You Say Geotourism,
I Say **Tourism Geology!**

Second Edition

Yudi Satria Purnama

Printed version ISBN: 978-623-5745-32-9
eBook version ISBN: 978-623-5745-33-6
Second Edition, 2022

Cover photo by Gesit Mutiarta
Cover design by Rezza Alam Islami
Cover photo: a geologist is standing on the Eocene Sandstone of the Bayah Formation, West Java, Indonesia

I would like to dedicate this book to
my great father,
my dear mother,
my helpful sisters,
my lovely wife, Nurul, who full of patient,
my cute little princess & prince: Desti and Dhirgham
... great thanks for your great support!

This book also dedicated to
anyone who dares to be different

Respect Your Dreams!

Respect your dreams!
Because it represents yourself
Without it, you are nobody

Respect your dreams!
Without it, your life is emptiness...
and you don't have your own Heaven.

Although it impossible to be achieved...
Keep respect for your dreams!
Without it, your soul has no spirit

October 2004

Table of Contents

Table of Contents v
Preface vii
Acknowledgments xi
List of Abbreviations xiii
List of Figures xv
List of Tables xx

Chapter 1   Introduction 1
General description of what will you get in this book

PART I: GETTING FAMILIAR TO TOURISM GEOLOGY 13

Chapter 2   Reshaping Geology and Tourism Relation 15
Arguments of why does tourism geology able to be redefined

Chapter 3   Tourism Geology Scope 95
The complete package of geological knowledge that specially
design for tourism-related professional. In general it cover wide
variety of attraction, activity (include safety and difficulty rating),
and impact

Chapter 4   Research and Cooperation Importance 213
The need of research and cooperation with practitioner and
tourism-related professional and demonstration of research from
tourism geology point of view might deliver different outcome
compare to geotourism

Chapter 5   Make It More Clear 235
Demonstration of different geological specialties might have
different point of view during assessing the same landscape and
the possible challenge ahead during developing geotourism

PART II: RESEARCH DEMONSTRATION **255**

Chapter 6   **Identifying Tourist Attraction Potential in Samarinda and Surroundings, Eastern Kalimantan** **257**
Describe potential tourist attraction from geological point of view in Samarinda

Chapter 7   **Geological Control on Identification of Aesthetic and Safety Factors for Swimming in Southwestern Nearshore of Banten, Western Jawa** **277**
Geological factors contributes to determine aesthetic and safety aspects on safe waters for swimming in case of Southwestern of Banten

Chapter 8   **Geological Approach for Tourist Destination Planning in Gunung Batu, Western Jawa** **315**
Geological translation effort to be understandable knowledge for tourism-related professional in case Gunung Batu

Chapter 9   **Assessment of Geological Variable to Mountaineering Difficulty Rating and its Application to Mountaineering in Cereme, Slamet, and Semeru Volcanoes** **341**
Construction of new mountaineering difficulty rating and description geological variables influence during mountaineering in case of Cereme, Slamet and Semeru Volcanoes

This chapter is written in collaboration with Aridy Prasetya, Febrio Baroes, Joko Wiyono, Suwondo and Sapto Wibowo

Chapter 10   **Highlights of the Geological-Related Attractions and Tourism Development of Rinjani - Lombok Geopark and Lombok Island** **393**
Geological interpretation to unlock tourist attraction potential and contribute to tourism development in case of the Lombok Island.

This chapter is written in collaboration with Nicolaus Lumanauw and Heryadi Rachmat

Glossary **427**
Index **439**
Author Bio **449**

Preface

Since '90 decades, we know geotourism as the only one relation of geology and tourism. Through this work, I declare tourism geology as the other relation. No intention to show which one is the best. Tourism geology and geotourism has different purposes.

I have been organizing the concept since 2001. The process was really time-consuming. Because, it was difficult to build arguments against mainstream views, to liberate wild ideas, to dare to be different. Since I had a scratch of tourism geology idea, I found a million reasons to discontinue developing it. But I have a motivation to keep move forward until now: tourism geology idea is a beautiful mind! I believe geology can do more for tourism. Finally, I am glad to share this interpretation so you can use it to change your world.

What are my goals?
My short-term goal is to establish a new scientific journal of tourism geology. Such a journal is media of research accumulation. Its collection able to stimulates innovation. I believe, there are unexposed knowledge of geological variables interaction that relate to tourist attraction. I encourage you to explore such knowledge by research.

My long-term goal is to generate a profession of tourism geologist. Who will be interested? They are maybe volcanologist, structural geologist, mineralogist, outdoor enthusiast, tour guide, park manager or other professions. Who knows when your mindset change, an opportunity will come to you!

As the history of applied geologies told us, the profession will flourish when market demand grows. It is like a seed creation. It can turn to be fruitful trees which will become a food source. Yet, the seed requires the finest soil, the best natural fertilizer, nurtured by the most diligent farmer, and sufficient time to grow. Then, the market will give their recognition to our garden. Recall Henry Ford's quote, the founder of the Ford Motor Company (1863 – 1947):

> "coming together is a beginning,
> keeping together is a progress, and
> working together is a success"

Since I started develop geological knowledge dedicated for tourism, I found many interesting ideas of geological knowledge applied to many aspects of our life. Some ideas already within the scope of applied geology disciplines, and some need to be nurtured. Until today we recognize about ten applied geologies, and what I am doing is to add a new one -Tourism Geology- which made by design. My message: it is possible to make a new applied geology by re-explore the relation of geology and the subject we would like to connected with, starts with exploration of our mind.

Applied Geology		
• Engineering Geology	• Urban Geology	• Agricultural Geology
• Petroleum Geology	• Medical Geology	• Archaeological Geology
• Economic Geology	• Forensic Geology	• *Tourism Geology*
• Environmental Geology	• Military Geology	*My Proposal*

In this century, geology needs to adapt to the new community demand, for geology to be more humanistic in the next decades. We also need to make people understand that they need geology more than they realize. In the age of artificial intelligence, we should never forget the soul of geology.

Why tourism? Personally I enthusiast when I see the jaw-dropping landscape, when I observe the natural wonders, and when I watch the physical outdoor activities in nature. Tourism certainly strongly relate to having fun. When we think tourism, we show our big smiles to escape from daily routine life, thinking what desire to bring, take their friends, relatives or spouse, to having new experiences, to feel a small piece of heaven on earth and tell the stories later.

The value of this book is knowledge the state of the art of tourism geology, including all aspect of geological feature relate to tourism, and opportunities as consequence. After reading this text, whether you as a geologist, a tourism-related professional or a tourist, I hope it inspires you to act: *the world is changed by those who dare to act differently.*

Let's Rock the World!

Yudi Satria Purnama
Email: yudigea93@gmail.com
yudi@yudispurnama.com

Jakarta
July, 2022

Visit **www.yudispurnama.com**
for my progress of Tourism Geology

Follow me ......

 yudigea93@gmail.com
yudi@yudispurnama.com

 @yudi_s_purnama

 @yudi_s_purnama

Acknowledgments

There are many people involved during my thought construction whom I would like to thank for their support to:

- Nicolaus Lumanauw (Environment Tourism Social and Development Centre, Indonesia), the first person who introduced me to the importance of geology in tourism. Many valuable discussions with him during construction of tourism geology until now.

- Andang Bachtiar (GDA Consulting, Indonesia) who encourages me and gave me opportunities to develop tourism geology in several field studies with GDA Consulting during the early years.

- Prof. R. P. Koesoemadinata (Institut Teknologi Bandung, Indonesia) for precious discussion especially during informal 'final academic test' in early 2005. It encouraged me to keep move.

- Prof. Jafar Jafari (University of Wisconsin-Stout, USA) who sent me tourism educational materials, allowed me to understand his perspectives, and encouraged me to continue developing the idea;

I also would like to thank to Susilawati, M.Sc. (independent construction consultant, Indonesia); Prof. Martin Chulshaw (University of Birmingham, United Kingdom); Kamil Szafrański and Stace Beaulieu (InterRidge; International Cooperation in Ridge-Crest Studies) for hydrothermal vent data permission; Fajar Lubis (LIPI; Indonesian Institute of Sciences); Sugeng Wijanto (Civil engineer, Indonesia); Angus M. Robinson (Leisure Solution, Australia); Thomas Krassmann (Germany geologist); Soffian Hadi (Sidoarjo Mudflow Mitigation Agency, 2007-2017); Matt McKee (Utah Department of Transportation); Harry Nelson (Washington State Department of Transportation); Andri Subandrio and Agus M. Ramdan (Geological Department, Institut Teknologi Bandung); Gesit Mutiarta (GDA Consulting); Irsal Budi Darmawan (HSSE PHE Tuban East Java); Nabila Shadrina Arief and Gusti Ayu Eka Purnatika (Exploration Think Thank Indonesia); Darwin Kadar (independent paleontologist); Stan VanderWerf (Mountaineer, US); Dasep Sabarudin (independent mineralogist); Management of GDA Consulting for their support to publish Chapter 6; Board of Indonesia Geologists Association (IAGI) Directors for their permission to publish Chapter 7; Aridy Prasetya, Febrio Baroes, Joko Wiyono, Suwondo and Sapto Wibowo who support me to wrote Chapter 9; Heryadi Rachmat (Indonesian Geotourism Practitioner) who support me with Lombok geological information in Chapter 10; Miroslava Seregova and Lenka Vargová Jurková of Košice Región Turizmus for Jasovská Cave photo; Nataniel Mangiwa (independent geologist) and Purnama Ari Suandhi (GDA Consulting) for discussion; Adam Long (UK photographer) for BASE jump photo; Samuel Edge (US) for Eel river and viewing stone photo; Octinur Alam (independent translator), Dady Hendarmin (Exploration Think Tank Indonesia), Risa Triandari (former personnel of GDA Consulting), Sarah Risda Nafisah (PHE Randugunting) and Cemara Dinda (independent translator) for reviewing my grammar; Dhony Afriyantho and Sandi Jatmika (PHE Randugunting) as models and Andi Krisyunianto (GDA Consulting) for his cowboy hat in the promotion material; and Rizal Rabas as interior book designer.

List of Abbreviations

AAPG	:	American Association of Petroleum Geologist
APGN	:	Asia Pacific Geopark Network
BASE	:	Building, Antenna, Span (bridge), Earth
BPJ-1	:	Banjar Panji-1 (well)
BPLS	:	Badan Penanggulangan Lumpur Sidoarjo
CC-BY	:	a Creative Commons license that let other to distribute, remix, tweak and build upon someone's work, even commercially, as long as they put credit for the original creation.
COVID-19	:	Corona Virus Disease 2019
CT (scan)	:	Computerized Tomography
CTX	:	Context Camera, a high resolution camera.
E	:	East
Hr	:	hour
HSSE	:	Health Safety Security and Environment
HOSV	:	Human Occupied Submarine Vehicle
IAGI	:	Ikatan Ahli Geologi Indonesia
IUCN	:	International Union for Conservation of Nature
JPL	:	Jet Propulsion Laboratory
Km/h	:	kilometer per hour
Km	:	kilometer
LROC	:	Lunar Reconnaissance Orbiter Camera
LUSI	:	Lumpur Sidoarjo / Sidoarjo Mud flow
m^3/d	:	meter cubic per day
M	:	meter
MMI	:	Modified Mercalli Intensity
MPV	:	Multi Purpose Vehicle
MSSS	:	Malin Space Science Systems
Mt.	:	Mount
N	:	North
NAC	:	Narrow Angle Camera.
NASA	:	National Aeronautics and Space Administration
NE	:	Northeast

NOAA	:	National Oceanic and Atmospheric Administration
NW	:	Northwest
PMEL	:	Precision Measurement Equipment Laboratory
ROV	:	Remotely Operated Vehicle
S	:	South
SARS	:	Severe Acute Respiratory Syndrome in 2002-2003
SE	:	Southeast
SW	:	Southwest
US	:	United States
UK	:	United Kingdom
UNESCO	:	The United Nations Educational, Scientific and Cultural Organization
USG	:	(medical) ultrasonography
USGS	:	United States Geological Survey
VEI	:	Volcanic Explosivity Index
W	:	West
WHOI	:	Woods Hole Oceanic Institution

List of Figures

1.1   Research locations Part II..   9

2.1   Path of thinking in this study...   24

2.2   Division of the "larger group" of geology......................................   27

2.3   Analogue of three categories of tourism in the form of an iceberg.........   31

2.4   Comparison of five major visitor activity statistics in the Grand Canyon,
       Yellowstone national parks and John Day Fossil Beds national monument....   35

2.5   Statistical data of how many visitor groups were interested to study
       interpretative topics in Grand Canyon National Park.....................   36

2.6   Comparison of the top seven visitor activities during 2006, 2011, and 2012
       in Yellowstone National Park...   37

2.7   An analysis of tourism types in Geoparks, based on 37 Geoparks..........   38

2.8   An analysis of the geology and tourism relationship...................................   38

2.9   A general building construction project...   42

2.10   Summary of principal steps in upstream oil and gas industry.................   48

2.11   Workflow of geologist work in each industry / service...............................   64

2.12   Satellite image of Lebak Area, southwestern coast of Jawa, Indonesia...   66

2.13   Map of potential tourist activities in Gunung Batu, Indonesia...................   69

2.14   Geological cross-section along routes of the Cereme Volcano.................   71

2.15   Landform Zone Map for geological-related attraction 72

2.16   Two ways geology and tourism interact 89

3.1   Simplified relation model among tourist, host / local culture, and wildlife, with geological, meteorological, and hydrological features in a natural tourist destination. 100

3.2   Volcanic strata exposure in Tanah Lot, Bali, Indonesia 108

3.3   The small bay of Seger Beach in Lombok Island 113

3.4   Three-dimension form of the deep marine western slope of Bahama Bank ... 116

3.5   BASE jumping in Monte Brento, Italy 118

3.6   Jasovska Cave of Slovakia that well known for speleotherapy 132

3.7   Viewing stone hunting in Eel river, California 137

3.8   Sidoarjo mud or LUSI, Sidoarjo, Indonesia 143

3.9   Giant gypsum crystals, Naica cave mine, Mexico 149

3.10   Sinus Iridum, also called "Bay of Rainbows" area of the Moon 154

3.11   Spectacular high sun view of the Mare Tranquillitatis pit crater Moon 155

3.12   Comparison of conglomerate outcrop on Mars with similar outcrop on Earth 156

3.13   An unnamed crater mimicking a "happy face" 158

3.14   The amazing Eberswalde Delta 160

3.15   Simplified distribution of earthquakes and volcanoes. 168

3.16   Graph relation of earthquake magnitude and average annually 169

3.17   Relation of tsunami wave height to earthquake magnitude based on known tsunamis from 2004 – 2011 174

3.18   Anak Krakatau volcano eruption on 24 August 2008 in VEI 2 178

3.19   The "Candelabra" black smoker in the Logatchev Hydrothermal Field on the Mid-Atlantic Ridge 180

3.20   Hydrothermal vent distribution within various tectonic settings 181

3.21   182 hydrothermal Vents as potential tourist attractions worldwide 183

3.22   Tubeworm concentration in "Tempus Fugit Vent Field" in the vicinity of Galapagos Island 191

3.23   Cruise itinerary map from Barcelona to Naples 192

3.24   A reminder sheet of tourism geology 205

4.1   The upstream part of Rogue River in Oregon, US 223

4.2   Sibayak crater full of graffiti 2.0 227

4.3   Lava lake of Erta Ale, Ethiopia 228

5.1 An imaginary landscape shows two settlements separated by a long limestone hill... 240

5.2 Graphical Illustration of tourism geology and geotourism differences 249

6.1 Satellite image of Samarinda and the Modern Mahakam Delta 269

6.2 Stratigraphy of the Kutai Basin.. 270

6.3 Geological Map of the Samarinda and surrounding area Lower Kutai Basin 270

6.4 Position of potential tourist attractions investigated in Samarinda.......... 272

6.5 A group of explorationist landed in mouth bar of modern Mahakam Delta... 273

6.6 Gas and oil seepages in Bambu Kuning Area.. 273

6.7 An active mud volcano in Batuputih Area 274

6.8 Outcrop of sandstone channel shows lateral accretion 275

6.9 Outcrop of delta in the Palaran Stadium Gate...................................... 276

7.1 Study area on the southern coast of the Western Part of Jawa Island.... 296

7.2 Simplified profile of the coastal area shows the principal zones of wave... 297

7.3 Rip current anatomy consists of rip vortex, rip neck and rip head........... 298

7.4 Four cross section types from shore to nearshore zones 299

7.5 Stratigraphy of Banten Block shows three sedimentation cycles 301

7.6 Geographic Map of Study Area shows the three locations of Manuk Island, Ciantir, and Legon Pari Bay... 302

7.7 Geological Map of Investigation Area 303

7.8 Satellite Image of Lebak Area shows sediment suspension in the western part.. 304

7.9 Situation Map of the Manuk Island Bay.. 305

7.10 Beach and sea bed profiles of the Manuk Island Bay 306

7.11 Situation Map of the Ciantir Bay... 307

7.12 Situation Map of the eastern part of the Ciantir Bay............................. 308

7.13 Beach and sea bed profile of the eastern part of the Ciantir Bay 309

7.14 Situation Map of the Legon Pari Bay 310

7.15 Beach and sea bed profile of the Legon Pari Bay................................. 311

7.16 Google Earth image of the Manuk Island Bay 312

7.17 Google Earth image of the Ciantir Bay... 313

7.18 Google Earth image of the Legon Pari Bay 314

8.1	Aerial photo of Northern Bandung	331
8.2	Topographic Map and its profiles of the Gunung Batu	332
8.3	Slope map of the Gunung Batu	333
8.4	Geomorphologic Map of Gunung Batu.	335
8.5	Geologic map of Gunung Batu, Geological cross-section, and stratigraphic column.	336
8.6	Gunung Batu landform shows the northern cliff as a fault plane or fault scarp	337
8.7	Attraction Map of Gunung Batu	338
8.8	Activity Map of Gunung Batu	339
9.1	Visualization of a slope	363
9.2	Illustration of slope beside the route	364
9.3	Satellite image of volcano distribution in Jawa Island	366
9.4	Geological Map of Cereme Volcano	366
9.5	Mountaineering Route Map of Cereme Volcano on topographic map	368
9.6	Geological section along route of the Cereme Volcano	369
9.7	3D topographic model of Cereme Volcano along routes	370
9.8	Narrower track and Walet Cave of Cereme Volcano	375
9.9	Crater rim and soil slide of Cereme Volcano	376
9.10	Geological Map of Slamet Volcano	377
9.11	Mountaineering Route Map of Slamet Volcano on topographic map	378
9.12	Geological section along the ascending route, Slamet Volcano	379
9.13	3D topographic model of Slamet Volcano along routes	380
9.14	Tree line and finer grained pyroclastic near of Slamet Volcano	383
9.15	Geological Map of Semeru Volcano and surrounding area	384
9.16	Mountaineering route Map of Semeru Volcano on topographic map	386
9.17	Geological section along the ascending route, Semeru Volcano	387
9.18	3D topographic model of Semeru Volcano along ascending route	388
9.19	Steep slope in the loose pyroclastic zone, crater rim, and Ranu Kumbolo of Semeru Volcano	391
9.20	3D topographic model of 75 Blank Zone, Semeru Volcano	392
10.1	Geographical Map of Lombok Island	417
10.2	Satellite Image of Lombok Island	417
10.3	Geological Map of Lombok Island	418

10.4 Volcanic Hazard Map of Rinjani Volcano 419

10.5 Earthquake frequency in Lombok Island from 1979 to 2019 419

10.6 Earthquake epicentrum in Lombok Island and surrounds during
1979 – 2019 420

10.7 Earthquake Hazard Prone Map of Lombok Island 420

10.8 Ground Motion Vulnerability Zone Map of Lombok Island 421

10.9 Tsunami Prone Map of Lombok Island 421

10.10 Methodology used in this study 422

10.11 Landform Zone Map for Geological-related attractions 424

10.12 Northern coast character of the Lombok Island 426

List of Tables

2.1 Summary of Subject-Matter and Focus of Interest of Petroleum Geology, Geophysics and Petroleum Engineering Disciplines 51

2.2 Status of Attraction and Activity on each Landform unit 73

2.3 Summary of Case Studies. 75

2.4 Main characteristics of Geotourism and Tourism Geology. 83

3.1 Relation between Tourist Attraction Type related to geological feature, Tourism Market Segment, and example of Geological Features. 106

3.2 Landscape Types and examples. 112

3.3 Relation of Outdoor activity types with landform 120

3.4 Summary of Geologic Environments and Geologic Material with Curative Effects related to Tourism. 123

3.5 TThe Giant Crystal Caves in the world. 147

3.6 Earthquake Magnitude (Richter Scale) and Average Annual Number Earthquakes each Magnitude 165

3.7 Modified Mercalli Intensity (MMI) Scale 166

3.8 Comparison of Earthquake Magnitude and Intensity 167

3.9 Simplified Tsunami Intensity Scale and its possible correlation with tsunami/wave height 172

3.10 Simplified Volcanic Explositivity Index 176

3.11 List of 182 hydrothermal vents as future tourist destinations 184

4.1 Systematic Knowledge Matrix in Tourism Geology 219

6.1 Simplified lithostratigraphy of the Samarinda Area 271

6.2 Potential tourist attraction in Samarinda and surroundings 271

7.1 The Beaufort Scale 300

7.2 Beach profile measurement of the Manuk Island Bay 306

8.1 Components of Supporting and Prohibitive Factors and the impact possibility 328

8.2 Sensitivity Scale on Geoconservation 329

8.3 Relation of variable, collecting data technique, data analysis and synthesis ... 330

8.4 Slope classification and geomorphic process 334

8.5 Summary of Attraction and Activity in Gunung Batu. 340

9.1 Description of terrain and route condition variables of Mountaineering Difficulty Rating 365

9.2 Simplified volcanic rock unit of Cereme Volcano and its description 367

9.3 General information of ascending route through Palutungan Route, Cereme Volcano 371

9.4 Difficulty rating and its variables of ascending route through Palutungan Route, Cereme Volcano 372

9.5 General information of ascending route through Linggajati Route, Cereme Volcano 373

9.6 Difficulty rating and its variable of ascending route through Linggajati Route, Cereme Volcano 374

9.7 Simplified volcanic rock unit of Slamet Volcano and its description 377

9.8 General information of ascending route through Guci Route, Slamet Volcano. 381

9.9 Difficulty rating and its variables of ascending route through Guci Route, Slamet Volcano. 382

9.10 Simplified volcanic rock unit of Semeru Volcano 385

9.11 General information of ascending route through Ranu Pane Route, Semeru Volcano. 389

9.12 Difficulty rating and its variables of ascending route through Ranu Pane Route, Semeru Volcano. 390

10.1 General stratigraphic column of Lombok Island 418

10.2 The 22 geological sites of the Rinjani-Lombok Geopark 422

10.3 Status of attraction and activity on each Landform Unit 425

Visit **www.yudispurnama.com**
for my progress of Tourism Geology

🌟 It is possible to produce a NEW member of applied geology which I proved it by Tourism Geology where it was made by design

Applied Geology

- Engineering Geology
- Petroleum Geology
- Economic Geology
- Environmental Geology

- Urban Geology
- Medical Geology
- Forensic Geology
- Military Geology

- Agricultural Geology
- Archaeological Geology
- *Tourism Geology*

🌟 **New Applied Geology** ➡ **New Knowledge** ➡ **New Opportunities**

🌟 *"Every science begins as philosophy and ends as art; it arises in hypothesis and flows into achievement"* (Will Durant, 1885 - 1981)

Follow me ......

✉ yudigea93@gmail.com
yudi@yudispurnama.com

📷 @yudi_s_purnama

in @yudi_s_purnama

CHAPTER 1

Introduction

Highlights

- This book is about how geology studies tourism, called tourism geology. Book discussions include:
  - Utilizing geological features to fulfill various tourist interests on the earth' surface, subterranean levels, the ocean floor, and on extra-terrestrial objects like the Moon and Mars.
  - Geological features that might be harmful for tourists.
  - Impacts of tourist activity.

- Message if you are a geologist:
  - Geologist effort in tourism geology: how to translate geological data to be understandable knowledge for tourism-related professionals.
  - Main concern: how geology acts as a best kind of contribution to support every tourism type.

- Message if you are a tourism academician or tourism-related professional:
  - Tourist attractions related to geology are not only geological history.
  - There is more that geologists can do to support you.

- Tourism geology is not to compete with geotourism, but mainly to establish:
  - A particular journal of tourism geology.
  - A new profession of tourism geologist.

Abstract

This introductory chapter will tell you what you will find in this book. It is the idea of how geology studies tourism, where geological knowledge is used to fulfill various tourist interests, including safety issues and impact. Moreover, this idea can be used not only on earth surface but also the ocean floor and the Moon and Mars.

The idea, however, has little relation to the themes of geotourism, geoheritage, geoparks, or geoconservation. However, profession practitioners or academicians in tourism, geology, geotourism, and geoparks are welcome to read.

What makes this book different is the discussion of geology using a unique perspective, which I call tourism geology. Geologists' efforts in tourism geology are how to translate geological data to be understandable knowledge for tourism-related professionals. Moreover, the main concern is how geology acts as a best kind of contribution to support every tourism type.

There are two messages for tourism-related professionals. First, geological history is not the only single tourist attraction in the destination. Second, there are more that geologists can do to support your job. In addition, the purpose of tourism geology construction is not to compete with geotourism, but mainly to establish a particular journal of tourism geology, and to establish the new profession of tourism geologist.

Finally, there are two parts in this book. The first part is about getting familiar with tourism geology. It is about the know-why knowledge, in four chapters. The second part is composed of five research demonstrations, to show you what research looks like in tourism geology.

Keywords: tourism geology, tourist attraction, tourism-related professional

1.1. INTRODUCING THE IDEA

Within this work, you will find an idea of how geology studies tourism. It is about how to utilize geological feature to fulfill various tourist interests on earth's surface, subterranean levels, the ocean floor, and on extra-terrestrial objects like the Moon and Mars. It also discusses the geological features that might be harmful for tourists, and the impacts because of tourist activity. Thus the ideas can be used on earth's surface, also on ocean floor, and on the Moon and Mars. My expectation is that you can accomplish many things with this new understanding.

The centerpiece of this book, however, has a small discussion on geotourism, geoparks, geoheritage, natural conservation, and geoconservation. Nevertheless, you will find a different view when observing the geological features. This is what make this book unique compared to geotourism books.

If you are a geologist, geological discussion in this book is uncommon, because discussion uses a new perspective, that of tourism geology. There is no geological data anomaly. Nonetheless, when geotourism and tourism geology analyze the same data, there are distinct outcomes. From a tourism geology perspective, the main effort of a geologist is how to translate geological data for tourism-related professionals in an understandable language. Later, they will repackage the translation for tourists as things to see and to do. The main concern of tourism geology is how geology acts as a best kind of contribution to support every tourism type.

Hence, tourism geology is user-oriented. This means the task of the geologist is to fulfill geological data and information according to user needs. On the contrary, geotourism is (geological) conservation-oriented.

The effort of geologists in tourism geology is similar to geological support in other applied types of geology. For instance, engineering geologists' effort to support geological data for civil engineers during construction projects, where they understand what they should do from those data. Similarly for petroleum geologists' effort to support geological data for drilling engineers during exploration well-drilling, where they know the consequences of those data for drilling. Whether engineering geologists or petroleum geologists, their geological data support is translated to meet the requirement of civil engineer or drilling engineer.

If you are a tourism academician or tourism-related professional, I have two messages. The first is that tourist attraction related to geology is not only geological history. The second is that there is more that geologists can do to support you. In this context, examples of tourism-related professional types include park managers, recreation workers, tour and travel guides, tour operators, and park rangers.

In 2015, I published a book entitled *Introducing Tourism Geology (It Is NOT Geotourism)*. I used it to get feedback from selected people. So that this book is the revised version where I put additional ideas.

My proposal of tourism geology is not to compete with geotourism. However, it is mainly to establish a particular journal of tourism geology, and to establish the new profession of tourism geologist. Other reasons are to support tourism for more growth, to complete the geological contribution to tourism, to address the safety issues and risk value in the tourism business, to explore the use of geological knowledge for society's needs and wants in the next decade.

There are two parts in this work. The first part is getting familiarized with tourism geology. The second part is for research demonstration. I recommend reading the first part to have a better understanding. To get a deeper understanding, I present five chapters of my research in the second part, as an example of the know-how knowledge.

Those five research chapters reflect my idea development during the construction of tourism geology. What I need to show is what the investigation looks like in tourism geology.

I wrote Chapters 1 to 8. Chapter 9 and 10 were written in collaboration with my colleagues. Let's have a brief look at the description of Parts I and II.

1.2. SUMMARY OF PART I

Part I is composed of four chapters that describe the character of tourism geology.

- Chapter 2. This chapter discusses tourism geology's philosophy: reshaping the relation of geology and tourism. It provides know-why knowledge, and what makes it differ with geotourism. When we grasp know-why understanding, we have a better quality of know-how knowledge. This chapter discusses philosophical issues: extracting the new meaning and consequences from the known facts. I review the background of geology and tourism relations, the philosophy of geology, tourism and established applied geologies. The main purpose is a faith in what more geology can do for tourism. In this chapter, I describe the case studies contained in more detail in the second part.

- Chapter 3. The chapter discusses the scope of work of tourism geology. The scope exposes tourist attractions related to geological features, activity with safety requirements, and impact issues. The purpose of the scope of work is to build communication among geologists—as supplier knowledge—and the user. This mean that geologists should understand what should be delivered to the user. Likewise, a tourism-related professional as the user should recognize what should be asked of the geologist. Therefore, they communicate in the same scope, so that there is a commitment of supply and demand relationship among them.

More interestingly, I describe many tourist interests that refer to geological features. To invoke your mind: interests related to scenic beauty, curative activity, and outdoor activity. However, there are particular features that are my favorite. These include the unique features such as drilling-related accidents, giant crystal caves, powerful geologic processes, Moon and Mars features, and hydrothermal vents in the deep ocean floor. Let me tell you a few spectacular things within that particular feature.

- The largest mud volcano in the world, in Sidoarjo, Indonesia, still erupts violently since 2006 and most likely will continue for the next decades.

- Only in cave mines do crystals grow to a giant size. For instance, researchers found gigantic crystals in Naica cave mine, Mexico (Badino et al., 2009, p. 1767).

- Vacation to the extraterrestrial objects such as Moon and Mars is likely to occur in the coming decades. Just a few examples: Sinus Iridium of the Moon, Eberswalde fossil delta, and a crater mimicking a happy face on Mars.

- In the future, it will be possible for us to perceive whether the incoming powers of landslide, earthquake, tsunami, and volcano eruption are a threat or an attraction. The condition is when scientists will be able to predict accurately when, where, and how big the geological power will come. For instance, if we choose the smaller scale of earthquake (4.0 to 5.5 magnitude), then we have potential attraction average per year is ± 1,150 to ± 32,000 earthquakes annually (USGS, 2016).

- Hydrothermal vents in the deep ocean floor are a place where mineral sources spew out. It is the next interesting tourist attraction where available submarines will be able to take more passengers to the deep. Using inventory data by Beaulieu (2015), I select 182 vents as future tourist destinations, which situated around the globe.

As a result, many tourism types are influenced by tourism geology (e.g., sun and beach tourism, health tourism, sports tourism, or adventure tourism.) Let's think of the future: Mars tourism, deep ocean floor tourism, volcano eruption tourism, or tsunami tourism. My attention lies in how geology contributes to every tourism market segment.

- Chapter 4. I emphasize the research importance to strengthen tourism geology. I give several examples of research subjects to invoke your imagination or experience. In addition to developing tourism geology, I describe the importance of cooperation of geologists with tourism-related professionals and practitioners.

  This chapter ends with comparison of geotourism investigation and tourism geology research. The underlining matter is that despite geotourism and geology studying the same subject matter, both have a different focus of interest since they are designed for distinct purposes.

- Chapter 5. My purpose in this chapter is to make obvious the differences between tourism geology and geotourism. I give an imaginary case of a unique landscape where two settlements are separated by a long hill.

Four imaginary geological specialties are presented to show how they value the landscape according to their focus of interest, comparing their outcomes and response of the local people. To close this chapter, I give three possible challenges during developing tourism geology: scope definition, the conservation mission, and environmental issues.

1.3. SUMMARY OF PART II

I arrange Part II for research demonstration, using a tourism geology perspective. After reading the second part, I believe you will come up with a more challenging research subject and a better method in your area of interest. Because of my limitation, the research was performed in my own country such as Kalimantan, Jawa, and Lombok Islands (Fig. 1.1).

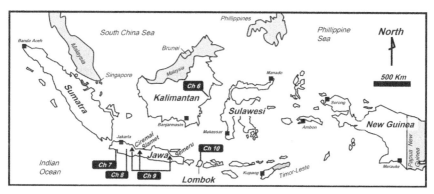

Figure 1.1 The Indonesia archipelago with the five biggest islands: Sumatra, Jawa, Kalimantan, Sulawesi, and (the western part of) New Guinea. Other countries shown in gray color are Malaysia, Singapore, Brunei, Philippines, Timor-Leste, and Papua New Guinea. Research locations discussed in Part II of this book were situated in Kalimantan (Ch. 6), Jawa (Ch. 7 to 9), and the Lombok Islands (Ch. 10). "Ch." means "Chapter."

- Chapter 6. This chapter is about geological attraction identification in Samarinda City, Eastern Kalimantan Province (Fig. 1.1). I found undeveloped tourist attractions related to geological features such as hydrocarbon seepages, mud volcanoes, abandoned wells, and rock exposure. Those attractions have the potential to be developed into attractive destinations.

- Chapter 7. This chapter is the analysis of aesthetic and safe waters for swimming in Lebak, on the southwestern coast of Jawa (Fig. 1.1). It is easier to define the aesthetic nearshore. But it is a different case for safety issues. Identification of safe waters for swimming falls to the oceanographic domain. However, my observations show the safest location is controlled geologically.

Originally, this paper was a part of Indonesian Geologists Association's (IAGI) report for the government of Lebak Regency,

Banten Province. It is part of a geological socialization program in 2002. During the program, I shared geological knowledge for tourism with the local government and encouraged them to promote the breathtaking beauty of the locality. In this work, I repackage the report for research presentation.

- Chapter 8. This chapter is about the geological approach to develop a tourist destination. It is the case of Gunung Batu, Western Jawa (Fig. 1.1). It is a small hill, but proven attractive, where we can adore the scenic beauty of the Bandung Highland.

  I conducted research to translate geological information into understandable information for tourist destination planners who usually are non-geologists. Outcome generated two maps: attraction and activity maps from tourism geology perspective. These suggest where particular attractions are and what activities might be performed.

  My work was originally published in the 33rd Indonesian Association of Geologists (IAGI) Annual Convention and Exhibition, 29 November – 1 December 2004. I translated the paper into English and repackaged it for research presentation.

- Chapter 9. This chapter describes the relation of geological variables to mountaineering difficulty rating. I wrote this chapter with Aridy Prasetya, Febrio Baroes, Joko Wiyono, and Suwondo and Sapto Wibowo. They went to the mountains and collected data while I analyzed the data to be synthesized.

  There are many rating systems built, but they did not satisfy me. Thus we constructed a new rating composed of four variables: terrain, route condition, weather, and physical ability. Moreover, we describe several consequences of each rating in the context of time, distance, special techniques, and probable geological hazards that might be encountered.

  The rating was applied during analyzing data from mountaineering on three volcanoes: Cereme, Slamet, and Semeru Volcanoes (Fig. 1.1).

Rating application generated mountaineering route maps, with the difficulty rating on each route segment. Tables are generated to contain information such as distance, ascending duration, difficulty rating, and potential geological risks. The table accompanies the route map.

- Chapter 10. This chapter is about characterizing geological-related attractions in Lombok Island, including the Rinjani-Lombok Geopark area in the northern part of the island (Fig. 1.1). Since the Geopark was established in 2018, I am interested in contributing my knowledge to the whole island.

  Traditionally, when we talk about geoparks, then we think that geotourism works for the geoscientific tourist interest type, to learn geological information of a site. In reality, geological features make it possible to fulfill various tourist interests, such as scenic beauty, outdoor activity, and curative interests.

  In addition, tourism development highlights are arranged based on particular characteristics identified. These include exploration (of new destination), mitigation (of injury and fatality), and impact monitoring (of tourist impact).

  I wrote this chapter with Nicolaus Lumanauw (my mentor of tourism) and Heryadi Rachmat (Indonesian geotourism practitioner). This chapter was presented at the 6th Asia Pacific Geoparks Network (APGN) Symposium, 3rd – 6th September 2019 in Mataram, Lombok Island.

There is a geologic term glossary at the end of this book, so that you can examine the meanings of particular terms. Moreover, you can find my updated work of tourism geology, including free e-books, on my website, https://yudispurnama.com. I hope that you will enjoy reading this work!

Reference Cited

Badino, G., Ferreira, A., Forti, P., Giovine, G., Giulivo, I., Infante, G., Lo Mastro, F., Sanna, L. & Tedeschi, R. (2009) The Naica Caves Survey. p.1767, In: White, W.B. (ed) Proceedings of 15th International Congress of Speleology, Kerrville, Texas-USA. 3, 19-26 July 2009, pp.1764-1769.

Beaulieu, S.E. (2015) InterRidge Global Database of Active Submarine Hydrothermal Vent Fields: prepared for InterRidge, Version 3.3. World Wide Web electronic publication. vents-data.interridge.org Version 3.4. Accessed January 2017.

USGS (2016) Earthquake Fact and Statistics. Accessed January 2017 through www.usgs.gov/natural-hazards/earthquake-hazards/earthquakes or go to tinyurl.com/ujn3bf9

Getting Familiar to Tourism Geology

This section explains why and how geological knowledge is applied to tourism from different point of view described in four chapters

CHAPTER 2

Reshaping Geology and Tourism Relation

Highlights

- Geotourism is not the only relation of geology and tourism anymore.

- The author proposes two ways that geology and tourism interact:
  - The first interaction is the tourism concept relying on geological features and man-made work related to geology, where geotourism is the result.
  - The second relation is an application of geological concepts to tourism, with tourism geology as the outcome.

- Tourism geology as applied geology is the (new) member of the applied geology group.
  - Subject-matter is a geological feature that can be safely visited.
  - Focus of interest of tourism geology is geological features as tourist attractions, which are able to fulfill geoscientific and non-geoscientific tourist interests, or to be just tourist attraction.

- Tourism geology has the same character with engineering geology or petroleum geology in professionalism.

- This idea opens the opportunities for geology to study tourism in new ways.

Content

2.1	INTRODUCTION	19
2.2	BACKGROUND	21
2.3	THE CHALLENGES	22
2.4	THE CHALLENGE-SOLVING METHOD	23
2.5	ANALYSIS	24
	2.5.1 Characteristics of Geology and Tourism	24
	2.5.1.1 General Character of Geology as Science	24
	2.5.1.2 General Character of Tourism	28
	2.5.1.3 Visitor Behavior in Tourist Destination	34
	2.5.1.4 Relation of Geology and Tourism	38
	2.5.2 Analysis of Applied Geology Character	40
	2.5.2.1 General Character of Engineering Geology	40
	2.5.2.2 General Character of Petroleum Geology	44
	2.5.2.3 Formulation of Applied Geology General Characteristics	53
	2.5.2.3.1 First Character	53
	2.5.2.3.1.1 Subject-Matter Relation	54
	2.5.2.3.1.2 Focus of Interest Relation	56
	2.5.2.3.1.3 Wrapping Up the First Character	59
	2.5.2.3.2 Second Characteristic	59
	2.5.2.3.3 Third Characteristic	60
	2.5.2.4 Logical Consequence	61
	2.5.3 Case Studies	64
	2.5.3.1 Relation of Geological Feature and Tourist Destination Identification	64
	2.5.3.2 Aesthetic Nearshore Identification	65
	2.5.3.3 Identification of Safe Waters for Swimming	65
	2.5.3.4 Safety Concern While Seeing Lava in Kilauea, Hawaii	67
	2.5.3.5 Tourist Destination Planning from Geological Point of View	68
	2.5.3.6 Geological Variable Influence in Mountaineering Difficulty Rating	70
	2.5.3.7 Geological-related Attraction Characterization in Lombok Island	71
	2.5.3.8 Synthesis of the Empirical Proofs	73
2.6	COMPARING DEFINITIONS	77
	2.6.1 Geotourism General Characters	77
	2.6.1.1 Geotourism Background	78
	2.6.1.2 Geotourism Purpose	79
	2.6.1.3 Geotourism Definition	80
	2.6.1.4 Geotourism Research	82
	2.6.2 Distinction of Tourism Geology with Geotourism	83
	2.6.2.1 Purpose	84
	2.6.2.2 Variable Type	84
	2.6.2.3 Knowledge Type Generated	84
	2.6.2.4 Outcome	85
	2.6.2.5 User Type	85
	2.6.2.6 Tourist Interest Type	86
	2.6.2.7 Tourism Market Target	86
	2.6.2.8 Geologist Role	86
	2.6.3 Comparing Previous Definitions of Tourism Geology	87
2.7	CONCLUSION	88

Abstract

The traditional relation of geology and tourism refers to geotourism, which means tourism that relies on geological features. I propose tourism geology as the other relation, meaning geological application to tourism. The method to construct tourism geology is composed of conceptual approaches and clarified by empirical study.

This study reveals there are two ways that geology and tourism interact. The first interaction is as the tourism concept relying on geological features and man-made work related to geology, with geotourism as the result. The second interaction is as an application of geological concepts to tourism, where tourism geology as the outcome.

Tourism geology as applied geology has subject matter that is geological features that can be safely visited. The focus of interest of tourism geology is geological features as tourist attractions that are able to fulfill geoscientific and non-geoscientific tourist interests, or just tourist attractions. Tourism geology has the same characteristics as other applied geologies such as character of engineering geology or petroleum geology in professionalism.

Tourism geology indeed differs with geotourism. For instance, supporting geoconservation, to be sustainable tourism, to improve visitor experience, and to encourage local economic growth, are all geotourism aims. On the other hand, tourism geology's purpose is to support tourism by delivering proper geological knowledge to make the tourism-related professional able to solve a tourism problem linked to the geological feature. The main variables in geotourism are mostly non-geological variables, while mostly geological variables are involved in tourism geology. The market of geotourism is geotourism itself, and perhaps also ecotourism. On the contrary, tourism geology has consequences for all tourism markets that use geological feature as tourist attractions, such as sun and beach tourism, adventure tourism, and health tourism. This idea of tourism geology open opportunities for geology to study tourism in new ways and strengthen geological contributions to tourism.

Keywords: tourism geology, geotourism, geological feature, tourist attraction, applied geology

2.1. INTRODUCTION

We acknowledge geology and tourism interaction since UNESCO launched the Geopark Program in the 1990s. Geopark is a geographical area where geological heritage sites are part of a holistic concept of protection, education, and sustainable development (UNESCO, 2014, p.3). The presence of protection and sustainability ideas suggests that geological conservation is important within the program.

Until now, the popular concept of geology and tourism is geotourism, which is based on conserving geological features. Thus, if the general perception is summarized, then the terms of geological conservation (geoconservation), geotourism, (public) education, sustainable development, and Geopark are one entity.

The first person who defined and popularized the term "geotourism" was Thomas A. Hose. In his definition, the word "geo" means geology. In 1995, Hose (p.17) defined geotourism as follow:

> The provision of interpretative and service facilities to enable tourists to acquire knowledge and understanding of the geology and geomorphology of a site (including its contribution to the development of the Earth sciences) beyond the level of mere aesthetic appreciation.

Jonathan Tourtellot (in Stokes et al., 2003) also introduced the "geotourism" term. But the word "geo" in his term refers to geographic and the meaning encompasses all aspects of travel. His definition is:

> Tourism that sustains or enhances the geographical character of a place being visited, including its environment, culture, aesthetics, heritage and the well-being of its residents.

In this work, I refer to geotourism definition as defined by Hose (1995, p.17).

Ibrahim Komoo (1997, p. 2970) introduced another idea of geology and tourism, called tourism geology. His statement is:

> *A specific discipline that deals with the application of geological knowledge for the development of ecotourism activities through a systematic search for and geological characterization of new and existing tourism destinations.*

He explained that the tourism packages arising from these efforts are called "geotourism activities."

Kadderi (2000, p.197), who echoed Komoo's idea, stated tourism geoscience is a paradigm to understand the earth environment for long-term non-destructive use of earth heritage. Kadderi (2000, p.200) redefined the thought as follows.

> *Tourism Geoscience is a new subdiscipline in geoscience education that emphasizes fusion of evaluating, planning and managing of geologic assets and resources in an ecosystem for sustainable development of a quality human habitat.*

The "tourism geology" term is also popular in China, where they have their own understanding. Through their book *The Principles of Geotourism*, authored by Chen et al. (2015, p. 2), they put tourism geology into a group called "tourism earth science." Chen et al. (p. 2) stated that tourism earth science is composed of tourism geology and tourism geography. It was born from the marriage of earth science and tourism science.

Furthermore, it is interesting to scrutinize this Chen et al. (p. 2) statement:

> *Tourism earth science should study not only the object of tourism—tourism resources—but also two subjects of tourism—tourism markets and media as well as tourism services and facilities. In a word, all the three elements of tourism have*

earth scientific topics and rules pending to be explored by earth scientific workers.

In this chapter, I demonstrate the construction process of tourism geology. The purpose is to make you understand why I describe the relation of geology and tourism differently.

2.2. BACKGROUND

The idea of tourism geology was originated based on etymological and empirical reviews. Etymological review relates to the applied geology meaning, while empirical review is based on field study.

There are two meaning of the applied geology term. The first meaning is application of various geological sub-disciplines to a discipline or a particular society interest group. The examples are engineering geology, petroleum geology, and medical geology. The particular society interest group, discipline, business, or industries relating to those applied geologies are (civil) engineering for engineering geology, petroleum for petroleum geology, and medical for medical geology.

The second meaning is the application of particular geological subdisciplines to various society interest groups or disciplines. It refers to the field such as applied sedimentology, applied paleontology, applied mineralogy, and applied structural geology. In this work, I use the first meaning of applied geology since tourism is the particular society interest group.

The term "applied geology" is analyzed etymologically. For instance, engineering geology is "geology to support the construction business." Similarly, petroleum geology is "geology to support the petroleum industry." Those etymological reviews bring a speculative idea that tourism geology is "geology to support the tourism business." If that is true, it brings a consequence: tourism geology is a member of applied geology.

On the other hand, empirical review shows that geological variables in outdoor activities play important roles. For example, determination of the difficulty rating in river rafting relies on the interaction between the paddler, geological variables, and hydrological variables. The interaction is the size of catchment area of rainfall, river current, water debit, riverbed architecture, slope, boulders, rock type, and structural geology features. Similarly, in other cases, geological variable interaction is hypothetically important in determining difficulty degree for other outdoor activities, such as rock climbing, mountain biking, or mountaineering.

Those geological variables are indeed geological subject matter. Consequently, those variables are the domain of geologists, and they are able to study them. If those geological variables have influence on those outdoor activities, then the geologist has a right to study the cause-and-effect consequences of the variables with the activities.

These thoughts have a potential in generating problem sets to be solved in applied geology, which is relatively unfamiliar until the present. As those problems relate to outdoor activities or in general concern tourism, the discipline can be designated as tourism geology. For that reason, tourism geology is a member of applied geology.

2.3. THE CHALLENGES

Etymological and empirical reviews generate a hypothesis that turns out to be a major question: "Is it true that tourism geology is a member of applied geology?" A sentence is true if it has verified meaning. As a consequence, the speculative statement brings five challenges, as follow.

- First: what is the relationship between tourism and geology?

- Second: what is the requirement for tourism geology to be accepted as a field of applied geology?

- Third: what are the plausible consequences if tourism geology is a member of applied geology?

- Fourth: what is empirical clarification of the consequence?

- Fifth: if tourism geology is clarified as a branch of applied geology, then what are its differences from geotourism and earlier concepts of tourism geology?

2.4. THE CHALLENGE-SOLVING METHOD

A method to answer those five challenges is developed, as follow.

- The first challenge, the geology and tourism relationship, is solved by first identifying the philosophy of geology and of tourism, followed by reviewing the statistics of visitor behavior at the destination.

- The second challenge, tourism geology requirement, is solved by analog study with engineering geology and petroleum geology.

- The third challenge, the consequence of tourism geology as applied geology, is solved by integrating the answer of the first and the second challenges.

- The fourth challenge, the empirical clarification, is solved using field studies and library research.

- The fifth challenge is solved by comparing the definitions and statements of geotourism and the earlier concepts of tourism geology with my concept.

If all challenges can be answered properly, then the statement "tourism geology is a member of applied geology" is a correct statement. If the difference of my version of tourism geology from earlier concepts is clarified, then my version contributes to the new understanding of the relationship between geology and tourism. Fig. 2.1 shows the path of problem-solving as the black box so that everyone able to track my logic of thinking.

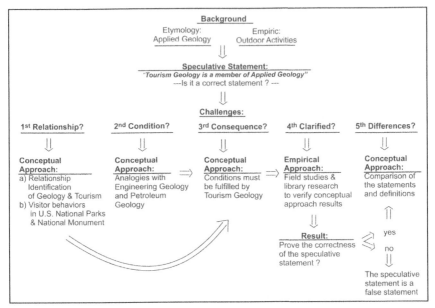

Figure 2.1. Path of thinking in this study. It was commenced from background, speculative statement, and challenges. Eventually, this study was closed with the conclusion about whether the speculation statement is true or not. If it is true, the outcome compares to published statements and definitions.

2.5. ANALYSIS

The analysis below attempts to solve these challenges. Conceptual approaches were directed by library studies. Most of the empirical proofs were handled by field studies.

2.5.1. Characteristics of Geology and Tourism

Geology and tourism relation identification is intended to find out how those two interact. It is conducted by scrutinizing the character of geology, the nature of tourism, and tourist behavior statistic at destinations.

2.5.1.1. General Character of Geology as Science

What is geology? It is related to the natural elements such as the fossil antiquity, the power of volcanic blasts, and earthquakes the importance of oil, coal, and metal deposits; the mountain belt scenic beauty; and the billions of years of history of the earth itself. The features mentioned refer to abiotic features and biotic features of dead matter in the surface and subsurface, its processes and history.

Nowadays, most people say geology is the study of the earth, particularly of the geosphere as the solid part of the earth. In practice, geologists study the earth's crust only by visual observation (Prof. R. P. Koesoemadinata, 2011, personal communication). On the other hand, earth study by measuring physical characteristics through instrument is conducted by geophysicists.

Geologists observe, analyze, and synthesis geological feature visually, with or without instrumental aid. Those features range from outcrops, minerals, fossils, airborne photos, satellite images, to seismic sections and natural processes such as volcanic explosion and deltaic sedimentation.

As a science, geology has subject matter and a focus of interest. Subject matter is the matter studied, while focus of interest is the particular way to study the matter. There are three types of geological subject matter: solid, fluid, and process. The solid and fluid have a non-dynamic character, while the process involves solid and fluid in a dynamic character. All of those types are mostly situated in the geosphere, the solid part of the earth. Brief descriptions are as follow:

- The solid matter is in the form of mineral, stone, and rock, from dust to mountain sized, that comprises the earth's surface to subsurface. It includes remains of prehistoric organisms, or trace animals.

- The fluid matter is all fluid originated from rock and/or contained in rocks, such as CO_2, H_2S, groundwater, and hydrocarbons.

- The process is natural dynamic processes in the earth's surface and crust, such as volcanic eruptions, earthquakes, landslide, and tsunamis.

Moreover, geology also includes the solid part of the extra-terrestrial object such as planets and their moons, meteorites, comets, and asteroids. The discipline, also known as planetary geology or astrogeology, means study of the geology of the extra-terrestrial object. Hence, geological subject matter is not only on earth, but also on another extra-terrestrial objects. In this chapter, I will use the term "geological feature" frequently, which refers to geological subject matter.

The focus of interest of geology is earth history within four-dimensional frames, wherein three dimensions represent the landscape and one dimension represents a time frame of billions of years (Prof. Soejono Martodjojo, 1993; Dr. Andang Bachtiar, 2005; personal communications). This means that the earth crust of a region, or of the whole regions, both on surface and sub-surface, evolve from time to time.

Most definitions of geology involve "study of earth." We should realize that the earth is a system composed of many spheres: the biosphere (including anthroposphere), atmosphere, hydrosphere, geosphere, and cryosphere (ice). Study of geology mostly concerns the geosphere in the view of four dimensions (time). Thus, a concise definition of geology should be "study of earth history," while geologist is "the earth historian."

The reason geologists think in four dimensions is because of 4.6 billion years of the earth's age. Time is a different dimension. Although geologists learn the earth's history, the outcome is not just about the past. The result is to be used to predict the future, for civilization continuity and living in balance with the nature. For instance, by understanding the earth's dynamic history through plate tectonic theory, geologists explain the distribution of earthquakes, volcanoes, and tsunamis. The knowledge is used to predict where the areas are with the most severe of those natural processes. When linked with other disciplines such as civil engineering, or other users such as government, the knowledge is used for societal needs.

To point out a few examples: how strong should a bridge be built to respond to earthquake shock? How should marine erosion be controlled in a coastal area? How should groundwater be managed in a metropolitan environment? Or how should the nearest geothermal force be used for electric power?

In this work, geology as "the larger group" can be divided into geological science and applied geology (Fig. 2.2). Some might call geological science "pure geology." Geological science is the (natural) science of geosphere that studies particularly the earth's history. Applied geology is geology to support a particular discipline, society interest group, business, or industry. Geological science is the foundation to support the existence of applied geology.

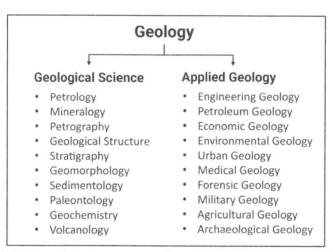

Figure 2.2. Division of the "larger group" of geology composed of geological science and applied geology and its examples.

Geoscientists or geologists document geologic knowledge in many geologic journals. According to *SCImago Journal & Country Rank* updated in 2020 within the subject area of earth and planetary sciences and subject category of geology, there are 278 journals. To name a few: *Gondwana Research Journal*, published by Elsevier; *Journal of Metamorphic Geology*, published by Wiley-Blackwell; and *Lithosphere*, published by the Geological Society of America.

Popular applications of geology are mitigation and exploration. It means that these geological applications are related to specific societal needs. Mitigation is our attempt to prevent casualties from natural causes such as landslides, tsunamis, or volcanic eruption. Exploration is our endeavor to find and to extract natural resources for energy demand such as coal, oil, and gas. Examples of applied geology that deal with mitigation are engineering geology and medical geology, while those that deal with exploration are petroleum geology and economic geology.

2.5.1.2. General Character of Tourism

Activity related to tourism was started at least during the ancient Egyptian era, about the third millennium BCE. They traveled for leisure where hospitality centers and main roads were available in major townships (Mill, 1985, pp. 2-3). During the industrial revolution, tourism expanded rapidly when mass transportation became available such as the steamship and commercial flights.

Etymologically, Theobald (2005, p. 9) suggested the word "tour" derived from Latin "tornare" and Greek "tornos," It means "the movement around a central point or axis." However, I found interesting opinion in an old book published in the 1970s and authored by Porrath (1978, in *Currant*, 1978). It is stated that the term "tour" was derived from a Hebrew term meaning "learning, studying, and searching."

As stated in the Hebrew Bible of Torah, Porrath (1978, in *Currant*, 1978, p. xix) explains that the term dates back to the history of Moses. It told us when twelve men were designated to penetrate the land of Canaan, Israel's future promised land. Those men were charged to "tour" the land, to research the country's resources, to assess its productivity, and to study its assets and liabilities, while posing as tourists (pp. xix-xx). Furthermore, *"a tour still, indeed, represents an attempt by the traveler to discover something about a place he visits"* and *"a tourist is one who learns, studies and searches for data of interest to him"* (Porrath, 1978, in *Currant* 1978, p. xx).

What will people think when they interpret the word tourism today? They think activities linked to the many themes. Mill (1985, pp. 42-46) describes the themes are pleasure, leisure time, vacation, escape, fresh air, health, adventure, family togetherness, companionship, and satisfaction of inner desires. Although modern tourism generally means having fun away from home, it still contains three main components. They are to study, learn, and search—despite different degrees in each activity.

Today there are many tourism types worldwide. For instance, wildlife tourism, medical tourism, culinary tourism, pilgrimage and spiritual tourism, ecotourism, cruise tourism, rural tourism, cultural tourism, film tourism, and educational tourism. So that geo(logical)tourism is one of many tourism types.

Based on personal communication with Nico Lumanauw (2020), my mentor in tourism, he concludes that tourism can be viewed in three categories: direct providers (Category I), support services (Category II), and tourism development (Category III). Direct provider (Category I) provide the things needed by the traveler. They are the entities such as the lodging, food service, and transportation industries; the attraction sector; tour and travel agents; and retail shops.

Those providers are supported by support services (Category II). Their services are directly to the direct providers, but indirectly affect to the travelers. Support services include contract food services, contract laundries, food suppliers, tour organizations, and travel publications.

The last is about tourism development (Category III). It works indirectly to direct providers and travelers, and directly to support services. Tourism development includes components of the public sector and private sector such as planners, government agencies, local communities, travel industry associations, financial institutions, real estate developers, and educational, vocational, and training institutions. Support services and tourism development are mostly managed by governments, institutions, and the private sector, which don't have direct contact with the tourist.

If those three categories are put into the form of an iceberg, category I is in the upper part while categories II and III are in the middle and lowest part, respectively (Fig. 2.3). Let's call the iceberg the tourism iceberg. The upper part of the iceberg is easily seen by the people in the boat (tourist); while the middle and lowest parts are hidden beneath the sea. In other words, those hidden parts support the existence of the upper part.

As consequence of the tourism iceberg model, most people think that tourism is only about direct providers, which can easily be seen because they are situated above sea level. This is the effect of the iceberg on the world of tourism. The work of support services and tourism development are hardly seen, because they work behind the stage. In reality, without their support, it is hard for direct provider to serve the tourist. Therefore, for the discussion of tourism development and planning to be comprehensive, it must involve all categories.

Tourism is sensitive to the world situation, where nowadays the news spreads easily around the globe in the blink of an eye. Interesting news spreads through social media (e.g., Instagram, Facebook, YouTube). For instance, when an event held or a new local attraction goes viral through social media, it will attract people from other countries.

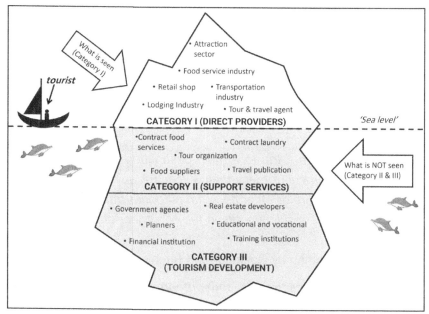

Figure 2.3. Analogue of three categories of tourism in the form of an iceberg, called the tourism iceberg. Category I is positioned in the upper part, which is above the sea level. Categories II and III are hidden below sea but support the existence of Category I. The people in the boat represent tourists easily to see in the upper part of the iceberg.

Nonetheless, unpleasant news also has a tremendous impact. For instance, natural catastrophes (e.g., Indian Ocean tsunami in 2004, Eyjafjallajökull eruption in 2010); terrorism (such as the Bali bombing in 2002, or the 11 Sept 2001 attack); economic crises (e.g., 1997 Asian crisis, 2007-2008 global crisis); and health crises (such as SARS in 2002-2003, COVID-19 from 2020 onwards). News has many consequences for the tourism business: destinations closed, canceled events, and travel restriction or even travel bans. It affects demand and supply in generating and destination countries.

Although "tourism" is the word we are used to hear, unfortunately, there is no universal definition of tourism. It is because the word "tourism" means different things for different people (Theobald 2005, p. 8). I collected several tourism definitions to prove the variety. For instance, the United Nations (2016, p. 237) defined tourism as a social, cultural and economic phenomenon which entails the movement of people to countries or places outside their usual environment for personal or business/professional purposes.

In other document of the United Nations (2010, p.10), it is stated that *tourism refers to the activity of visitors.* In addition, *a visitor is described as*

a traveler taking a trip to a main destination outside his/her usual environment, for less than a year, for any main purpose (business, leisure or other personal purpose) other than to be employed by a resident entity in the country or place visited.

The tourism definition by Goeldner and Ritchie (2009, p. 6) is:

the processes, activities and outcomes arising from the relationships and the interactions among tourists, tourism suppliers, host governments, host communities and surrounding environments that are involved in the attracting and hosting of visitors.

On the other hand, Jafari's definition (2000, p. 585) is:

the study of man (the tourist) away from his usual habitat, of the touristic apparatus and networks responding to his various needs and of the ordinary (where the tourist is coming from) and non-ordinary (where the tourist goes to) worlds and their dialectic relationships.

However tourism is defined, it is indeed a worldwide social phenomenon. It involves people traveling across countries that are associated with various service industries such as the travel, lodging, food, and attraction sectors. Tourism shows many relations, such as sociocultural phenomena among the tourist and the resident and the two different governments' relation when people from abroad visit other countries. Thus, tourism has multiple social dimensions.

There are many academic ways to approach tourism. Goeldner and Ritchie (2009, pp.21-25) suggested approaches to tourism study such as institutional, product, historical, managerial, economic, sociological, and geographical. On the other hand, Jafari and Ritchie (1981, pp.15-19 developed four components for a tourism framework:

- Study of man (the traveler who does the touring).

- The travel industry.

- The setting (sociocultural fabric and physical environment including natural resources, man-made resources, and sociocultural resources).

- The encounter (the host-guest relation).

Tourism has subject matter and a focus of interest. In my discussion with Nico Lumanauw (personal communication, 2014), he concludes that the subject matter of tourism is the tour as the holistic system. The focus of interest is tourist attraction. This means the tourism-related professional views the social or natural phenomena as the tourist attraction, which has potential to evoke or to improve the tour as a system. The system itself is composed of many components, such as tourism goods and services, the sociocultural fabric, and host-guest relations.

Nico Lumanauw (personal communication, 2014) also concludes that tourism's scope captures the natural and social features and integrates it with industries. Those integrated features are transformed to be a tourism product. The process includes tourism planning and development.

As a social science, tourism has journals. According to *SCImago Journal & Country Rank*, last updated in 2020, there are 124 journals referring to the subject area of Business, Management and Accounting, and under the subject category of tourism and leisure and hospitality management. To name a few: *Annals of Tourism Research, Tourism*

Management, both published by Elsevier; and *Journal of Sustainable Tourism*, published by Routledge.

Until today, tourism is still considered profitable to be developed by governments due to its positive economic impacts, such as creating employment, increasing resident income, and generating economic activities. But tourism can generate negative impacts, such as resident negative attitude, increased crime rate, migration of inhabitants to the tourist destination, and environmental pollution. Keeping everything in balance is the most challenging task.

2.5.1.3. Visitor Behavior in Tourist Destinations

The Park Studies Unit, University of Idaho, conducted a visitor behavior study in U.S. National Parks and Monuments. The study report used in this work was chosen on destinations that rely on geological feature as the main attraction. They are the Grand Canyon National Park, Yellowstone National Park, and the John Day Fossil Beds National Monument.

Littlejohn et al. (2004, p. 28), Littlejohn and Hollenhorst (2004, p. 30), Manni et al. (2007, p. 40), and Lee et al. (2005, p. 29) presented statistical visitor activities of those national parks and the national monument (Fig. 2.3). It shows that main visitor activities are sightseeing, scenic driving, walking, photography / painting / drawing, and shopping. Those activities are non-geologic activities.

In this context, I describe geologic activity as a tourist activity to understand geologic information in the destination. Such activity includes learning interpretative topics, visiting a geological museum, studying fossils, and joining a geological tour. The highest rank of geologic visitor activities only appears in the John Day Fossil Beds National Monument (Fig. 2.4). I conclude that non-geologic activities were more dominant than geologic activities.

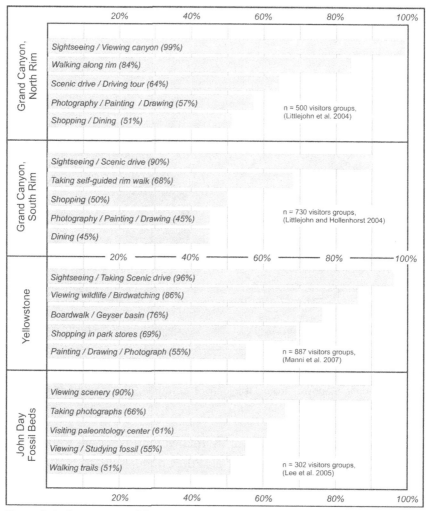

Figure 2.4. Comparison of five major visitor activity statistics in the Grand Canyon, Yellowstone, and John Day Fossil Beds. Statistic data show non-geologic activities were dominant. Total percentages of visitor activities do not equal 100 because visitors could choose more than one answer. Redrawn based on works of Littlejohn et al. (2004, p. 28), Littlejohn and Hollenhorst (2004, p. 30), Manni et al. (2007, p. 40), and Lee et al. (2005, p. 29).

There are many interpretative topics in the Grand Canyon that talk about the canyon formation, water role, plants and animals, ancient history, and modern cultures. However, the statistics suggest that most of visitors are not interested in studying those topics (Littlejohn et al., 2004; Littlejohn and Hollenhorst, 2004; Fig. 2.5). Those facts suggest non-geologic activities were more dominant than geologic activities.

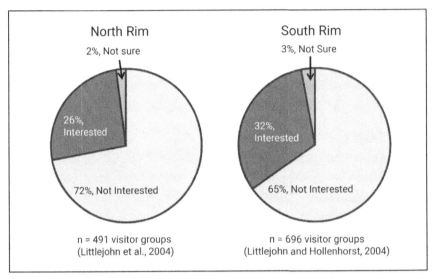

Figure 2.5. Statistical data of how many visitor groups were interested to study interpretative topics in Grand Canyon National Park. Data show non-geologic interest was dominant. Redrawn from Littlejohn et al. (2004, p. 33) and Littlejohn and Hollenhorst (2004, p. 35).

I compare top seven activities in Yellowstone National Park during 2006, 2011, and 2012 (Manni et al., 2007, p. 40; Kulesza et al., 2012a, p. 41; Kulesza et al., 2012b, p. 41; Fig. 2.6). It indicates minor change in dominant visitor activities where non-geologic activities were more dominant. Type of non-geologic activities are sightseeing / taking a scenic drive, viewing wildlife / birdwatching, shopping, and painting / drawing / taking photographs.

Moreira and Melendez (2012, p. 205) studied the other tourism types in Geoparks. They conducted the study with 37 members of the Global Geopark Network, from 18 countries including European, Asian, North America, and South America Geoparks. The outcome (Fig. 2.7, p. 206) suggest that Cultural Tourism is the most popular (94%), followed by Ecotourism (83%), Historical Tourism (81%), Rural Tourism (75%), Culinary Tourism (64%), and Adventure Tourism (61%). The others (25%) are religious tourism, beach tourism, fishing tourism, scientific tourism, cruise ship tourism, and thermal tourism.

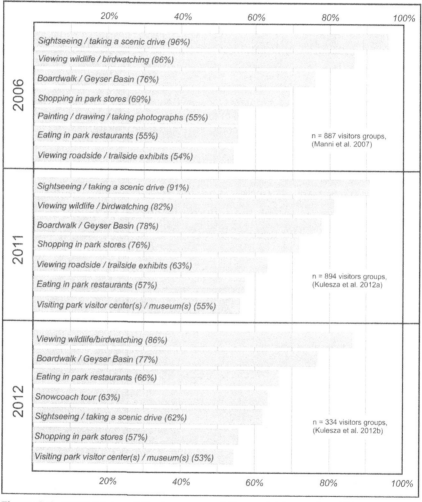

Figure 2.6. Comparison of the top seven visitor activities during 2006, 2011, and 2012 in Yellowstone National Park (Manni et al., 2007, p. 40; Kulesza et al., 2012a, p. 41; Kulesza et al., 2012b, p. 41). Statistic data show non-geologic activities were dominant. Total percentages of visitor activities do not equal 100 because visitors could choose more than one answer. Redrawn from Manni et al. (2007, p. 40), Kulesza et al. (2012a, p. 41), and Kulesza et al. (2012b, p. 41).

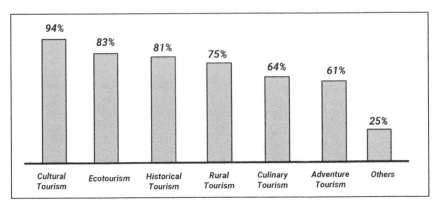

Figure 2.7. An analysis of tourism types in Geoparks, based on 37 Geoparks. Geotourism, although it was not a part of the analysis, certainly existed in all Geoparks. Figure is modified with permission from Moreira and Melendez (2012).

2.5.1.4. Relation of Geology and Tourism

There are two ways to understand the relationship of geology and tourism. The first is to link the nature of geology as science with the nature of tourism. The second is related to visitor behavior statistics (Fig. 2.8).

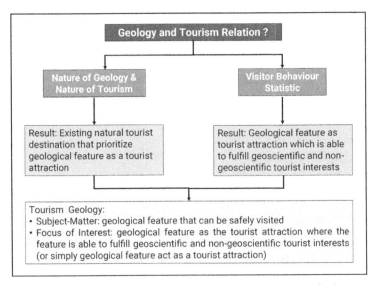

Figure 2.8. An analysis of the geology and tourism relationship that further interprets the subject-matter and focus of interest of tourism geology.

The first way—which is to link the nature of geology as science and the nature of tourism—has another two means. However, the outcomes are the same. Firstly, based on a common idea, the relation of tourism and geology refers to the existing national park that prioritizes geological features as a tourist attraction (e.g., Grand Canyon and Yellowstone). Secondly, using Jafari and Ritchie's thought (1981, pp.15-19), tourism has natural resources components. It also refers to the existing natural tourist destination (e.g., a national park) as a tourist attraction. Those two indicate the geology and tourism relation is the existing natural tourist destinations that prioritize geological features as a tourist attraction (Fig. 2.8).

The second way that is related to visitor behavior statistics in destinations shows that non-geologic tourist interest and its activities also relate to the geological feature. This means that the geological feature as a tourist attraction is able to fulfill geoscientific and non-geoscientific tourist interests (Fig. 2.8).

Hence, the final statement for the relation of geology and tourism is *existing natural tourist destination that prioritizes geological features as tourist attractions, where the features can fulfill geoscientific and non-geoscientific tourist interests*. Hence, the statement answers the first challenge about the relation of tourism and geology.

Those statements can be further elaborated as to what are the subject matter and the focus of interest of tourism geology. The subject matter is the existing natural tourist destination. Nonetheless, to open opportunities in the future, new or undeveloped geological features could be the destination, the subject matter could be further interpreted as geological features that can be safely visited. The focus of interest of tourism geology is geological feature as the tourist attraction, where the features are able to fulfill geoscientific and non-geoscientific tourist interest (or simply geological feature act as a tourist attraction as; Fig. 2.8).

In a tourism context, we call such geological features "tourism resources" or "natural assets." Tourism-related professionals might call them "the things to see and to do" for tourists. In a natural conservation context, it is called natural heritage, geological heritage, or geodiversity.

In practice, geologists interpret the kinds of tourist interests related to geological features as a tourist attraction only for geoscientific interest. Perhaps this situation is due to the worldwide spirit of geoconservation and eagerness to disseminate geological knowledge to the public. What is geoconservation? It is defined by Burek and Prosser (2008, p. 2) as *"an action taken with the intent of conserving and enhancing geological and geomorphological features, processes, sites and specimens."*

Empirical review shows that there are more kinds of tourist interests related to the geological features; an example is outdoor interest. *The point is that geologists and tourism-related professionals should consider that there are many tourist interests and their activities relate to the geological feature.* We will review those tourist interest types in Chapter 3.

2.5.2. Analysis of Applied Geology Characteristics

To identify the general character of applied geology, I used popular applied geology as an analogue. In this work, I select engineering geology and petroleum geology. Those two disciplines have proven their contribution, are responsible for building modern civilization, and have a long history of their development. Such histories are not bedtime stories. They contain messages for the next generation. The outcome is to understand the applied geology characteristics that should be contained in tourism geology.

2.5.2.1. General Character of Engineering Geology

We need to learn the history of civil engineering and geology to understand why and how geology became involved in civil engineering.

Prior to the 20th century, civil engineers overlooked geology as an important part of their work.

Engineering geology became of interest after construction failures such as dam disasters in the Bouzey Dam in France, 1895; Austin Dam in Texas, 1900; and the St. Francis Dam in Southern California, 1928, where 426 people lost their lives. The disasters occurred due to lack of civil engineering interest in the geological conditions where the dam foundations were constructed. Those disasters caused civil engineers to realize how important it is to understand the soil and rock nature at the site proposed.

Since they place the building foundation onto the soil and rocks, civil engineers needs to understand their nature, which is studied by geologists. However, the focus of interest of civil engineering on the soil and rock is the structure where mitigation is a requirement. Mitigation means to make the building structure stable. Hence, the focus of interest of engineering geology is also mitigation, as required by a civil engineer.

In practical work, geologists deliver the natural character of the materials to the civil engineer after geological site investigation is conducted on the soil and rock. It includes predictions of what would happen if the materials are subjected to the specific load of the structure. Finally, civil engineering anticipates by structure design. The purpose is to control the soil and rock response to the foundation.

Thus, what a civil engineer needs from an engineering geologist is the ability to translate all geological data and information for their practical need. This means that descriptions and interpretations of rock and soil conditions at a work site need to be stated in understandable technical terms by the civil engineer. For instance, a sedimentary rock description should focus on weathering and fracture spacing description, rather than focus on a depositional environmental history interpretation.

Engineering geological study outcome is scientific information on the characteristics of rocks, soil, and geological processes should the soil and rock be subjected to structure loads. Engineering geologists should provide the technical input needed by the civil engineers. In this relation, engineering geologists act as the supplier of knowledge and civil engineers act as the user.

In the case of a general building construction project, I present a general workflow to show the engineering geologist working together with the civil engineer, architect, and mechanical and electrical engineers (Fig. 2.9). The engineering geologist's task is mainly during the site survey as part of design development. To a lesser degree, during preliminary design, the engineering geologist also contributes to the design. The engineering geologist also contributes during the construction phase by monitoring and recording ground response (compiled from Susilawati and Prof. Martin Culshaw, 2012, personal communication).

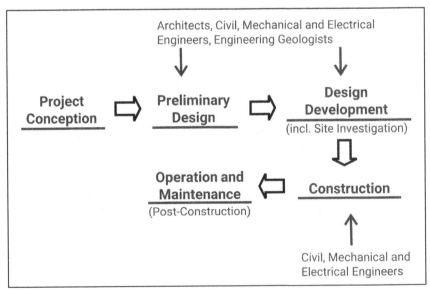

Figure 2.9. A general building construction project. The engineering geologist's role is mainly in site investigation as part of the design development phase. I compiled the project phase from Susilawati and Prof. Martin Culshaw, 2012, personal communication.

Over the time, engineering geology's contribution is multi-faceted, covering a wide range of applications. For example, engineering geology applies to the land use planning process, geohazard and risk assessment and mitigation, quarry, pit and mine design, urban development, regeneration and conservation, and assessment and mitigation of the contaminated land (Prof. Martin Culshaw, personal communication, 2011). The wide range of applications of engineering geology are best described in the International Association for Engineering and the Environment's (IAEG) statutes (1992), as follows:

> *Engineering geology is the science devoted to the investigation, study and solution of the engineering and environmental problems which may arise as the result of the interaction between geology and the works and activities of man as well as to the prediction of and the development of measures for prevention or remediation of geological hazards.*

The subject matter of engineering geology is rocks, soils, fluids, and their natural dynamic process, which have causes and consequences in relation to the subject matter of civil engineering. The focus of interest of engineering geology is mitigation. Particular knowledge generated in this field is rock and soil mechanics. It includes methods and techniques such as borehole testing, in-situ deformation and stress measuring, and deformation monitoring techniques.

There are many user types for the work of engineering geologists. In this context, the next users or the direct users of the engineering geologist's input, other than civil engineers, are developers, contractors, and the government. The end-users are the people who use the buildings, such as the tenants and pedestrians.

Today, engineering geology studies are kept updated as shown by various scientific journals. To mention a few: *Bulletin of Engineering Geology and the Environment,* the official journal of IAEG published by Springer; *Engineering Geology,* published by Elsevier' and *Quarterly*

Journal of Engineering Geology and Hydrogeology, published by the Geological Society of London.

The subject matter of civil engineering is buildings such as roads, bridges, tunnels, dams, and runways including the foundation where it is placed in the subsurface. Hence, the subject matter of engineering geology is the ground where the building foundation will be placed.

The focus of interest of civil engineering is the structure characteristics, including design, implementation, and monitoring (Sugeng Wijanto, personal communication, 2019), where mitigation is a requirement. Mitigation is used by engineering geology as a focus of interest. In this work, mitigation means to make the rock able to withstand the weight of the building without causing engineering failure, or to prevent geological processes from weakening the condition of a constructed building.

The result of engineering geology investigation is dedicated to the civil engineer as the next-user. The result is in a form of scientific information as input for them to make decisions. Thus, the engineering geologist's task is to explain and to predict geologic features related to man-made buildings. The outcome is used by the civil engineer to control the response of buildings to geological processes. It also means they do not dedicate the result of engineering geology for the end-user such as tenants or pedestrians.

2.5.2.2. General Character of Petroleum Geology

Petroleum is a naturally occurring complex liquid hydrocarbon, which after distillation produces a range of combustible fuels, petrochemicals, and lubricants. The name "petroleum" covers both crude oil and petroleum products. Most petroleum products are combusted to provide energy. Those products include diesel fuel, kerosene, and gasoline. Crude oil can provide petrochemical industries for a wide range of uses. It can be used as products themselves and as chemical feedstock to make other products. These petrochemical products include pharmaceuticals, plastics, synthetic rubber, insecticides, fungicides, and fertilizers.

In in earlies time, petroleum was used to fulfill people's needs such as for asphalt for building roads, waterproofing ships, an ointment to cure certain illness, and for a cheaper and more flexible source of illumination. In fact, it was also used for weapon defense by pouring hot oil onto the enemy below when the enemy tried to break down the fortress' gate. Those societies discovered oil through surface seepages where it was easily available. For instance, Imperial Russia produced 3,500 tons of oil in 1825 from Baku—in present-day Azerbaijan—where the oil had flowed freely to the surface for many centuries. In most cases, they still did oil extraction by hand.

The "black gold rush" began in the mid-19th century. It was started by oil distillation invention to substitute whale oil for illuminating fuel. However, to produce oil from underground was still not considered effective. It wasn't until August 28, 1859, in Titusville, Pennsylvania, when Edwin L. Drake succeeded in discovering oil with a drilling machine at a depth 69.5 ft. (21.2 m). The drilling site was where the surface oil seepage located. His main contribution established the drilling prototype that was initially used for drilling salt wells. Drake's effort was supported by William A. "Uncle Billy" Smith, who had mechanical skills and made the tools to drill the salt wells. At that time, the well produced about 12 to 20 barrels a day. With the spread of their technique to discover oil, the area saw an oil boom.

From early to modern days, petroleum exploration has been evolving. One of the earliest exploration methods that is still used is the anticlinal theory of oil entrapment. It was put forwarded by Thomas Sterry Hunt in 1861, and also by Ebenezer Baldwin Andrews in the same year. Petroleum exploration was dominated by identification of the anticline structure based on surface geological surveys.

A surface geological survey could only predict subsurface structure within a shallower depth. Geophysical methods such as gravity, magnetic, and seismic refraction were introduced and applied to exploration in the mid-1920s. They were used to understand deeper structures unobserved from the surface and where the larger petroleum accumulation might be located. In the same period, geophysical methods were also applied to borehole logging, with the first electric log run at Pechelbronn, France, in 1927.

Major advances in geophysics occurred in the 1970s, when the 2D seismic reflection method was introduced. Seismic images could be displayed on continuous seismic sections. In the 1980s, increasing computing power led to the development of 3D seismic surveys. They enabled seismic images to be displayed in any orientation. Today, geophysics data are a vital exploration tool.

The method of extracting petroleum accumulation on the subsurface in petroleum engineering is by drilling. During early times, the drilling method used cable-tool drilling, which had a depth shallower than 1000 m. The rotary drilling method displaced the old method in the 1920s. It permitted the drilling process to be faster, more efficient, and to penetrate deeper. With the new rigs, the wells were soon taken deeper. In fact, geological information derived by the new rigs brought new geological knowledge, such as basin structure and its histories, due to deeper depth.

The driving force of petroleum exploration and production is energy demand to move the engines of economics and politics to dominate the planet. When Henry Ford introduced the Model T in 1908, gasoline demand rose. World Wars I and II emphasized that oil was urgently needed to win wars through tanks, trucks, warships and fighter planes. We also saw how the West was dependent on oil from the Middle East during oil shocks in 1970s and the Gulf War of 1990. Moreover, the power of the U.S. dollar is unlikely to be strong without its influence on the oil trade.

We witness how oil has changed our world over the course of more than 160 years ever since Edwin Drake drilled a well in Pennsylvania. The change is not only how we can move the goods and people with their idea of farther and faster. Oil also changes the world of politics and the economy. For sure, the world needs oil, and we are addicted to it.

In the briefly mentioned petroleum exploration history, I realize that the history of engineering geology emergence is different from petroleum geology history. The history of engineering geology taught that there were the supplier party (geologist) and the user party (civil engineer). Those two are needed each other. Their communication finally gave birth to engineering geology.

Petroleum geology history in United States taught that the professions of petroleum engineer and geophysicist were developed from the (petroleum) geologist (Prof. R. P. Koesoemadinata, 2014, personal communication). Perhaps the only user party during the early periods of the oil industry was the entrepreneur, who needs geologist to find oil. Therefore, I conclude that petroleum geology emerged due to increasing demand of oil.

Nowadays, the term "petroleum geologist" is used for a geologist who looks for oil. Moreover, it was used for the name of the American Association of Petroleum Geologists (AAPG) since 1917. The association is one of the world's largest professional geological societies, with over 300,000 members in 116 countries at the beginning of the 21st century.

In the context of the petroleum industry, there are two main sections: upstream and downstream. The upstream section deals with exploration, development, and production stages. The downstream section deals with transportation, refining, and marketing. Petroleum geologists, petroleum geophysicists, and petroleum engineers work in the upstream section, called the exploration and production department (Fig. 2.10). In this context, "petroleum geologist" and "petroleum geophysicist" are simply written as "geologist" and "geophysicist."

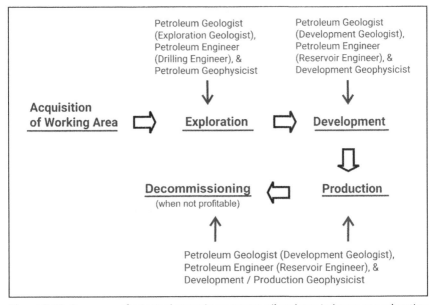

Figure 2.10. Summary of principal steps in upstream oil and gas industry or exploration and production oil and gas industry, with major profession types involved in each stage. A geologist who works in the exploration stage is called an "exploration geologist." Geologists who work in development and production stages are called "development geologists" and "production geologists."

Industry employs geologists and geophysicists—both are also called geoscientists—because of their expertise in applying earth science to explain and to predict geologic processes that form petroleum deposits. Petroleum engineers are employed because of their capacity to extract or to produce petroleum. Those three professions work as a multidisciplinary team.

Geophysics is the study the earth and its environment, which covers the geosphere, atmosphere, and space, by using the principles and practices of physics. In this context, discussion of geophysics is focused on the geosphere. Geophysical data are derived from observation using tools, such as the seismograph, gravimeter, and magnetometer. Those tools measure the earth's physical features from the surface using sound waves, earthquake waves, or magnetic pulses. Thus, knowledge derived from geophysics methods such as seismic reflection, gravity, and magnetic methods is basically derived from indirect methods.

Geophysics methods are similar to methods used by medical experts to analyze the inner part of our body, such as X-rays, USG, or CT scan methods. The resultant observation depicts the earth structure and its content. In more detail, the goal of geophysics is to show subsurface structures including the size, shape, depth, and other physical properties, including fluid character.

Without geophysics data, it would be hard for a geologist to predict petroleum accumulation in the subsurface. It would also be hard for petroleum engineers to drill, since geophysics provides knowledge on the size, shape, depth, and other physical properties including fluids. Today, it is mandatory for an exploration and production company to have geophysics data in their working area.

Petroleum geology itself is the study of why and how the rocks are able to produce petroleum. Thus, geologists must be able to explain and to predict petroleum accumulation in the subsurface, since it has accumulated in a specific region, at a particular depth, and in a certain rock layer.

Once geophysics data are acquired and processed, geological explanation and prediction is applied to the data (e.g., seismic image). Using geophysical data, coupled with the geological concept of petroleum systems, the geologist is able to explain and predict where petroleum accumulated and where to drill.

Without geological knowledge, it is impossible for geophysicists and petroleum engineers to understand petroleum accumulation in the subsurface. Geology provides knowledge of why and how the earth acts as a natural machine that produces petroleum. Without geological knowledge, geophysics data will remain "a body without a soul." On the other hand, without geophysics data, geological knowledge will remain "a soul without a body."

After a specific location and target depth are defined by the geologist and geophysicist, the next step is to extract petroleum. The knowledge of producing or extracting petroleum falls to the petroleum engineering discipline. In more detail, petroleum engineering is concerned with drilling an exploratory well, establishing the reserves of an oil field, determining distribution of petroleum within a reservoir, and the most effective way to produce it. Without petroleum engineering knowledge, geologists and geophysicists would be unable to produce petroleum. It is because the petroleum engineer understands how to control the wild subsurface environment by drilling a well and how to bringing oil to the surface. Without petroleum engineering knowledge, petroleum accumulation will remain deeply buried down there, forever.

The subject matter and focus of interest of petroleum geology, geophysics, and petroleum engineering are summarized in Table 2.1. The subject matter of those three disciplines is slightly different, but focused on the same thing, petroleum, due to a cause-consequence relationship. What makes them work as a multidisciplinary team is their similarity of focus of interest as well as the cause-consequence of their subject matter.

Despite producing petroleum being mainly the task of petroleum engineering, geology and geophysics also have related sub-disciplines, such as production geology and developmental geophysics. However, the production scope in geology and geophysics is different from the production scope in petroleum engineering. For instance, a production geologist is responsible for understanding the geological framework of a reservoir that influences fluid flow within a producing reservoir. On the other hand, a production engineer attempts to maximize production in a cost-effective manner by designing equipment to extract and treat petroleum from a petroleum well.

Table 2.1 Summary of subject matter and focus of interest of petroleum geology, geophysics, and petroleum engineering disciplines

Discipline	Subject-Matter	Focus of Interest	Remark
Petroleum Geology	Rocks related to petroleum	Exploration and production	Exploration and production by exploration play concept construction to explain and to predict petroleum
(Petroleum) Geophysics	Physical characters of rocks related to petroleum	Exploration and production	Exploration and production by analyses on geophysics character to predict petroleum
Petroleum Engineering	Petroleum	Production	Production by engineering approach to control subsurface environment and to produce petroleum

Regarding the position of the supplier knowledge and the user, the position is interchangeable among geologists and geophysicists. Sometimes a geophysicist is a supplier where, he or she provides geophysics data ready to be interpreted by the geologist. On the other hand, a geologist is a supplier where he or she provides a geological concept to be implemented by a geophysicist in geophysical data. The outcome of geoscientist's work is utilized by petroleum engineers as the next-user. The geoscientist's outcome is a certain location to be drilled, at a certain depth; rock composition will be penetrated and a particular rock layer contains petroleum to be extracted.

In a company, there are other next-users of a geoscientist's work, such as managers and investors. The end-user of petroleum is the people who use petroleum as the final product, such as electric power in their home, transportation fuel in their vehicle, or as petrochemical products in their garden (e.g., insecticides, fungicides).

Since the time of the "black gold rush" began, knowledge formulation related to oil commenced to accumulate. To name a few researchers, other than Thomas Sterry Hunt, there was Sir Boverton Redwood. He was a chemical engineer who published the first comprehensive text on petroleum in 1896, *Petroleum: A Treatise* (Sorkhabi, 2011, p. 51). Another researcher was Edward Hubert Cunningham, a Scottish geologist who published a purely petroleum geology text title *Oil Finding: An Introduction to the Geological Study of Petroleum* in 1912 (Sorkhabi, 2011, p. 51).

The long history of petroleum exploration in various case studies around the globe generates systematic knowledge. Today, we call the Petroleum System for systematic knowledge of petroleum geology. Magoon and Dow (1994, p. 10) defined the Petroleum System as:

> *A natural system that encompasses a pod of active source rock and all related oil and gas and which includes all the geologic elements and processes that are essential if a hydrocarbon accumulation is to exist.*

Thus, petroleum geology is the study of petroleum system itself.

Today, petroleum geology knowledge is documented in various scientific journals. To mention a few, *Petroleum Geoscience,* published by the European Association of Geoscientists and Engineers and the Geological Society of London; *Petroleum Science and Engineering Journal,* published by Elsevier; and *AAPG Bulletin,* published by the AAPG.

Based on petroleum geology characteristics described, I conclude that petroleum geology was developed because of increasing market demand and development of various exploration methods. Such development causes specification of the subject matter and focus of interest (Table 2.1). And it is finally a call for specialization: that is, petroleum geology, geophysics, and petroleum engineering. The subject matter of those three disciplines is slightly different, but pointing at the same thing—petroleum—due to the cause-consequence relation.

Thus, petroleum geology is a field of geology to support the petroleum industry in exploring and producing petroleum. The subject matter is rocks related to petroleum, while exploration and production are the focus of interest.

Petroleum geologist tasks are to explain and to predict geologic characteristics and processes related to petroleum occurrence. The outcome of petroleum geology investigation is in a form of scientific knowledge. It is dedicated for next-users such as petroleum engineers. The purpose is to make them able to take scientific-based decision during problem-solving. The scientific knowledge is then utilized by petroleum engineer to control the subsurface environment during producing petroleum. It also means that the result of petroleum geology is not dedicated for the end-user who use petroleum product as the final product.

2.5.2.3. Formulation of Applied Geology General Characteristics

The result of analogue study is a general characteristic of applied geology. If tourism geology is a member of applied geology, then it should have applied geology characteristics. I extracted three characteristics of applied geology, and I will now use them to answer the second challenge. The challenge is about tourism geology's requirement to be accepted as a member of an applied geology.

2.5.2.3.1. First Characteristic

Applied geology is a discipline connector among geology and a particular discipline, society interest group, business, or industry. I use petroleum geology and engineering geology as models of applied geology. Hence, petroleum geology is a discipline connector between geology and petroleum engineering. Engineering geology is also a discipline connector between geology and civil engineering.

Applied geology activity is scientific research. Its outcome is a scientific report. The user type of research outcome is called the next-user. They are the people in a discipline, business, industry, or society interest group; this list could be simplified to be "discipline." Their profession might be scientist, engineer, government, manager, investor, or politician.

On the other hand, applied geology's position is supplier knowledge. Therefore, petroleum geology is supplier knowledge, and petroleum engineering is the next-user. Engineering geology is also supplier knowledge and civil engineering is the next-user.

The next-user integrates geoscientific reports with other reports from other disciplines. Based on those reports, the next-user decides on actions to design and produce a final product. Gasoline, electricity, and petrochemical products are the final products related to the petroleum industry to which petroleum geology contributes. Tunnels, bridges, and towers are the final products in the construction business, where engineering geology plays an important role. The user of the final product is the public consumer, called the end-user.

I conclude the reason why geology is able to apply its knowledge to a discipline. It is because there are two relations. The first is subject-matter relation. The second is the focus of interest relation. Although geology and the discipline have their own subject matter and focus of interest, the two relations among them exist to build "unique communication." My effort describes how such "unique communication" occurred.

2.5.2.3.1.1. Subject-Matter Relationship

The relation of subject matter refers to the subject matters of geology and of the discipline in the same problem discussed, which shows a cause-consequence relation. It is the same thing to do the business. Variables play in the discipline's subject matter or the problem discussed, geological variables. Those variables are related to the earth's solid part (i.e., minerals, stone, rocks), fluids contained, and their natural processes.

Let me give two examples in engineering geology and petroleum geology. In the construction business, the civil engineer needs to put a foundation of the thirty-floor hotel deep into the ground. The foundation is the lower-most part of a building. It is needed to transfer the building's weight into the subsurface, so that the building is able to stands stably. In addition, a particular foundation type needed is determined by the subsurface character and building weight. Hence, a subsurface character needs a particular foundation type. Therefore, there is a cause-consequence relation of the foundation and the subsurface.

The engineer needs to understand the subsurface character composed of soil and rock. It is a domain of geology and studied by geologists. From this view, civil engineers and geologists have the same subject matter along with a cause-consequence relation. It is geological feature of the subsurface where the foundation will be placed.

In the case of the petroleum industry, a private company intends to explore and to produce oil in an onshore area where oil seepages are situated. The seepages flow from reservoir in the ground through fractures. It means there is an oil accumulation deep in the subsurface, which is stored in a reservoir of rock layers.

A drilling engineer intends to produce the oil from reservoir. But he or she needs to understand the natural character of rocks that will be penetrated, and the reservoir depth target. It is the domain of geology and studied by geologists. Therefore, the drilling engineer and geologist have the same subject matter along with a cause-consequence relation. It is geological feature of the subsurface where oil from the reservoir will be produced.

2.5.2.3.1.2. Focus-of-Interest Relation

The subject-matter relation should be followed by the second relation. It is the focus-of-interest relation. It means, geology and the discipline have the same perspective to assess the subject matter or the problem discussed. By the two relations, geologist and the next-user are able to communicate. In other word, it is because they have the same thing to do the business, and the same view on how to run the business.

In this relationship, the geologist should understand the next-user's problem. Hence, geology borrows the discipline's focus of interest. Furthermore, geologists should be able to interpret the problem into several geological variable interactions, because it has cause-consequence relation. Then, the geologist will know the kind of variables needed to solve the next-user's problem. The variables are geological data and information, simplified to be knowledge.

During process of "borrowing" the discipline's focus of interest, geologists learn the nature of the discipline. It is a way to make geological knowledge compatible for a particular next-user. Therefore, when a geologist delivers the geological knowledge needed, the geologist knows what kind of consequences will be faced by the next-user. The knowledge will be used as scientific input in a decision-making process. Then, the next-user will understand what they should do.

In this stage, geology serves as the supplier of geological knowledge dedicated for a discipline. In other words, geology has transformed into a discipline connector (applied geology), which is dedicated to a particular discipline (next-user).

Proper geological knowledge means it should be needed and understandable by the next-user, so that they will be able to use it to solve their problem. The geologist might develop a new method or new interpretation to deliver the proper knowledge. Without geological support, they are unable to solve the problem. If they say "it is nice to have it" or "nice to know it" to geological knowledge delivered, then actually it is not useful.

Let us continue to review the previous case in the construction business. A civil engineer needs to put a foundation for the thirty-floor hotel into the subsurface. His first problem is he does not know the safe bearing capacity of the subsurface and how it will respond to the building. The rock in the subsurface should be strong to support a building. If a building is rested on weak rock, then it will be damaged. It may crack, tilt, or collapse. Moreover, the subsurface character will determine the particular foundation type needed.

It is a risk if he insists on building a hotel without geological knowledge of the subsurface. If he decides to use a shallow foundation type while the strong rock is evidently in deeper depth, then the building will be damaged. Although the response may be slow, it is certain, and it will need more cost to repair. Eventually, his reputation will decrease.

What should appear in the mind of a civil engineer regarding geological knowledge is mitigation. It is his focus of interest. To avoid disaster, he discusses the problem with a geologist. During discussion, the civil engineer's position is next-user, while the geologist is the supplier of knowledge. To understand his problem and to deliver proper knowledge, the geologist borrows his focus of interest – that is, mitigation.

The geologist explores data and information on the subsurface where the engineer will construct the hotel. It ranges from literature review to ground check (e.g., soil test). Data and information are interpreted into understandable geological knowledge to the engineer. The outcome should fulfill what the engineer needs. Moreover, the engineer should be able to realize its consequences for the foundation type needed.

In this context, the geologist acts as engineering geologist in the field of engineering geology, who works in construction business. His or her focus of interest is mitigation. His or her support is particular geological knowledge dedicated to civil engineering works. In this case, engineering geology is geology to support construction works by mitigating engineering failure due to geological causes.

Let us continue to review previous case from the petroleum industry. A drilling engineer needs to produce oil from a reservoir deep in the subsurface. To achieve it, he needs to drill an exploration well. However, he does not know the geology of the area. This refers to factors such as how deep the reservoir target is and what kind of rock layers will be penetrated. Geological knowledge will determine matters such as exploration well design, the drilling rig type needed, and the particular drilling mud type.

It is a risk if he insists on drilling without geological knowledge. The risk is he or she doesn't know how deep, how hard, and how long to drill. If the engineer runs out of budget before reaching the reservoir target, then he or she will need to ask for more. Eventually, it will ruin the engineer's reputation.

What should appear in the mind of a drilling engineer regarding geological knowledge is production. It is his or her focus of interest. To meet the objective, the engineer consults with a geologist about the problem. During the discussion, the drilling engineer's position is next-user, while the geologist is the supplier of knowledge. To understand problem and to deliver proper knowledge, the geologist borrows his or her focus of interest, which is production. However, before producing oil, the geologist needs to explore the geology of oil accumulation in the area. Hence, the geologist's focus of interest is exploration and production.

The geologist explores data and information on the subsurface where oil seepages are found. It ranges from literature review, to interpreting rock layers in the subsurface, to geophysical data and field surface mapping. Data and information are interpreted into understandable geological knowledge for the next-user. Finally, the drilling engineer understands the geological knowledge of the depth reservoir objective and rock layer types that will be penetrated. Most important is that the engineer understands the consequences to drilling well design, particular drilling rigs, and certain types of drilling mud needed.

In this context, the geologist acts as petroleum geologist in the field of petroleum geology who works in the petroleum industry. His focus of interest is exploration and production. His support is particular geological knowledge dedicated to drilling engineering. In this case, petroleum geology is geology to support the petroleum industry by exploring and producing oil in a drilling works.

2.5.2.3.1.3. *Wrapping Up the First Characteristic*

Based on the previous description, the first character of applied geology is *geological knowledge support,* which should be important to solve the next-user's problem. In this characteristic, geologist's focus of interest is the same as the next-user's. The geologist works in a particular discipline where his or her support is particular proper geological knowledge dedicated to the next-user in the discipline.

2.5.2.3.2. Second Characteristic

Geologists carry on scientific investigations to find the proper knowledge for the next-user. The outcome is knowledge. Over the time, the knowledge accumulates. Eventually, the accumulation allows geologist to generate a theory as systematic knowledge. Theory is a set of explanations of why a feature might occur, consisting of causal relationships of various variable interactions. Based on the theory, geologist and engineer able to explain, predict, and control.

The main theory of petroleum geology is the petroleum system. Using the theory, a petroleum geologist is able to explain and to predict petroleum accumulation in the subsurface. The controlling task is conducted by the petroleum engineer.

The main theory of engineering geology is rock and soil mechanics. Engineering geologists use the theory to explain and to predict geologic response to the man-made building that will be built in an area. The controlling task is conducted by civil engineer.

A theory generated by applied geology is generally only applicable to solve the problems in the applied geology itself. This is because every applied geology theory has a particular focus of interest. As a result, a common theory generated by applied geology is unable to solve the problems belonging to another applied geology. For instance, petroleum system knowledge is generated by investigations in the petroleum geology discipline, not researches in engineering geology. Similarly, the knowledge of soil mechanics in engineering geology is hardly able to solve the problems for finding oil needed by the petroleum industry.

Therefore, the second characteristic is *an applied geology study generates a particular systematic knowledge.* Certainly, a new applied geology should show its potential to produce particular systematic knowledge. Generating such knowledge requires time and support from many parties.

2.5.2.3.3. Third Characteristic

An applied geology outcome is geoscientific information. It is used by the next-user as technical knowledge input during making a decision. In addition, every applied geology has its own next-user.

In the case of engineering geology, the result of engineering geological investigation is scientific information dedicated to the civil engineer. In the case of petroleum geology, the outcome of petroleum geology study is scientific information dedicated to the petroleum engineer.

The civil engineer will hardly use the outcome of a petroleum geology study to understand ground character. Similarly, a petroleum engineer also will hardly use the study outcome of engineering geology to produce oil. Thus, the third characteristic is that *an applied geology study outcome is designated for a particular next-user.*

Hence, those are the three general characters of applied geology. It is also the requirement for tourism geology to be accepted as a field of applied geology of the second question.

2.5.2.4. Logical Consequences

If tourism geology is applied geology for tourism, then it should fulfill the three main applied geology characteristics. It is the third question of the plausible consequences if tourism geology is a member of applied geology.

When tourism geology is a member of applied geology for tourism, then it is a discipline connector among geology and tourism. Therefore, tourism geology should follow the relation of subject matter and focus of interest. The next-user of tourism geology outcome is the tourism-related professional, while the end-user is the tourist.

Thus, the same thing to do the business among tourism-related professionals and the geologist is on the natural tourist destination. Variables playing important roles in the destination are geological variables. Those variables are related to the solid part of the earth— minerals, stones, and rocks—and the fluids contained and their natural processes.

In focus of interest relation, the geologist and professional should have the same perspective to assess the geological feature. The professional perspective on the feature is a tourist attraction where many tourist interests and their activities relate to a geological feature. Geologists also assess the geological feature as tourist attraction where many tourist interests and activities are able to be fulfilled by the feature. Hence, the focus of interest is the same among them that is geological feature as tourist attraction.

Within a destination, there are problems related to geological feature as attraction that should be solved by tourism-related professionals. Using the same perspective, the geologist should be able to support them by analyzing the problem into several geological variable interactions, because there is cause-consequence relation. In this relation, geologist's role is to supply knowledge dedicated to the professionals. Geologists should understand particular geological knowledge needed, so that the professionals are able to use it to solve their problem and understand the consequences as well.

Hence, the first characteristic of tourism geology is *geological knowledge support should be important in solving tourism-related professional problems in regard to geological features as a tourist attraction*. The problem involves many tourist interests and activity types, as long as they relate to the geological feature.

The second characteristic is related to the ability of an applied geology to generate particular systematic knowledge. Such knowledge derives from research accumulation. The purpose of systematic knowledge is to explain the cause-consequence relation of variable interactions. Based on the knowledge, the geologist and the professional are able to explain, predict, and control.

An applied geology knowledge is unique because every applied geology has a particular focus of interest. Tourism geology as a member of an applied geology must be able to produce unique systematic knowledge that cannot be generated by other applied geology. Therefore, the second characteristic is *tourism geology studies should have the potential to generate particular systematic knowledge*. For sure, to construct such knowledge will be time-consuming. But the most important thing is that it is possible and can be faster with the support of many parties.

The third characteristic is related to the next-user who will use the study outcome of an applied geology. Because every applied geology is unique, its study outcome is used by a distinct next-user, not the end-user. The particular next-user of tourism geology study outcome is tourism-related professionals, not tourists. Thus, the third characteristic is that *tourism geology study outcome* should be *dedicated to tourism-related professionals.*

Tourism-related professionals will capture the features, derived from many study outcomes, and integrate them with industries. Those integrated features are transformed to be a tourism product. The final product is then ready to be used by tourist as the end-user.

Let me wrap up the three logical consequences of tourism geology:

- First characteristic: *tourism geological knowledge support should be important in solving tourism-related professional problems in regards to a geological feature as a tourist attraction.*

- Second characteristic: *tourism geology studies should have the potential to generate particular systematic knowledge.*

- Third characteristic: *tourism geology study outcome should be dedicated to tourism-related professionals.*

Those are three logical consequences for tourism geology to be accepted as a member of an applied geology (third challenge). If the speculative statement "tourism geology is a member of applied geology" is a correct statement, then those three consequences need to be clarified empirically. The empirical clarification is the answer of the fourth challenge.

The cases of an engineering geologist who works in the construction business and a petroleum geologist who works in the petroleum industry are used as models of applied geology. Hence, the work of a geologist in the tourism business, or let's say a tourism geologist, should be the same way with an engineering geologist or petroleum geologist (Fig. 2.11).

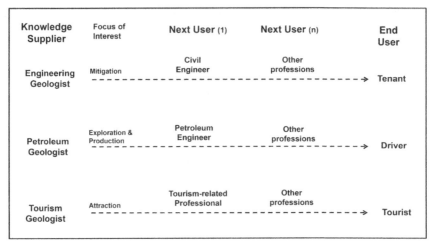

Figure 2.11. The workflow of an engineering geologist in the construction business and a petroleum geologist in the petroleum industry are used as models for "tourism geologists" who work in the tourism industry. Mitigation, exploration, production, and (tourist) attraction are the focus of interests of each profession.

2.5.3. Case Studies

I refer to several field studies and library research to answer the fourth question. Those studies are discussed in detail in the second part of this book. In this part, I briefly discuss the case studies.

2.5.3.1. Relation of Geological Feature and Tourist Destination Identification

Many attractive tourist destination areas were probably selected because of their scenic beauty or potential for adventure-related activity without scientific study. So that developing an area to be a tourist destination is easily constructed with no scientific investigation.

Purnama (2002a) carried on a geologic investigation for tourist destination verification in the Samarinda area, Indonesia (see also

Chapter 6). He carried out field observation and discovered several attractive geological features for tourist destinations, concerning geologic and non-geologic kinds of tourist interest. To name a few: caves, scenic view sites, hydrocarbon seepages, mud volcanoes, and abandoned oil wells. Those features are not found in most tourist's daily lives. It was one of the reasons to be upgraded to be a tourist destination. This research type is apparently abundant in the geotourism theme.

2.5.3.2. Aesthetic Nearshore Identification

Understanding geology and oceanography of an attractive area is useful when determining a nearshore area to be developed as a tourist destination. In this context, I use Lebak nearshore study, on the southwestern coast of Jawa, Indonesia (Purnama, 2002b; see further discussion in Chapter 7).

The first consideration was whether to decide on a nearshore aesthetic or not, particularly for swimming activities. Commonly, an aesthetic nearshore should be free of suspended sediment, because no tourist is willing to bathe in turbid water. Free sediment suspension area is also important for the safety factor, because the lifeguard can easily see injured swimmers or even sharks below the water surface. For that reason, the presence of suspended sediment affects the aesthetic nearshore and safety. Using a satellite image, I define a relatively cleaner nearshore on the eastern coast (Fig. 2.12). It was the eastern coast area, comprised of Manuk Island, Ciantir, and Legon Pari bays.

2.5.3.3. Identification of Safe Waters for Swimming

Every tourist requires personal safety during his or her activity, including swimming. For obvious reasons, a swimming area should fulfill safety requirements. When safety is considered, this means there is a potential threat. Purnama (2002b) stated that most parts of the southwestern nearshore of Jawa are unsafe for swimmers because of strong rip current, presence of waves and breakers up to three meters high, and the presence of lots of rocks/reefs. Rip current is a current flow perpendicular to the beach that is able to drag a swimmer into the open ocean. It is the main cause of casualty during swimming.

After the aesthetic area was selected, it was continued with choosing a swimming safe area. Purnama (2002b) concluded that safety issues for swimming in the selected bays apparently were geologically controlled. He observed the cape distance of each of three bays and their rock composition (Fig. 2.12). The cape width of Manuk Island, Ciantir, and Legon Pari Bays was 300 m, 3.3 km, and 450 m, respectively. Those capes were composed of hard rocks: limestone and volcanic breccia.

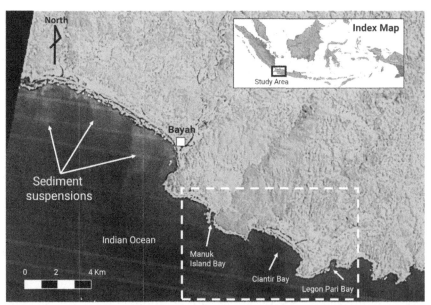

Figure 2.12. Satellite image of Lebak Area, southwestern coast of Jawa, Indonesia. Sediment suspension area observed in the western nearshore shows turbid waters, which affect the aesthetic factor. Free sediment suspension area was observed in the eastern nearshore (Manuk Island, Ciantir, and Legon Pari Bays). Purnama (2002b) interpreted it as aesthetic nearshore for tourist destination candidates. Satellite image courtesy of Indonesia Geologists Association.

Field observation showed that the lower wave energy develops in the maximum 450 m of cape distance. It has the consequence of reducing the rip currents developed in the bay. So that he considers the Manuk Island and Legon Pari Bays relatively safe for swimming. It should be noted that the shoreline in the study area is relatively parallel to the wind direction (east and west monsoons).

Purnama (2002b) concluded that the characteristics of safe waters for swimming in the study area have two features:

1. Bay with a cape width of up to 450 m. This ensures the distance allowed to guarantee a swimming safe area.

2. The cape consists of hard rock that juts into the sea. Hard rock is a natural barrier to reduce stronger waves and to prevent stronger rip currents from developing. This in turn prevents swimmers from being dragged and drifting into the rough seas.

Someone might use this knowledge as a hypothesis to determine safe waters for swimming in similar geological environments where the coast faces the open sea. For example, this hypothesis can be used in the western coasts of Sumatra or South America.

2.5.3.4. Safety Concern While Seeing Lava in Kilauea, Hawaii

Volcanoes, despite having a unique appeal during a visit, also have risks. For example, the impact of an injury due to falling pyroclastic or an earthquake during a volcanic eruption. Risks can also be linked to weather, such as acid rain when volcanic gases erupted are carried away by the wind.

One of the most-visited volcano destination is Hawaii. Seeing lava eruption will be an unforgettable experience. Admiring the lava of Mt. Kilauea, which flows into the sea, is an impressive memory. White clouds appear when lava interacts with sea water, looking like a beautiful cloud. However, it actually releases toxic gases and can cause fatality. When lava settles on the shore, it forms new land and becomes a tourist attraction. Even so, many accidents occurred because tourists stood too close to witness better the ongoing geological process.

Johnson et al. (2000) state that when hot lava settles on the shore, it explodes and forms hot water vapor, hot boiling water, tephra, or steam bursts. The debris of hot lava is then covered with a layer of lava flow, forming a "bench," which gives a false impression about the solid ground. Because the bottom and middle of the "bench" are still soft lava, it must have cracked and slid into the sea. Tourists who stand on such "benches" suffer injuries. In such cases, we need geological knowledge to understand the potential threat of sightseeing in active volcanic areas.

2.5.3.5. Tourist Destination Planning from a Geological Point of View

When the attraction is strongly related to a geological feature, we should use geological information for tourist destination planning. The next-user is the people, such as land developers, land owners, or park managers who will follow up the project. Geological information translation for them is useful, because they are non-geologists. They will use the translation to make scientifically based decisions. A case study of a tourist destination development at Gunung Batu, West Jawa, Indonesia, shows geological data were translated into supporting and prohibitive factors (Purnama, 2004; see also Chapter 8). The study purpose was for tourist destination planning. One of the research outcomes is a map of potential tourist activities in Gunung Batu (Fig. 2.13).

Supporting factor is geological character to draw visitor attention and develop activities. It includes attraction, visitor activity, and geodiversity value. Prohibitive factor is geological feature that decreases visitor activities and/or decreases all of the supporting factors. The purpose of prohibitive factor identification is to minimize physical loss or to minimize the decreasing attraction.

In the case of Gunung Batu, Purnama (2004) concluded that the supporting factors in the study area are composed of (1) the attractions, that is, geological, man-made geological, and recreational attractions; and (2) the activities, that is, geological and outdoor activities. The prohibitive factors are composed of sensitivity scale of the geological features (e.g., sensitive to rock mining and rock vandalism) and geological features as hazard potentials (e.g., earthquake, ground movement, and low risk area of pyroclastic fall from the nearest volcano).

The study's main point is how to translate geological data for tourist destination planners who usually are non-geoscientists. You might develop a different method during the translation process. It is the planner's decision, however, as to what theme in the destination will be used, which strongly related to profitability.

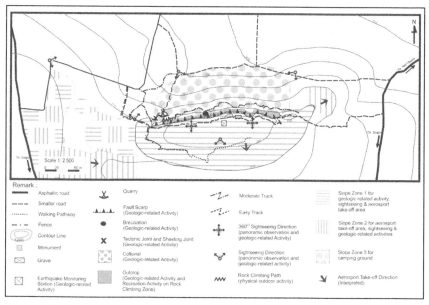

Figure 2.13. Map of potential tourist activities in Gunung Batu, Indonesia. It shows the kinds of activities ranging from geo-scientific, panoramic observation, camping, aero sport, and rock climbing (after Purnama, 2004).

2.5.3.6. *Geological Variable Influence in Mountaineering Difficulty Rating*

Mountaineering difficulty rating is measured to understand how much effort is needed (i.e., energy and skill required) to reach the peak. One of the difficulty components in mountaineering is geological variables, since the mountain itself is a geological feature, whether it is a volcano, fold mountain belt, or granitic rock.

Purnama et al. (in this volume, visit Chapter 9), constructed four main variables influencing mountaineering difficulty, composed of terrain, route condition, weather, and physical ability. Among those variables, terrain component—composed of slope and route surface type—is the only geological variable. Purnama et al. (in this volume, see Chapter 9) applied the difficulty rating during mountaineering in Cereme, Slamet, and Semeru volcanoes of Jawa Island.

During activity, variables were documented to measure difficulty rating. The variables were route surface types and position, slope, altitude, route, distance, travel time, coordinate position, vegetation, and geological hazard potential. One of the research outcomes suggests that different rock types and/or soil in the surface might have a different slope steepness. This has consequences for evaluating the difficulties in each route segment. Another outcome was geological hazard potential on the steeper slope, such as soil slide, pyroclastic sand or stone.

The user of the study might be a park ranger or mountaineer, as awareness for better preparation prior the activity. One of the study outcomes is a geological cross-section along the ascending and descending routes (Fig. 2.14). It will improve the understanding of difficulty rating in relation to geological variables.

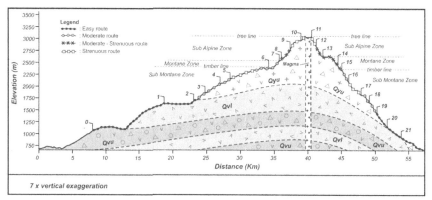

Figure 2.14. Geological cross-section of ascending (Stop 0–Stop 11) and descending (Stop 11–Stop 21) routes of the Cereme Volcano. The subsurface geology interpretation of the profiles was based on a geological map of Cereme Volcano (after Djuri, 1973). Numbers are stop sites. Qyu, Qvl, and Qvu are rock units. Qyu is undifferentiated volcanic (e.g., breccia) and pyroclastic rock unit. Qvl is Lava deposit unit. Qvu is undifferentiated volcanic unit.

2.5.3.7. Geological-Related Attraction Characterization in Lombok Island

The designation of Rinjani-Lombok Geopark by UNESCO in 2018 and the MotoGP event of 2022 brought more tourism business opportunity in the Lombok Island. The Rinjani-Lombok Geopark area is situated in the northern part of the island. Within the area, there are about 22 geological sites to be promoted in the geotourism market segment.

Purnama et al. (2019, in this volume in Chapter 10), intend to characterize the geological-related attractions of the whole island through desk study on a regional scale. It is based on the belief that geological features are able to fulfill various tourist interests, such as scenic beauty, outdoor activity, and curative interests. In addition, there is a need to understand the consequence of tourism development highlights from the characterization outcome.

In geological-related attraction characterization context, the outcome shows Lombok's geomorphology comprises four landscape types, subdivided into to eleven landform units. It comprises landscapes of volcanic (four landform units), coastal (three units), faulted hill (two units), and karst (two units; Fig. 2.15; Table 2.2).

Based on the data, Purnama et al. (2019, Chapter 10) define statuses (proven, probable. and possible) of tourist attraction and activity on each landform unit. Tourism development highlights are also arranged on each landform unit: exploration (of new destination), mitigation (of injury and fatality), and impact monitoring (of tourist impact; Table 2.2).

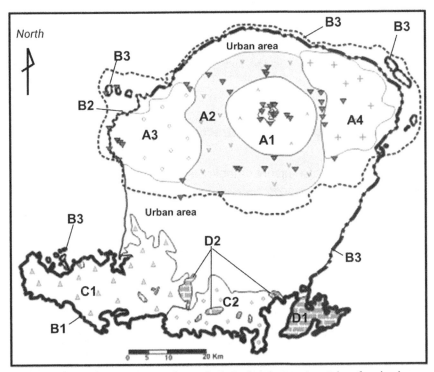

Figure 2.15. Landform zone map for geological-related attraction. It has four landscape and eleven landform units (see Table 2.2). The Rinjani-Lombok Geopark Area is within Volcanic Landscapes (A1, A2, A3, A4), Malimbu Rocky coast (B2), and northern part of the Rinjani Sandy Coast (B3). The triangles are the twenty-two geological sites of the Geopark.

Today tourist activities are mostly in the southern and the western coasts where other identified geological-related attractions mostly fall to probable and possible statuses. Tourism development highlights as examples are expected able to offer destination choices, distribute tourist pressure on the environment, and increase undeveloped community wealth.

Table 2.2. Status of attraction and activity on each landform unit.

Land-scape Type	Landform Unit Code	Landform Unit Name	Attraction & Tourist Activity Status			
			Geologic History	Scenic Beauty	Particular Landform for Outdoor Activity	Curative
Volcanic Landscape	A1	Rinjani Upper Cone	proven	proven	proven-probable	proven-probable
	A2	Rinjani Lower Cone	proven	proven	proven-probable	possible
	A3	Punikan Volcanic Cone	proven	proven-probable	proven-probable	possible
	A4	Pusuk-Nangi Volcanic Cone	proven	proven-probable	proven-probable	proven-probable
Coastal Landscape	B1	Pengulung-Kuta Rocky Coast	proven	proven	proven-probable	proven
	B2	Malimbu Rocky Coast	proven	proven	proven-probable	possible
	B3	Rinjani Sandy Coast	proven	proven-probable	proven-probable	possible
Faulted Hill Landscape	C1	Pengulung Undulated	possible	proven-probable	proven-probable	possible
	C2	Kuta Undulated	possible	proven-probable	proven-probable	possible
Karst Landscape	D1	Ekas Carbonate	possible	proven-probable	possible	possible
	D2	Pengulung Isolated Carbonate	possible	possible	proven-probable	possible

2.5.3.8. Synthesis of the Empirical Proofs

I use those case studies to answer the fourth challenge. It is the query of empirical clarification towards the three logical consequences. The outline of case studies is given in Table 2.3.

The first logical consequence of tourism geology is *tourism geological knowledge support should be important to solve tourism-related professional's problem* (Table 2.3). In addition, the case studies presented concern geologic and non-geologic interests. The problems of the case studies are typical in tourism, called tourism problem. Those problems are also associated with the geological feature. So that, geological variable interaction with the feature becomes knowledge. Thus, geological knowledge is proven able to support tourism problem solving. In my perspective, those geological supports in those cases are important. Hence, the case studies clarify the first logical consequence.

However, I should measure how important those geological supports. So that, three scales were made and used to measure the level of support in the studies (Table 2.3), as follows:

- Low to medium: Geological support carries the better outcome, especially on geoscientific interest identification. Nevertheless, non-geologists are also able to define the attraction of non-geoscientific interest.

- Medium to high: Geological support has the further result on causal explanation and prediction. The practitioner is also good on identification, although less so in explaining and predicting.

- High: Only geological support is able to explain and to predict. The level of importance is different among the cases. A decision on whether geological support is needed or not is in the hand of the next-user.

The second logical consequence is *tourism geology studies should have the potential to generate particular systematic knowledge*. Those study results show its potential to establish systematic knowledge, particularly in case number 3, 5, 6, and 7 (Table 2.3). If similar studies applied worldwide, there is the potential to form a theory or method. For instance, a theory of geological control on identification of safe waters for swimming, or how to predict mountaineering difficulty rating from geological or geomorphological maps. We will discuss this idea in further detail in Chapter 4. Thus, the studies deal with the second logical consequence.

Table 2.3. Summary of case studies.

No	Case Studies	Tourist Interest Kind	Tourism Problem	Geological Support Scale for Tourism
1	Identification of potential tourist destination (Samarinda, Eastern Kalimantan)	Geologic and non-geologic	Identification tourist attraction	Low – Medium
2	Aesthetic nearshore identification (Lebak, Western Jawa)	Non-geologic	Identification tourist attraction	Low – Medium
3	Safe swimming nearshore identification (Lebak, Western Jawa)	Non-geologic	Identification safety area	Medium – High
4	Safety sightseeing lava (Mt. Kilauea, Hawaii)	Geologic and non -geologic	Identification safety area	High
5	Tourist destination planning (Gunung Batu, Western Jawa)	Geologic and non -geologic	Geological data translation for tourist destination planning	High
6	Geological variable influence in mountaineering difficulty rating (Cereme, Slamet and Semeru Volcanoes, Jawa Island)	Non-geologic	Identification of mountaineering difficulty rating	Medium – High
7	Lombok Island including the Rinjani-Lombok Geopark	Geologic and non -geologic	Identification of attraction and activities and tourism development highlight from attraction character	High

The third logical consequence is *tourism geology study outcome should be dedicated for tourism-related professionals.* The research outcomes produce a set of geologic knowledge in the form of a scientific paper or report. It is dedicated to the tourism-related professional, in particular someone who works in the attraction sector. Hence, the studies clarify the third logical consequence.

Absolutely, the outcome is not dedicated for the tourist (end-user). If it will be used for them, then it needs to be repackaged by the science communication discipline. It is about how to communicate a scientific topic to public. Therefore, the studies successfully answered the fourth challenge. It is the search of the empirical verification of the three logical consequences. For that reason, the speculative statement of "tourism geology is a member of applied geology" is a correct statement.

Using this understanding, we able to interpret several attributes of tourism geology and the geologist, as follows.

- The geologist acts as geologist with tourism geology mind, who works in tourism, especially in the attraction sector.
- The focus of interest of the geologist is tourist attraction related to the geological feature, which able to fulfill geoscientific and non-geoscientific tourist interests.
- Geological support is particular geological knowledge applied for the tourism-related professional, particularly who works in the attraction sector.
- Tourism geology's purpose is to support tourism by delivering proper geological knowledge to make the tourism-related professional able to solve tourism problems linked to the geological feature.

2.6. COMPARING DEFINITIONS

To answer the fifth challenge, I scrutinized the definitions and statements related to geotourism from published papers and books. The challenge is about the differences of my tourism geology version with geotourism and the earlier concepts of tourism geology.

2.6.1. Geotourism General Characteristics

I refer to two geotourism leaders for geotourism descriptions. The first is Thomas A. Hose, whose geoconservation context in geotourism became his main background. The second is Ross Dowling, where his geotourism point-of-view is discussed in a tourism context. Some of Dowling's publications were written in collaboration with David Newsome.

Thomas Alfred Hose or Tom Hose is the first person who popularized the term "geotourism" since 1995. His LinkedIn profile tells us that he is a consultant, writer, and editor in the field of geotourism, geoconservation, and landscape tourism. He has worked in museums (1988–1991), which support his interest in geotourism. He has Bachelor of Science (BSc) in Geology, Master of Arts (MA) in Museum and Gallery Administration, and Doctor of Philosophy (PhD) in Geotourism. Today, he serves as an Honorary Research Associate in School of Earth Sciences, University of Bristol, United Kingdom.

Scrutinizing the profile of Ross Dowling from a book that he authored: he is a global contributor of tourism development in the fields of geotourism and geoparks (at least since 2005), cruise ship tourism, and ecotourism. He conducts many international research projects in those fields. In fact, he has over 200 publications including 16 books. In addition, he was awarded the Medal of the Order of Australia in 2011 for his excellent contributions to tourism education and development. He has a BSc in Geology, Master of Science (MSc; Hons) in Geography, and PhD in Environmental Science. At this moment, he serves as an Honorary Professor of Tourism in Edith Cowan University, Australia.

David Newsome is an Associate Professor in Environmental Science and Ecotourism and member, Nature Based Tourism Research Group, School of Environmental Science at Murdoch University, Australia. He is an environmental scientist with expertise in wildlife tourism, geotourism, and biophysical impacts of natural area tourism. He is also in an advisory role, predominantly to the state government and IUCN on ecotourism. Wildlife tourism, geotourism, and biophysical impacts of natural area tourism are his research areas.

Apparently, Thomas Hose, Ross Dowling, and David Newsome share the same messages. It is geological features as main tourist attractions for geoscientific tourist interest, great attention to increasing visitor experience on geological features, in context of a geoconservation spirit, sustainable tourism, and to stimulate local economic growth with positive environmental impact.

2.6.1.1. Geotourism Background

The emergence of Hose's thought derived from his own experience, including many geosite losses. Meanwhile, the geoscience community failed to bring natural conservation issues to the wider political arena and planning and public communities. This led him to develop a research program on "site-specific geologic interpretation" during the early 1990s (Hose, 2011, p. 349).

Hose (2011, p. 345) stated that the inception geotourism study was developed as a way for geology and geomorphology to be promote, identify, protect, and conserve geological sites. Thus, geotourism and geoconservation have a strong relationship in Hose's mind. His first definition in 1995 gained popularity when UNESCO developed the Geopark program in the late 20th century.

On the other hand, Dowling (2009, pp. 25-26) carries different approaches on geotourism principles. His background on the world of tourism clearly shows his mindset of how geotourism should be.

He emphasizes geological atmosphere in every tourism aspect. He describes his principles of geotourism as follows:

1. Geologically based or based on the earth's geoheritage.
2. Sustainable, i.e., economically viable; community enhancing; and fosters geoconservation.
3. Geologically informative, which is achieved through geo-interpretation.
4. Locally beneficial.
5. Generates tourist satisfaction.

The first three characteristics are essential products of geotourism. The last two characteristics are desirable for all tourism forms.

2.6.1.2. Geotourism Purpose

At the outset, Hose et al. (2011, p. 340) envisaged that geotourism would promote, build, and provide funding for geoconservation of geosites and geomorphosites when Europe's governments were unwilling to provide financial support. As a consequence, it would open up and maintaining access to geosites and geomorphosites through the development of sustainable tourism products and services (Hose et al., 2011, p. 339).

In my view, the heart of Hose's geotourism is geoconservation. He emphasizes the importance of geoconservation through geotourism by provision strategy. His thought is also a reminder of the natural conservation spirit and marked geotourism movement in welcoming the new age of the 21st century.

Dowling (2009, pp. 26-27) has a slightly different point of view. He has a broader view of geotourism which also concerns the local community, visitor experience, and economy. He mentioned the goals of sustainable geotourism development, as follows:

1. To develop greater awareness and understanding of the significant contributions that geotourism can make to the environment, local communities, and the economy.

2. To promote equity in geo-development.

3. To improve the quality of life of the host community.

4. To provide a high quality of the geological experience for the visitor.

5. To maintain the quality of the geoheritage on which the foregoing objectives depend.

2.6.1.3. Geotourism Definition

Among many parties' definitions of geotourism, I choose the definition of Hose compared with the Newsome and Dowling version. Hose (2012, p. 11) defined geotourism as:

> The provision of interpretative and service facilities for geosites and geomorphosites and their encompassing topography, together with their associated in-situ and ex-situ artifacts, to constituency build for their conservation by generating appreciation, learning and research by and for current and future generations.

Hose (2016, p. 4) also formulated four key interrelated aspects that underpin geotourism: geohistory, geoconservation, geointerpretation, and geosites or geomorphosites.

Another geotourism definition is derived from Newsome and Dowling (2010, p. 3). They stated:

> Geotourism is a form of natural area tourism that specifically focuses on geology and landscape. It promotes tourism to geosites and the conservation of geodiversity and understanding of earth sciences through appreciation and learning. This is achieved through independent visits to geological features, use of geo-trails and viewpoints, guided tours, geo-activities and patronage of geosite visitor centres.

Moreover, Newsome and Dowling (2006, p. 5) described three components within the geotourism scope: form, process, and tourism.

The components of form and process (e.g., landscapes and deposition) are geological features. The components of tourism—attraction, accommodation, tours, activities, interpretation, planning, and management—mean visiting, learning, and appreciating geological sites.

The geotourism definition might be explained in context of subject matter and focus of interest. Subject matter of geotourism includes geosite, geomorphosite, landscape, and geosite; and also covers artifacts such as visitor center, geological museum, old textbooks, and sculpture from rocks. It is similar to tourism geology but extended to man-made products.

The main purpose of geotourism is conservation of geological features. Other activities in geotourism, such as visiting geosites or geotrails, appreciation, and learning, are the means to get (public) attention to support conservation of geological features.

My conclusion is that geotourism subject-matter is a geological feature and man-made work related to geology. The focus of interest of geotourism is conservation (of geological features). In other word, the geotourism practitioner assesses the geological feature mainly to be conserved.

In practice, however, the meaning of geotourism might be different between geologists and tourism-related professionals. As mentioned by Melendez et al. (2011, p. 98), during the process of making geology to be a touristic attraction, both geologists and the administration often design products and facilities that are more related to research and geodidactic. In other word, those products are intended to explain geology to school teachers, students, organized groups, and occasionally for tourist, rather than making geology to be an attractive subject for tourists.

2.6.1.4. Geotourism Research

Interpretation on geoscience information is needed since communication of geoscience to the public is an important aspect. Hose (2012, p. 17) defined geointerpretation as *the art or science of determining and then communicating the meaning or significance of a geological or geomorphological phenomenon, event or location.* Hose (2005, p. 30) mentioned that geotourism is also a geology-focused development of environmental interpretation. Such interpretation involves translating the technical language of a natural science into specific vocabulary and ideas, so that non-specialists can readily understand them.

According to Hose et al. (2011, p. 340), geotourism always encompasses an examination of the physical basis, interpretative media, and promotion of geosites and geomorphosites, documentation of geoscience knowledge growth, and geoscientist or geologist personnel themselves. Thus, geotourism's scope is not only about geosites. It also clear that geotourism study is a part of social science studies, not natural sciences studies. Several geotourism research examples are discussed in Chapter 4.

Following geotourism booming worldwide, several journals that strongly related to geotourism and geoconservation are published. They are as follow:

- *The Geotourism (Geoturystyka)* published since 2004 by AGH University of Science and Technology, Poland;

- *Geojournal of Tourism and Geosites,* issued since 2008 under the aegis of the University of Oradea, Romania and the Academy of Physical Education and Sports from Gdańsk, Poland.

- *Geoheritage,* published by Springer Verlag since 2009.

- *Acta Geoturistica,* published jointly since 2010 by the academic publisher SCIENDO, with the support of the Faculty of Mining, Ecology, Process Control and Geotechnologies (Technical University of Košice) and Institute of Geotechnics (Slovak Academy of Sciences).

- *The International Journal of Geoheritage and Parks,* since 2013 published by Elsevier B.V., where the copyright is held by Beijing Normal University.

- *Sustainable Geoscience and Geotourism,* published by SciPress Ltd since 2017.

2.6.2. Distinction of Tourism Geology from Geotourism

From those statements and definitions, I conclude the distinction of geotourism and tourism geology. It is discussed in several aspects, such as purpose, variable, knowledge type made, result, tourist type, and impact on tourism market (Table 2.4).

Table 2.4. Main characteristics of geotourism and tourism geology.

Aspect	Geotourism	Tourism geology
Purpose	To support geological conservation, to be sustainable tourism, to improve visitor experience and to encourage local economic growth.	To support tourism by delivering proper geological knowledge to enable the tourism-related professional to solve tourism problem linked to the geological feature
Variable Type	Mostly non-geological variables	Mostly geological variables
Knowledge Type Generated	Non-geological knowledge since social variables plays critical roles.	Geological knowledge
Outcome	Tourism products connected to geology	Geologic publication or report
User Type	end-user (tourist) and also next-user (tourism-related professional)	next-user (tourism-related professional and other practitioner)
Tourist Interest Type	Geologic interest	All tourist interest referred to geological feature
Tourism Market Target	Geotourism, Ecotourism (?)	All tourism market applied to geological feature
Geologist Role	Geologist specified in geoscientific interest and also to be a tourism-related professional	Supplier knowledge for the next-user

2.6.2.1. Purpose

Geotourism's aim differs when compared to the purpose of tourism geology. Geotourism's aim is to support geoconservation, to be sustainable tourism, to increase visitor experience, and to encourage local economic growth with positive environmental impact. Differently, tourism geology's purpose is to support tourism by deliver proper geological knowledge to make the tourism-related professional able to solve tourism problems linked to the geological feature. The problem refers to exploring tourist attractions, identifying a safety area, geological data translation effort for planning, and other things related to the geological feature for tourism-related professionals. We will review the tourism geology scope in Chapter 3.

2.6.2.2. Variable Type

Geotourism involves mainly non-geological variables during construction of its products, which include interpretative material, souvenirs, geotour itineraries, and tourism planning and development process. For instance, during developing a geotourism-related site, we need to understand variable interaction between visitor education level, visitor age, visitor behavior, media type, institutional arrangement, and site management. Such variables are social variables, hence beyond geological scope.

On the opposite, tourism geology covers only geological variables as well as non-living related variables, such as the steepness of the slope, rock type, and structure of the rock itself. Research examples in tourism geology refer to the cases of field studies as given previously.

2.6.2.3. Knowledge Type Generated

The distinctions in purpose and variable have consequences in the knowledge type generated. Since mainly social variable interaction plays a crucial role in geotourism, then the theory generated is non-geological knowledge. For instance, it is better to use simple words with analogy relating to daily life rather than more technical terms to explain geological information to the public. In addition, adding sketches of the paleoenvironment will be helpful to increase understanding.

Variable type in tourism geology is mostly geological variable interaction. As a consequence, knowledge achieved is geological knowledge. What kind of geological knowledge in tourism geology had been discussed in the case studies.

2.6.2.4. Outcome

Geotourism is able to generate final tourism products related to geology. As a consequence, it is able to be directly used by the end-users / tourists. For instance, interpretative geological panels, geological guidebooks, geological souvenirs, and geological tours. On the other hand, tourism geology's scope is able to produce geologic knowledge in the form of a scientific paper or report. Unfortunately, it is beyond the scope of tourism geology to generate products like geotourism products.

2.6.2.5. User Type

Tourism geology is user-oriented, where outcome only can be understood by tourism-related professionals, such as park managers, recreation workers, tour and travel guides, tour operators, park rangers, and others. User oriented also means the task of the geologist is to fulfill geological data and information according to user needs (will be discussed in Chapter 3).

The outcome of geotourism work can be used directly by the end-user (tourist) and also next-user (tourism-related professional) who need geological interpretation. In addition, geotourism is (geological) conservation-oriented.

2.6.2.6. Tourist Interest Type

Tourist interest type in geotourism is a focus on geoscientific interest where geological history is the centerpiece. In contrast, tourist interest type in tourism geology is all tourist interest connected to the geological feature (e.g., geologic, adventure, and scenic beauty interests).

2.6.2.7. Tourism Market Target

Geotourism has a particular tourism target market, such as geotourism and possibly ecotourism. In contrast, tourism geology has all of the tourism market target that is connected to the geological feature—such as adventure tourism, sports tourism, sun and beach tourism, and health tourism. This will be discussed in more detail in Chapter 3. It doesn't matter if geology has a smaller contribution in those tourism types. The most important thing is that geological contribution is recognized and needed.

My intention in explaining the distinction of tourism geology from geotourism is to show that those two terms are designed for different purposes. Although geotourism and tourism geology study the same subject-matter, that is, the geological feature, each has a different particular focus of interest and also a different scope. It is also clear that geotourism is not part of tourism geology, and vice versa.

2.6.2.8. Geologist Role

The geologist's role in tourism geology is basically as a supplier of geological knowledge for tourism-related professionals (the next-users), never reaching tourists (end-users). It is same situation in the other discipline. For instance, the engineering geologist's role in engineering geology is a supplier of knowledge for civil engineers, never reach directly to the tenant (end-user). Petroleum geologists' role in petroleum geology is to supply knowledge for the petroleum engineer; there is no way for them to interact with the driver who needs gasoline (end-user). Why do they never contact the end-user? Because their job description in their business is already described according to their focus of interest. Details of geological knowledge supply to tourist-related professionals will be discussed in Chapter 3.

It is a different situation, however, with the geologists' role in geotourism. They are the supplier of geological knowledge although the focus is on geoscientific tourist interest. Furthermore, they are able to reach more than geological scope, such as tour interpreter, tour guide, and products made with a geological connotation. Eventually, they are able transform to be tourism-related professionals, where they interact directly with end-users (tourists). This matter will be discussed in Chapter 5.

2.6.3. Comparing Previous Definitions of Tourism Geology

It is crucial to point out differences among earlier definitions of tourism geology with my interpretation of tourism geology. The most popular terms come from Malaysia and China. The first tourism geology definition originated in Malaysia, represented by Komoo (1997, p. 2970) and echoed by Kadderi (2000, p. 200). They stated that tourism geology is a part of geology dedicated to tourism. However, they stated that their version is only for ecotourism development and develops geotourism as a consequence. Thus, I conclude their concept of tourism geology relates closely to the geotourism concept.

In China, apparently geotourism has been named by geoscientists as tourism earth science (Chen et al., 2020, p. ix). The Association for Tourism Earth Science in China defined tourism earth science in Article 2 as "*a newly emerging interdisciplinary science, aims at investigating, studying, planning, developing and protecting tourism resources by applying its theories and methodology.*" The word *protecting* indicates the same concept as the geotourism idea, whereas tourism geology has a different approach about protection of the geological feature (further discussions will come in Chapters 3 and 5). Hence, there is no doubt that their concept of tourism earth science is the same as the geotourism idea.

My version of tourism geology is to support tourism by delivering proper geological knowledge to make the tourism-related professional able to solve tourism problems linked to the geological feature. Hence, my idea differs from earlier perceptions of tourism geology, whether they originated in China or Malaysia. Hence, those statements answer the fifth challenge. It is the challenge about differences of my tourism geology with geotourism and previous approaches to tourism geology.

2.7. CONCLUSION

Current understanding of geology and tourism relation refers to geotourism. Previously, it is believed that geotourism is the only one relation. My work intends to reveal the opportunity of the other relation.

I formulate the idea into the speculative statement that "tourism geology is a member of applied geology." The statement originated from etymological and empirical reviews. This work is the effort to verify the statement.

Methods to test the speculative statement validity use conceptual approaches, which are successfully verified by empirical proofs. Hence, the statement "tourism geology is a member of applied geology" is found to be a correct statement.

In addition, my study produces another two conclusions. I prove that my version of tourism geology has a different meaning from geotourism and earlier perceptions of tourism geology. So that, the first conclusion is there are two ways of geology and tourism interacting. The first interaction is as a tourism concept relying on geological features and man-made work related to geology, where the result is geotourism (and the earlier idea of tourism geology).. The second interaction is as an application of geological concepts to tourism, with the result is tourism geology (Fig. 2.16).

In this work, I simplify what I have been calling "the earlier idea of tourism geology" to be the same thing as geotourism itself. In addition, although you refer to the geotourism definition in Tourtellot's version, geotourism is still a tourism concept in a broader sense.

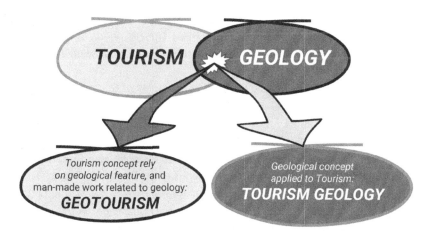

Figure 2.16. Two ways geology and tourism interact. The first interaction is as a tourism concept relying on a geological feature and man-made work related to geology, where the result is geotourism. The second interaction is as an application of geological concepts to tourism, in which the result is tourism geology.

I propose tourism geology as newly applied geology for tourism. The subject matter is the geological feature that can be safely visited. Tourism geology has the particular focus of interest that is a geological feature as a tourist attraction, which is able to fulfill geoscientific and non-geoscientific interests. The main purpose of tourism geology is to support tourism by delivering proper geological knowledge to make the tourism-related professional able to solve tourism problems linked to the geological feature. This idea opens new opportunity for geology to develop tourism and geology itself.

The second conclusion is that tourism geology should have the same characteristics as any other applied geology disciplines. It means, tourism geology has same level such as engineering geology or petroleum geology. Therefore, tourism geology is proof that there are many uses of geological knowledge for the community, other than mitigation of geological disaster and exploration for the extractive industry.

Reference Cited

Burek, C.V. & Prosser, C.D. (2008) The History of Geoconservation: An Introduction. p.2, In: Burek, C.V. & Prosser, C.D. (eds) *The History of Geoconservation*. Geological Society Special Publication No. 300, The Geological Society of London, 312 pp.

Chen, A., Lu, Y. & Ng, Y.C.Y. (eds) (2015) *The Principles of Geotourism*. Springer & Science Press Beijing. p.2, 264 pp.

Chen, A., Ng, Y., Zhang E. & Tian, M. (eds) (2020) *Dictionary of Geotourism*. Springer & Science Press Beijing. p.ix, 732 pp.

Djuri (1973) *Geologic Map of the Ardjawinangun Quadrangle*, Java, Scale 1:100,000. Geological Research and Development Centre, Bandung, Indonesia

Dowling, R. (2009) *The Growth of Global Geotourism*. p.25-27, pp.24-30, In: Carvalho, C. N. d. & Rodriguez, J. (eds), *New Challenges With Geotourism, Proceedings of the VIII European Geoparks Conference, Idanha-a-Nova, 14-16 September 2009*, 285 pp.

Goeldner, C.R. & Ritchie, J.R.B. (2009) *Tourism: Principles, Practices, Philosophies*. Eleventh edition, John Wiley & Sons Inc., p.6, 21-25, 624 pp.

Hose, T.A. (1995) *Selling the Story of Britain's Stone. Environmental Interpretation*, Vol. 10, No.2, p.17, pp.16-17.

Hose, T.A. (2005) Geotourism: Appreciating the Deep Time of Landscapes. p.30, pp.26-37, In: Novelli, M. (ed) *Niche Tourism*. Elsevier, 264 pp.

Hose, T.A. (2011) *The English Origins of Geotourism (as a Vehicle for Geoconservation) and Their Relevance to Current Studies. Acta Geographica Slovenica*, 51-2, p.345, 349, pp. 343-360

Hose, T.A. (2012) *3G's for Modern Geotourism*. Geoheritage, Springer-Verlag, Volume 4, p.11, 17, 7-24 pp.

Hose, T.A. (2016) Thee Centuries (1670 – 1970) of Appreciating Physical Landscapes. p.4,5. pp.1-23, In: Hose, T.A. (ed) *Appreciating Physical Landscapes: Three Hundred Years of Geotourism.* Geological Society, London, Special Publication 417, 248 pp.

Hose, T.A., Markovic, S.B., Komac, B. & Zorn, M. (2011) *Geotourism - A Short Introduction. Acta Geographica Slovenica,* 51-2, p.339, 340, pp.339-342

IAEG (1992) *Statutes.* Accessible via www.iaeg.info/wp-content/uploads/2018/12/iaeg-statutes.pdf or go to tinyurl.com/swwa94r.

Jafari, J. & Ritchie, J.R.B. (1981) *Toward a Framework for Tourism Education: Problem and Prospects. Annals of Tourism Research,* Vol. VIII, No. 1, Special Issue on Tourism Education, p. 15-19, pp 13-34

Jafari, J. (ed) (2000) *Encyclopedia of Tourism.* Routledge, p.585, 683 pp.

Johnson, J., Brantley, S.R., Swanson, D.A., Stauffer, P.H. & Hendley II, J.W. (2000) *Viewing Hawai'i's Lava Safely – Common Sense is Not Enough.* USGS Fact Sheet 152-00, Version 1.1, December 2000, Available via pubs.usgs.gov/fs/2000/fs152-00/fs152-00.pdf or go to tinyurl.com/rjsb27g. Accessed April 2004.

Kadderi, M.D. (2000) *Tourism Geoscience: A New Subdiscipline in Geoscience Education. Geological Society of Malaysia, Annual Geological Conference, 8-9 September 2000, Pulau Pinang, Malaysia,* p.197, 200, pp. 197-201.

Komoo, I. (1997) Conservation Geology: A Case for The Ecotourism Industry of Malaysia. p.2970, pp.2969-2974, In: Marinos, P.G., Koukis, G.C., Tsiambaos, G.C. & Stournas, G.C. (eds) *Engineering Geology and the Environment.* Balkema Publication, Rotterdam, Vol. 3. 3357 pp.

Kulesza, C., Gramann, J., Le, Y. & Hollenhorst, S.J. (2012a) *Yellowstone National Park, Visitor Study: Summer 2011.* Natural Resource Report NPS/NRSS/EQD/NRR–2012/539, University of Idaho, Park Studies Unit, June 2012, National Park Service, Fort Collins, Colorado, U. S. Department of the Interior, p.41, 136 pp.

Kulesza, C.Y., Le, Y. & Hollenhorst, S.J. (2012b) *Yellowstone National Park, Visitor Study: Winter 2012.* Natural Resource Report NPS/NRSS/EQD/ NRR–2012/611, University of Idaho, Park Studies Unit, December 2012, National Park Service, Fort Collins, Colorado, U. S. Department of the Interior, p.41, 104 pp.

Lee, Y., Schuett, M.A. & Hollenhorst, S.J. (2005) *John Day Fossil Beds National Monument. Visitor Study. Fall 2004.* Visitor Service Project Report 162, NPS-D81. University of Idaho. Park Studies Unit, April 2005, Social Science Program, National Park Service, U. S. Department of the Interior, p. 29, 88 pp.

Littlejohn, M.A. & Hollenhorst, S.J. (2004) *Grand Canyon National Park, South Rim, Visitor Study, Summer 2003,* Visitor Service Project Report 144, NPS D-728.

University of Idaho, Park Studies Unit, May 2004, Social Science Program, National Park Service, US Department of the Interior, p. 30, 35, 125 pp.

Littlejohn, M.A., Weber, K. & Hollenhorst, S.J. (2004) *Grand Canyon National Park, North Rim, Visitor Study, Summer 2003*, Visitor Service Project Report 143, NPS D-727, University of Idaho, Park Studies Unit, May 2004, Social Science Program, National Park Service, US Department of the Interior, p. 28, 33, 82 pp.

Magoon, L.B. & Dow. W.G. (1994) The Petroleum System. p.10, pp.3-24, In: Magoon, L.B. & Dow, W.G. (eds) *The Petroleum System-From Source to Trap*. AAPG Memoir 60, The American Association of Petroleum Geologists, 639 pp.

Manni, M.F., Littlejohn, M., Evans, J., Gramann, J. & Hollenhorst, S.J. (2007) *Yellowstone National Park, Visitor Study*. Visitor Service Project Report 178, NPS D-1210, University of Idaho, Park Studies Unit, June 2007, Social Science Program, National Park Service, U. S. Department of the Interior, p. 40, 102 pp.

Melendez, G., Fermeli, G., Escorihuela, J., Basso, A. & Moreira, J. (2011) *What Do We Mean When We Say Geotourism? Proceeding of International Congress Arouca 2011, Geotourism in Action, 9 – 13 November 2011, Arouca Geopark Portugal*, p.98, 99, pp.98-100

Mill, R.C. (1985) *Tourism: The International Business*. Prentice – Hall International Editions. p.2, 3, 42-46, 370 pp.

Moreira, J.C. & Melendez, G. (2012) It's Not Only Geotourism! Types of Tourism in Geoparks, An Analysis Based in 37 Geoparks. p.205, 206, pp.205- 206, In: Sa, A.A., Rocha, D., Paz, A. & Correia, V. (eds) *Proceedings of the 11th European Geoparks Conference, 19 – 21 September 2012, Arouca Geopark Portugal*, 319 pp.

Newsome, D. & Dowling, R. (2006) The Scope and Nature of Geotourism. p.5, In: Newsome, D. & Dowling, R. (eds.) *Geotourism: Sustainability, Impacts and Management*. Butterworth-Heinemann, 352 pp

Newsome, D. & Dowling, R. (2010) Geotourism: a Global Activity. p.3, In: Newsome, D. & Dowling, R. (eds) *Global Geotourism Perspectives*. Goodfellow Publisher Ltd., 250 pp.

Porrath, S.I. (1978) Foreword: The Role of the Professionals. p.xix, xx, pp.xi-xxvii. In: Currant, P. J. T. *Principles and Procedures of Tour Management*. CBI Publishing Company Inc., 151 pp.

Purnama, Y.S. (2002a) *Laporan Penelitian Geologi Pariwisata: Penelitian Potensi Kawasan Wisata Alam di Kotamadya Samarinda, Propinsi Kalimantan Timur*. Internal Research of GDA Consulting Jakarta, Indonesia (unpublished)

Purnama, Y.S. (2002b) *Laporan Penelitian Geologi Pariwisata: Penelitian Potensi Kawasan Wisata Alam di Pantai Selatan, Kabupaten Lebak, Propinsi Banten.*

Follow up to the Geology Socialization Program in the Regency Lebak, Komisi Geowisata dan Karst IAGI, Jakarta, Indonesia, p. 9-17, 23, 25, 30, 36 pp (unpublished)

Purnama, Y.S. (2004) *Pendekatan Geologi bagi Pengembangan Kawasan Gunung Batu, Kabupaten Bandung, Propinsi Jawa Barat, menjadi Kawasan Tujuan Wisata. 33rd IAGI Annual Convention and Exhibition, Bandung, 29 November - 1 December 2004,* p.2-3, 15, 18 pp

Sorkhabi, R. (2011) *History of Oil: Early Textbooks of Petroleum Geology. Geo ExPro Magazine,* Vol 8, No 6, December 2011, p.51, 93 pp

Stokes, A.M., Cook, S.D., & Drew, D. (2003) Geotourism: The New Trend in Travel, Travel Industry Association of America, p.1, 70 pp.

Theobald, W.F. (2005) The meaning, scope and measurement of travel and tourism. p.8,9 pp. 5-24. In: Theobald, W.F. (ed) *Global Tourism: The Next Decade.* Elsevier, 561 pp.

UNESCO (2014) *Guidelines and Criteria for National Geoparks Seeking UNESCO's Assistance to Join the Global Geoparks Network.* p.3, 12pp. Available via www.europeangeoparks.org/wp-content/uploads/2012/03/Geoparks_ Guidelines_Jan2014.pdf or go to tinyurl.com/rf6yfnn. Accessed March 2015.

United Nations (2010) *International Recommendations for Tourism Statistics 2008,* Series M No. 83 / Rev.1, Department of Economic and Social Affairs, Statistic Division, United Nations, p.10, 134 pp.

United Nations (2016) *International Recommendations for Tourism Statistics 2008 Compilation Guide,* Series M No. 94, Department of Economic and Social Affairs, United Nations, p.237, 277 pp.

CHAPTER 3

Tourism Geology Scope

Highlights

- Tourism geology scope describes whatever should be delivered by geologists and whatever should be asked of geologists by a tourism-related professional.

- Within this scope, geologists and tourism-related professionals work in the same context and the same content.
  - Context: tourist attraction.
  - Content: delivering proper geological knowledge to tourism-related professionals.

- There are two components and three relations in tourism geology.
  - Two components are tourist and geological features.
  - The three relations of those two components are attraction, activity, and impact.

- Generally, the geologist's task in the context of tourism geology is as follows.
  - Exploring geological features which potentially arouse the tourist's interest.
  - Recommending tourist activities with safety rule and determining the difficulty rating.
  - Predicting and monitoring environmental impact.

- Six tourist attraction types related to the geological feature.
  - Geoscientific, scenic beauty, particular landform, curative, art-related rocks and minerals, and particular features attractions.
  - The particular feature is composed of drilling-related accidents, giant crystal caves, powerful geologic processes, the Moon and Mars, and hydrothermal vent attractions.

Content

3.1 INTRODUCTION 99
3.2 SCOPE OF TOURISM GEOLOGY 99
   3.2.1 Geologist's Task 103
3.3 TOURIST ATTRACTION TYPE IN TOURISM GEOLOGY 104
3.4 ATTRACTION AS THE FIRST RELATION 106
   3.4.1 Geoscientific Attraction 108
   3.4.2 Scenic Beauty Attraction 111
      3.4.2.1 Landscape and Landform Scenery 112
      3.4.2.2 Scenic Subterranean Beauty 114
      3.4.2.3 Scenic Beauty on the Ocean Floor 115
   3.4.3 Particular Landform Attraction 116
   3.4.4 Curative Attraction 122
      3.4.4.1 Healing Through Water 123
         3.4.4.1.1 Bathing in water 124
         3.4.4.1.2 Drinking Mineral Water 125
      3.4.4.2 Healing Through Mud, Sand, Stone, Mineral and Clay Mineral 125
         3.4.4.2.1 Healing Through Mud 125
         3.4.4.2.2 Healng Through Sand 126
         3.4.4.2.3 Hot Stone Therapy 127
         3.4.4.2.4 Gemstone Healing 128
         3.4.4.2.5 Clay-Eating Therapy 129
      3.4.4.3 Healing Through Aerosol, Geomicro Climate and Gas in Subterranean Environment 131
         3.4.4.3.1 Salt Mine Tunnel and Dry Saline Aerosol 131
         3.4.4.3.2 Geomicro-Climate of Cave in Karst 131
         3.4.4.3.3 Ore Mine Tunnel and Radon Gas 132
      3.4.4.4 Healing through the Earth itself (Earthing) 133
      3.4.4.5 Toxic Substances and Pathogen in Geologic Material 134
   3.4.5 Art-Related Stone and Mineral Attraction 134
   3.4.6 Particular Feature Attraction 138
      3.4.6.1 Drilling Accident-Related Attractions 138
         3.4.6.1.1 Fly Geyser of Nevada 139
         3.4.6.1.2 Darvaza Gas Crater of Turkmenistan 140
         3.4.6.1.3 Sidarjo Mud Volcano of Indonesia 141
      3.4.6.2 Giant Crystal Cave Attraction 145
         3.4.6.2.1 Naica Cave Mine 148
      3.4.6.3 Moon and Mars Attraction 151
         3.4.6.3.1 Possible Natural Attraction in the Moon 152
         3.4.6.3.2 Possible Natural Attraction in the Mars 155
      3.4.6.4 The Potential Attraction of Powerful Geologic Processes 160
         3.4.6.4.1 Landslide Attraction 163
         3.4.6.4.2 Earthquake Attraction 165
         3.4.6.4.3 Tsunami Attraction 170
         3.4.6.4.4 Volcano Eruption Attraction 174
      3.4.6.5 Hydrothermal Vent Attraction in the Deep Ocean Floor 179
   3.4.7 Geologist's Task in Context of Attraction 193
3.5 ACTIVITY AS THE SECOND RELATION 197
   3.5.1 Safety as Primary Need 198
   3.5.2 Safety in Context of Difficulty Rating 200
   3.5.3 Geologist's Task in Context of Safety 200
3.6 IMPACT AS THE THIRD RELATION 202
   3.6.1 Geologist's Task in Context of Impact 203
3.7 SUMMARY 204

Abstract

Tourism geology has a particular scope. It provides whatever should be delivered by geologists to tourism-related professional as the next-user, and whatever should be asked of geologists by them. It is the way for two different professions to communicate in the same context and the same content. Tourist attraction is the context. Delivering proper geological knowledge for the tourism-related professional is the content.

There are two components in tourism geology: tourists and geological features. Those two components have three relations. The three relations are attraction, activity, and impact. This chapter discusses those relations.

Generally, the geologist's task explores geological features that potentially arouse the tourists' interest or have attraction value; recommend tourist activities with safety requirements and determination of difficulty rating; and predict and monitor environmental impact on the geological feature because of tourist activity. The outcome of the geologist's work is dedicated to the tourism-related professional as the next-user for input during the decision-making process.

There are six tourist attraction types that relate to the geological feature: geoscientific, scenic beauty, curative, particular landform, art-related rock and mineral, and particular features' attractions. The last is composed of drilling-related accident, giant crystal caves, powerful geologic processes, the Moon and Mars, and hydrothermal vents. This many tourist interest types might benefit the next-user for planning and development of tourism strategy, deciding on various products, market types, targeted tourists, and destination countries.

Keyword: tourism geology scope, geologist task, tourist attraction, activity, safety, impact, tourism market, tourism product.

3.1. INTRODUCTION

This chapter describes tourism geology's scope to be developed by cooperation of geologists and tourism-related professionals. The scope provides whatever should be delivered by geologists to tourism-related professionals and whatever should be asked of geologists by them. It is the way that two different professions to communicate in the same context and the same content. The tourist attraction is the context. Delivering proper geological knowledge for the tourism-related professional is the content.

3.2. SCOPE OF TOURISM GEOLOGY

Tourism geology is an effort to explore the relation between the environment and man in the context of tourism. The man acts as a tourist, visitor, or recreationist (I use interchangeably those terms in this book). The relation of tourist and environment is developed as follows. If someone uses his or her leisure time to do a pleasant thing different from a routine life of business, then he or she will choose a destination. If the destination fulfills his or her interest, then the destination is said to have an attraction. Later on, the tourist goes to the destination and performs activities according to interests, abilities (level of difficulty), and also safety procedures. The activities might have physical contact with the attraction. If he or she made physical contact, then this might cause a physical change as the consequence. From this reasoning, attraction is the main interest, activity is the derivative of the attraction, safety and difficulty rating are requirements, and impact is the consequence.

Several relations involving geological features on the site, tourists, host, wildlife, meteorological features, and hydrological features can be modeled for any tourist activity in a natural tourist destination, whether or not it is developed (Fig. 3.1). The model points out that tourists might interact with many variables, as follow.

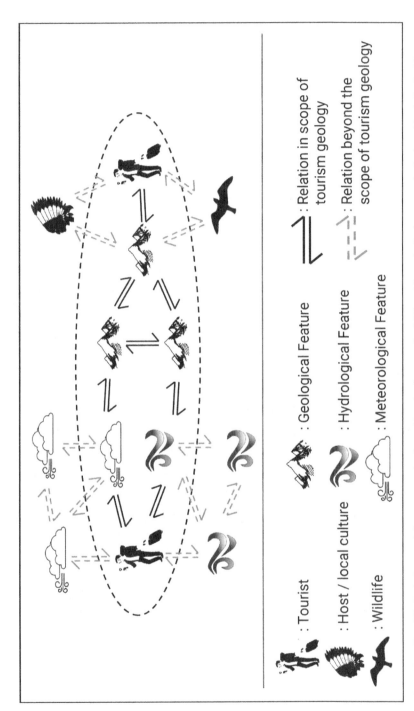

Figure 3.1. Simplified relation model among tourist, host / local culture, and wildlife, with geological, meteorological, and hydrological features in a natural tourist destination. Tourism geology scope is marked by a black dashed line. Symbols in the figure are designed by Freepik.

- Tourist – Host, e.g., cultural tour.
- Tourist – Wildlife, e.g., safari tour in national park.
- Tourist – Geological feature, e.g., geological tour, rock climbing, psammotherapy.
- Tourist – Hydrological feature, e.g., rafting, swimming.
- Tourist – Meteorological feature, e.g., paragliding.

In addition, host, wildlife, hydrological and meteorological features might directly relate to a geological feature.

A tourist attraction for some outdoor activities, which relate to hydrological or meteorological features, might be directly controlled by that feature. For example, the existence of river rapids allows us to do rafting trips with various difficulty ratings. Although river rapids are a hydrological feature, they exist because they are also controlled by geological features such as bedrock and boulder configuration, geological structures, or rock type distribution that controls the river slope.

A similar case goes for meteorological features. Ridge lift, also called slope lift or orographic lift, surrounds the mountain slope and is used for soaring in aero-sport activity (e.g., paragliding, hang gliding.) If there is no mountain slope, it is less likely the slope lift exists as well as the aero-sport activity. The presence of those geological features is the main reason of the existence of those attractions, which become one inseparable unity. Such attractions are discussed in tourism geology in the spirit of exploring geological knowledge usage for tourism.

In other cases, a geological feature might cause injury or fatality, constraining tourist activity. For instance, an avalanche of hot pyroclastic sediment boulder-sized at the volcano slope, or toxic gas emitting from an active volcano crater, might cause fatalities.

From this chapter onwards, what means by a geological feature is the geological subject-matter that supports the existence of the non-living natural attraction and tourist activities and also that constrain the activities. Geotourism scope is also the relation between geological features and tourists. However, the tourist interest is dedicated for geoscientific interest only.

It is important to emphasize that the main concerns of tourism geology are geological features in their natural condition on-site and the non-living related features. The reason is within the natural condition; it allows the construction of a particular geological concept that accommodates the existence of a particular attraction and activities. The concept will refer to a certain area, route, spot, on the surface or subsurface, which built naturally and refers to a typical geomorphological or geological environment. For instance, salt flats for racing car competition, caves in a karst environment for speleotherapy, and river with metamorphic provenance sediment for suiseki hunting.

Hence consider those mentioned characteristics in a sentence, tourism geology is defined as

> *"Study of tourist interaction with geological features where the features control non-living natural tourist attractions, tourist activity, carried out in varying degrees of difficulty (if any), and taking into account safety factors and the impact caused by tourist activity on the feature."*

Discussion of highly modified (man-made) structures on the rock that were built or reused for the sake of tourist attraction is also allowed. For instance, dirt bike racing on an open-pit mining slope. However, it is hardly to have a consequence for geological concept construction. Hence, such an attraction is beyond the scope of tourism geology.

The non-living natural tourist attraction includes geological feature related to geological subject-matter and also hydrological and meteorological attractions that are controlled by the geological features. How far the control level of geological features to the hydrological and meteorological attractions in each case will be a subject to be discussed.

Therefore, there are three roles of geological features in tourism geology, as follows.

1. As attraction, whether directly as an attraction (e.g. geologic history, scenic beauty) or supporting the existence of a hydrological or meteorological attraction.

2. As restriction of the attraction, in the context of safety or difficulty rating of an activity.

3. As part of an environmental impact or physical carrying capacity.

Hence, there are two components and three relations in tourism geology. The first component is human as a tourist, who in this context is focused by the aspects of interest, physical ability, and skill to do an activity. The second component is the geological features (geosite and geomorphosite) which can be elaborated into geological variable interactions. The three relations are attraction, activities, and impact. Those two components with three relations are the main concern of tourism geology.

I realize that some host and wildlife features as tourist attractions might strongly relate to a geological feature. However, those features are the living natural attractions while tourism geology concerns the non-living things.

3.2.1. Geologist's Tasks

Generally, geologist's tasks in the context of tourism geology are as follows.

1. Exploring a geological feature, potentially to arouse the tourist's interest or have an attraction value.

2. Recommending tourist activities, which can be conducted on-site, along with safety rules and determining the difficulty rating.

3. Predicting and monitoring environmental impact to the geological feature as a consequence of tourist activity.

Geologists should be able to translate tourism problems into geological variable interactions, so that the geologist delivers proper geological knowledge to tourism-related professionals. Eventually they are able to use it to solve the problem. Geologists need to describe interpretation of geologic features in understandable terms for the next-user.

The outcome of geologists' work is proper geological knowledge for the next-user, who can use it as an input during the decision-making process. Therefore, the geologist's work will have a high value for next-user—not just "nice to know" or "nice to have." Eventually, they will integrate it with other input from other disciplines and design it to be tourism ideas or products.

3.3. TOURIST ATTRACTION TYPE IN TOURISM GEOLOGY

Tourist attraction is a factor contained in a destination that pulls tourist to go to the destination. Tourist interest is an internal factor that pushes the tourist to visit the destination. When a tourist is able to reach, do something in a destination and satisfied, then it is said that tourist interest is fulfilled by the destination, where interest and attraction are connected.

In reality, there are various geological features able to fulfill various tourist interests. This explains why there are many tourism market types affected by tourism geology. As long as their interest relates to geological subject-matter, no matter how its dependency, then tourism geology has the right to put it on the list.

Geological features as tourist attractions in tourism geology are categorized into six types based on tourist interest type. This also relates to various tourism market types (Table 3.1). The six attractions are as follows.

1. Geoscientific Attraction is geological history information contained in the geosite. This attraction is the only one related to geoscientific interest.

2. Scenic Beauty Attraction is the earth scenery that arouses the natural aesthetic perception.

3. Particular Landform Attraction is the particular landform that enables the outdoor enthusiast to perform a particular physical activity in the landform.

4. Curative Attraction is the therapeutic effect of geologic materials or the things related to geologic materials in a geological environment to heal diseases or increase health.

5. Art-related Stone and Mineral Attraction refers to particular stone or minerals that arouse the aesthetic perception.

6. Particular Feature Attractions occur for a number of reasons, as follows:

   - Related to accident (e.g., drilling accident).

   - Require particular time to observe it (e.g., powerful geologic process).

   - Situated in a certain location and require technology to visit (e.g., the Moon and Mars, giant crystal caves, and hydrothermal vents).

There are many next-users of tourism geology other than tourism-related professionals. They may be a geologist with geologic interest who is looking for other outcrops for his own study, an outdoor enthusiast in particular landform for physical outdoor activity interest who likes to experience a new area, or a doctor looking for an alternative natural therapy. There may also be a drilling engineer interested in drilling-related accident attractions, a planetary geologist looking for something new to be observed, and a land owner or a business planner looking for a new business opportunity.

Table 3.1. Relation between tourist attraction type related to geological feature, tourism market segment, and example of geological features.

No	Tourist Attraction Type related to Geological Feature	Example Tourism Market Segment	Example Geological Feature
1	Geoscientific	Geotourism, ecotourism	Volcano, outcrop, fossil, mineral, cave
2	Scenic Beauty	Sun and beach tourism, ecotourism, recreation	Coast, karst, folded mountain, volcano crater, glacier
3	Particular Landform	Adventure toruism, sport tourism	Hill slope environment, volcanic neck, cave
4	Curative	Health tourism, medical tourism	Hot spring, salt mine tunnel, beach sand, cave, volcanic sand
5	Art-related Stone and Mineral	Suiseki hunting, gemstone hunting	River bank, hill slope
6	Particular Feature, composed of:		
6a	Relate to drilling	Disaster tourism?	Mud volcano of Sidoarjo, Indonesia
6b	Giant crystal cave	Cave tourism?	Giant crystal inside the cave mine
6c	Powerful geologic process	Volcano eruption tourism? Tsunami tourism, earthquake tourism?	Landslide, tsunami, volcano eruption, earthquake
6d	Moon and Mars	Mars tourism, Moon tourism	Sites in Moon and Mars
6e	Hydrothermal Vent	Deep sea tourism / Deep ocean floor tourism, (deep) marine ecotourism	Hydrothermal vent field (black or white smokers) on the ocean floor

3.4. ATTRACTION AS THE FIRST RELATION

The non-living natural attraction is described as the value contained in a feature that potential or proven able to satisfy one's interest. Attraction is an external factor or characteristic of the environment that pulls tourists to visit and do something at a destination.

Moreover, attraction is one of many top reasons why tourism exists. Attraction is tourism supply, while the things such as transportation and accommodation are tourism support (personal communication with Nico Lumanauw, 2019).

A geosite is a geologically related attraction situated naturally on a site or exposed within a man-made structure. Minimum modification of a geosite for the purpose of increasing attraction or to conserve the attraction is allowed. If the geological material as attraction in the site is small enough and can be moved, then it is expected the material won't be moved far away from its original location, so that the area still has its own character. The attractions might be in form of landscape, landform, rocks, sediments, minerals, fossils, fluid, or dynamic geological processes.

Attraction is a value creation to a geological feature. It will be better if identification of attraction value in a geosite has more than one to fulfill many tourist interests. In addition, various attraction values identified will be useful for tourism-related professionals for tourism resources inventory. Later on, they might use it make tourism products.

Eventually, the tourist might develop their own sense of place after visitation. Therefore, it is no longer placeless, not just an experience, but there is also meaning and emotion fused in their memory. It might drive them to repeat or extend visitation and support maintenance of the destination.

If a main attraction area has been determined, it is important to observe accessibility and transportation mode to the area. The chosen route might connect several supported attractions, while the chosen transportation mode might increase tourist experience, such as rafting through a river, biking through a tea plantation, or off-roading by four-wheel-drive vehicle through the shoreline.

3.4.1. Geoscientific Attraction

Geoscientific attraction is a geological history attraction contained in a geosite. This attraction fulfills geoscientific tourist interest. Geological feature characteristics might be site beneficial for research, training, or education (Fig. 3.2), significant in national or international scale (Ellis et al., 1996, p. 45), significant in geological development history (Prosser and King, 1999, p. 28), and/or scientifically important due to exceptional features (Ellis et al., 1996, p. 45).

Figure 3.2. Volcanic strata exposure in Tanah Lot, Bali, Indonesia was used for geological field trip. Most people visit the area for its scenic beauty and cultural attractions. Photo was picked up by the author, 2015.

However, in tourism geology, the site excludes the museum where the geological material might have been moved away from its original location found, and man-made geological attractions such as an old textbook or sculpture from rocks. Whatever the character, the challenge remains the same: to make the geological feature an interesting subject for tourist s (Melendez et al., 2011, p. 100).

Geological features of geologic interest might be called geoheritage. Brocx and Semeniuk (2007, p. 55) mentioned that in literature, geoheritage primarily relates to sites of mineral or fossil locations, type sections, classic locations that illustrate Earth history, and locations where Earth processes are operating today and locally with particular emphasis on classic sites where some principles of geology were first crystallized.

Examples of geosites are outcrop, dinosaur footprints, meteorites, hydrocarbon seepages, karst landscapes, volcanic craters, ex-mining land, geysers, and aftermaths of an earthquake, tsunami, or volcanic eruption. As long as the feature can be seen and visited—whether landscape, rocks and stone exposed, or geological processes—those features have the potential to be used for geologic attraction.

Geopark is the global trend for geological features that have international significance. It is a UNESCO program that arose in the mid-1990s, in response to the need to conserve and to enhance the value of geologically significant areas in earth history. By April 2021, there were 169 UNESCO Geoparks in 44 countries, and there will be more in the coming years. Geoparks are found from Rokua Geopark of Finland in the north to M'Goun Geopark of Morocco in the south, from Tumbler Ridge Geopark of Canada in the west to Batur Geopark of Indonesia in the east.

Despite the international significant contained in geosites as a priority, evidently Geopark is more than just geological features. As stated in a UNESCO Global Geoparks brochure (2016, p. 2), the purpose of a UNESCO Global Geopark is to explore, develop, and celebrate the links between geological heritage and all other aspects of the area's natural, cultural, and intangible heritages. It is also stated that even if an area has outstanding, world-famous geological heritage of outstanding universal value, it doesn't automatically qualify to be part of a UNESCO Global Geopark unless the area also has a plan for the sustainable development of the people who live there, which may take the form of sustainable tourism, mainly through geotourism (UNESCO, 2016, p. 10). The message is sustainable development for the local people, whereas geotourism is one of the ways.

It is interesting to recall the Arouca Declaration of November 12, 2011 as the outcome of the International Congress of Geotourism in Arouca Geopark, Portugal, November 9 to 13, 2011. The aim of the congress was to clarify the scope of the geotourism concept, whether geotourism refers to geo(logical)tourism of the Thomas Hose version, or refers to geo(graphy)tourism of the Jonathan Tourtellot version. Let me rewrite two of six points of the declaration:

Point 1: *We recognize that there is a need to clarify the concept of geotourism. Geotourism should be defined as tourism which sustains and enhances the identity of a territory, taking into consideration its geology, environment, culture, aesthetics, heritage and the well-being of its residents. Geological tourism is one of the multiple components of geotourism.*

Point 6: *We encourage territories to develop geotourism focused not only on the environment and geological heritage, but also on cultural, historical and scenic value.*

Since then, the meaning of geotourism in UNESCO Global Geopark documents refers to geotourism of the Jonathan Tourtellot version. Considering the dual geotourism concept, Tourtellot (2011) noted that special geotourism is a specialty focused on geological features, while general geotourism is a strategy for protecting, showcasing, and enhancing all the distinctive assets of a destination.

As consequences of the geo(graphical)tourism concept acknowledged within Geopark, no wonder that many tourism varieties work in Geopark, such as cultural tourism, historical tourism, culinary tourism, and adventure tourism (recall Moreira and Melendez, 2012, Fig. 2.7).

The acceptance of Tourtellot's idea by the committee, however, was regrettable to Hose (2016, p. 5), where he argued that the committee probably unwittingly had actually embraced ecotourism. His posting in Tourtellot's blog of 2011 also reflected his reluctance.

3.4.2. Scenic Beauty Attraction

Valuing scenery as scenic beauty is perhaps the easiest thing to do. But describing what makes it beautiful is harder. Those who live in a desert landscape might estimate the glacial landscape as the best scenery, since they have never visited it before. Whatever the reason, seeing the sight of fantastic scenery is a satisfaction.

Visually, landscape and its landform are considered as scenic beauty interest, which may be due to the color of the stone, mineral deposits, sediments, soil, snow, ice, or water. It may also be related to the form of mountains, hills, canyons, valleys, rivers, waterfalls, lake sediments, or beaches. Whatever the reason, there should be a point to see the scenic area. The location might be from the valley to the top, from the peak of the hill, the basket of a hot air balloon, or from a spaceplane window.

The scenic beauty of a landscape or landform is not the only thing we perceive by our eyes. The beauty, adored by our eyes, is actually integrated with the fresh air and coolness felt by our nose and skin and the whispering wind gusting into our ears.

It is better if a destination has an identity or a character in form of a particular landform or landscape that is part of local culture. Its role as natural icon or landmark of a destination is important. Nowadays, in most visitors' minds, sightseeing on a destination means taking photos or video recording with natural icons as backdrop, posting it to social media, and getting "likes," "comments," "new subscribers," or even going viral.

Generally, there are three types of earth scenery based on its position. They are scenery on the land (landscape and landform), subterranean scenery or cave rooms (cavescapes), and on the sea floor.

3.4.2.1. The Landscape and Landform Scenery

Geologically, scenic beauty interest can be found in many types of landscapes. These range from fold-and-thrust belt mountains to karst regions, from coastal areas to a glacial environment. Table 3.2 provides examples from each landscape type.

Table 3.2. Landscape types and examples.

No	Landscape Type	Example
1	Fold and Thrust Belt Mountains	Alps Mountains of Europe, Appalachians of North America, Zagros Mountains in Iraq and Iran, Himalayan of Asia
2	Fault-Block Mountains	East African Rift of Africa, Death Valley in California, Harz Mountain in Germany
3	Plateau Mountain	Colorado Plateau in US, Guiana Highland of South America, Ethiopian Highlands in the central part of Ethiopia, Western Plateau of the Australian Shield
4	Volcanic	Tengger Caldera and Rinjani Volcano of Indonesia, Giants Causeway of Northern Ireland, Leirhnjukur of Iceland, Yellowstone Caldera in Yellowstone National Park
5	Karst	Leuser and Gunung Sewu of Indonesia, Zhangjiajie National Park and Guilin Karst of China, El Torcal de Antequera of Andalusia, Nakanai Mountains of Papua New Guinea
6	Granite	Spitzkoppe of Namibia Desert, Half Dome of the Yosemite National Park, Granitic coast of the BangkaBelitung Islands, Indonesia
7	Impact Crater	Barringer Crater of Arizona, Wolfe Creek Crater of Australia, Amguid Crater of Algeria, Monturaqui Crater of Chile
8	Fluvial and Lake	Yellow River of China, Amazon River of South America, Mississippi River of New Orleans, Congo River of Africa, Tanganyika Lake of Africa, Baikal Lake of Russia, Vostok Lake of Antarctica

No	Landscape Type	Example
9	Coastal, Estuary and Delta	Labuan Bajo and Mahakam Delta of Indonesia, Koh Phi Phi of Thailand, Victoria coast of Australia, Baia do Sancho beaches of Brazil, Anse Lazio in Praslin Island of Seychelles, sand bar of Whale Harbor in Florida
10	Desert	Sossusvlei of Namibia Desert, Valle de la Luna of Chile, McMurdo Dry Valleys of Antarctica, Pinnacles Desert of Nambung National Park, Salar de Uyuni of Bolivia
11	Glacial and Periglacial	Pasterze Glacier of Austria, Glacier Bay of Alaska, Terra Nova Bay of Northern Victoria Land, Vestfold Hills of East Antarctica

Numbers 1 to 6 are landscape formed by endogenic forces. Number 7 is landscape genetically related to extraterrestrial forces, while numbers 8 to 11 depict the surface processes or exogenic forces that shape the landscape.

The landscape might be an integrated environment between exogenic and endogenic forces, e.g., Pasterze Glacier in the fold and thrust belt of the Alps Mountain, karst of the Mariana Island, and intrusive volcanic hills in the coast of Seger Beach in Lombok (Fig. 3.3).

Figure 3.3. The small bay of Seger Beach in Lombok Island bounded by Plio-Pleistocene intrusive volcanic hills. Photo was taken by author, 2019.

The breathtaking beauty of the landscape might be influenced by the color of biological matter. For instance, yellow canola flowers surround the conical hills on China's Luoping Basin every March; the orange, yellow, and red colors of bacteria on the edge of the Grand Prismatic Spring of Yellowstone National Park; and the red and yellow of the algal bloom in Cano Cristales River in Colombia between July and November each year.

3.4.2.2. Scenic Subterranean Beauty

Another interesting scenery is the scenery of the subterranean, or cave rooms. Let's call it a cavescape. A cave is found in volcanic rock (lava tube), formed by wave action (sea cave), formed by fracture through soluble minerals (fracture cave), or formed by melting ice (glacier cave). But most caves are formed by a dissolution process in limestone or dolostone rock. A cave might be flooded entirely, or a part of it, by fresh water or sea water (e.g., cenote, blue hole).

The main attraction of the cavescape is the room and ornaments decorated on the floor, wall, or ceiling. It is like a living room, which will be more interesting if decorated by desk, chair, carpet, coffee maker, stereo set, and a big-screen TV. The limestone or dolostone cave ornament is carbonate dissolution features in the form of speleothem, such as dripstone and flowstone. For instance, Puerto Princesa Subterranean River in the Philippines, Škocjan Cave of Slovenia, and Carlsbad Caverns National Park in the United States.

A cave also provides a particular environment for cave-inhabiting animals, which contributes to the cave's attraction. Some animals are unique because they are rare or never found on the surface. One is a species of glowworms that exclusively live in Waitomo Glowworms Caves, New Zealand. In fact, it is one of the main attractions in the cavescape.

Another cave attraction is the sound of stalactites when struck with a mallet. Each stalactite has unique tone. For those who recognize the particular tone on each stalactite, they can play a song in the cave, such as in Gong Cave in Pacitan, Indonesia, and Great Stalacpipe Organ in Luray Caverns, Virginia, United States.

3.4.2.3. Scenic Beauty on the Ocean Floor

Another type of earth scenery is underexplored in tourism. It is the scape covered by the sea. But it is hard to appreciate its beauty through direct visual observation. Our sight is limited because the scape is submerged by sea water. Moreover, the sunlight diminishes with increasing depth of water, where the most spectacular scenery is situated.

Yet, sea floor mapping allows us to understand the spectacular sceneries of the ocean floor. It is feature such as the deeply incised valley and the channel of Hudson Canyon in the northeast Atlantic Margin; Bahama slope underwater where large debris blocks in deep marine deposits (Fig. 3.4); and Davidson Seamount off the coast of Central California decorated by a large variety of deep-sea corals.

Nowadays, the most advanced technology to map the seafloor is multibeam echosounders. It is basically a type of sonar (sound navigation ranging) technique that uses sound propagation to detect the object under the water surface. Just a few of our seafloors have been mapped with this technology. The outcome is a fine-scale "landform," like the western slope of the Bahama Bank (Fig. 3.4).

Today, seeing those seafloor features by the naked eye is almost impossible. But leaving behind those scenic beauties will be regrettable. The next thing to be resolved is the technique to see those scapes (already mapped), like seeing the landscape on surface, to adore the beauty of the deep, so that the public appreciates the ocean and its seafloor features as one unity with the panoramic beauty of the landscape.

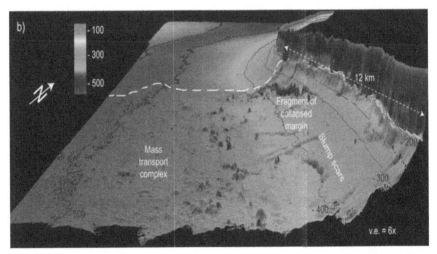

Figure 3.4. Three-dimension form of the western slope of Bahama Bank shows deep marine deposit in the slope. The deposit is composed of mass transport complex, fragments of collapsed margins, and slump scars. The figure was originally derived from extensive multibeam echosounder mapping. Vertical exaggeration is six times. Figure is adapted with permission from Schnyder et al., 2016. CC BY 4.0.

Our appreciation to the ocean should commence with our understanding of the ocean floor environment. In June 2017, a project called Seabed 2030 was launched. The project is a collaborative project between the Nippon Foundation of Japan and GEBCO. The project aim is to bring together all available bathymetric data to produce the definitive map of the world ocean floor by 2030. Moreover, they will make a map of the entire ocean floor available to all.

3.4.3. Particular Landform Attraction

A physical outdoor activity, also called adventure, might refer to an experience of an entirely new activity, exercises in new area, or a high-risk or bold action. Someone might consider that the adventurer is a thrill seeker or adrenaline-invited person. However, an adventure interest doesn't really need to be an extreme activity without reasoning. In fact, most of them are trained. The motivation might be personal challenge, self-development, or just recreation.

In this work, the terms "physical outdoor activities," "outdoor recreation," "adventure" or "extreme activities" refer to physical activities carried out in natural areas with very low to no modifications to the landform, with or without using sophisticated technology equipment or vehicles and performed at various levels of difficulty.

A particular physical outdoor activity is generally supported by a particular landform. The landform for the activity itself is composed of various component interactions, such as landform-forming rock type, landform geometry, slope, fracture, type of sediment (e.g., sand, soil, gravel, water), vegetation, and surface runoff. For instance, mountain biking is performed in slope with various steepness and surface cover types (e.g., mud, sand, or gravel); while the jumping point (exit point on earth) of BASE jumping activity is conducted from a cliff (Fig. 3.5). For mountain bikers, such a slope is an attraction, while in the BASE jumper's view, the cliff is an attraction.

Those landform components also support hydrological and meteorological attractions when they interact with hydrological and meteorological variables such as wind, river flow, waterfall, and rip current. Thus, the landform character contributes to those two attractions.

In this work, the physical outdoor activities can be categorized into six types, based on where the activities are mostly conducted. It is activity on the land, subsurface, water surface, in the water column, on the air, and based on particular season. The relation of each outdoor activity type with the landform is given in Table 3.3. In addition, within the same category, the activity can subdivide further by other categories. For instance, activity on the land might be categorized by whether it is motorized or not.

The landform has five roles in outdoor activity. The role is the landform as attraction, defining difficulty rating, defining safety, supporting meteorological attraction, or supporting hydrological attraction. In

Figure 3.5. BASE jumping in Monte Brento, Italy. The exit point altitude is about 1420 m, and the landing area is about 200 m altitude. Geological feature: Dolomite cliff of the Alps mountain range provides the exit point to jump. Image courtesy of Adam Long, 2007.

addition, there are four levels of geological variable interaction on the landform to define those roles in each activity: low, medium, high, and very high (Table 3.3). It is described as follows.

- Low: geological variable interaction has consequence to the existence of attraction.

- Medium: geological variable interaction has consequence to define safety factors of an activity

- High: geological variable interaction has consequence to the existence of attraction and defining the safety factor of an activity.

- Very High: geological variable interaction has consequence to the existence of attraction, defining the safety factor, and defining the difficulty rating of an activity.

A particular activity might have different geological variable interaction levels in the same outdoor activity types. For instance, geological variable interaction of downhill mountain bike in land-based activity define attraction, difficulty rating, and safety (very high level). But the same landform probably has different level for hiking activity, where geological variable interaction define attraction and safety factor (high level).

In some cases, particular landform characteristics influence the existence of a particular sport. For instance, the steep slope of Cerro Negro Volcano in Nicaragua is the landform chosen for the downhill mountain-biking speed record. It is a cinder cone that rises 728 m high above sea level or 500 m high from the flat area below. The surface is composed of volcanic sand and gravel. The slope is estimated at 20° to 30°. The fastest speed record by a bike on the volcano was 164.95 km/h, held by Markus Stockl in 2011. Another attempt was conducted on Atacama desert, a 45° slope on a 1200-meter course where Markus Stöckl rode a bike able to reach a speed of 167.6 km/h in 2016. However, the fastest downhill mountain bike record is held by Eric Barone in 2017 on a trail at the Vars ski resort, a snowy ski slope in the French Alps, where he reached 227.72 km/h.

Table 3.3: Relation of outdoor activity types with landform.

Outdoor Activity Types	Attraction	Description	Geological feature role					Level of geological variable interaction	Landform / Landscape Example	Example of Outdoor Activity
			as attraction	define difficulty rating	define safety	supports meteorological attraction	supports hydrological attraction			
Land-based activity	Slope and/or route surface types	Slope and/or route surface types define the route, also concern safety factor and difficulty rating	✓	✓	✓			Very High	Fold and thrust belt mountain, Desert, Cinder cone, Glacial	rock climbing, racing, downhill mountain bike, mountaineering
Air-based activity	Vertical height of a cliff	Landform provide minimum allowable height and the best point to jump	✓		✓	✓?		High	Fault scarp, Volcanic neck	Free fall, wingsuit flying, cliff jumping
	Natural arch, cliff, valley, etc	Landform variation increase difficulty rating	✓	✓	✓	✓?		Very High	Fault block mountain	proximity flying (Wingsuit BASE Jumping)
	Ridge lift in mountain slope	Interaction of slope and height of the mountain with wind produce ridge lift			✓?	✓		High ?	Coastal, Volcanic	soaring flight, hang-gliding
	Surrounding environment	Geological factor define safety issue in air-based, e.g. dust or volcanic sediment affect to pilot control on vehicle			✓			Medium	Volcano	Hang gliding

Outdoor Activity Types	Attraction	Description	Geological feature role					Level of geological variable interaction	Landform / Landscape Example	Example of Outdoor Activity
			as attraction	define difficulty rating	define safety	supports meteorological attraction	supports hydrological attraction			
Season-based activity	Freezing waterfall	Landform provide elevation waterfall to freeze				✓	✓	Low	Fault block mountain	ice climbing
	Freezing lake	Landform provide basin for water accumulation to freeze				✓	✓	Low	Lake	ice skating
	Snow on mountain slope	Landform provide slope for snow to be deposited		✓	✓	✓	✓	Very High	Fold and thrust belt mountain,	ski jumping, snowboarding
Water surface-based activity	Breaking wave for surfing	Interaction of seabed slope and wave / tide provide breaking wave for surfing		✓?	✓		✓	High - Very High?	Coastal	Surfing
	Rapid water and waterfall for rafting	Interaction of riverbed and water debit provide rapid for rafting		✓	✓		✓	Very High	Fault block mountain, Volcanic	rafting, kayaking
	Calm water and crystal clear	Interaction of geomorphic architecture and wave provide safety swimming nearshore			✓		✓	High	Coastal, Lake, River	swimming
Subaqueous-based activity	Subaqueous environment	Geological factor define safety issue in subaqueous activity, e.g. sediment suspension affect to diver's visibility			✓			Medium	Submerged cave, Delta	diving
Subsurface-based activity	Cavity network	Landform of carbonate rock provide cavity network	✓	✓	✓			Very High	Karst	caving

?: need more assessment

Particular slope is not the only slope aiming to reach the speed record. The broad and flat surface areas, such as the Bonneville Salt Flats or Bonneville Speedway, Utah, are ideal for setting the fastest land speed record since 1914. The race is only conducted during the summer, where the heat from the sun evaporates the water and the precipitated salt becomes a hard racetrack surface. However, heavy rain might cause mud deposition from surrounding mountains onto the flats and deteriorate the track.

3.4.4. Curative Attraction

Curative attraction is the capacity of geological material and/or the geologic environment to cure disease or to increase health by natural therapy on the natural destination or health resort. The therapeutic effect might be healing through water, mud, sand, stone, mineral, clay, liquid, or the environment. Geologically, it refers to geothermal, salt content, radioactivity, mud volcano, alluvial sediment, carbonated water, or cave environment as an intrinsic part with the geomicro climate. Table 3.4 is summary of geological material and environments that have had a therapeutic effect in the context of tourism.

Curative attraction is the direct use of geological material or environments by tourists without drastically changing its natural properties, except for removal of hazardous properties. This includes bathing in the water, mud, or sand; stone massage; mineral therapy; clay mineral (eating); drinking mineral water; and also inhaling where gas or aerosol gets into our lung through respiration. I describe geological material and geological environment used on the site or taken near the site for known therapeutic purposes, regardless the existence of medical evidence or advice. Some of examples listed can be used as an analog model.

Table 3.4. Summary of geologic environments and geological materials with curative effects related to tourism.

Geologically is linked to ...	Healing through							
	Water	Mud	Sand	Stone	Mineral	Clay Mineral (eating)	Gas, aerosol, and/or integrated with geomicro climate	The Earth (earthing)
Natural Spring	X							
Geothermal / Volcano	X	X	X				X	
Salt	X	X					X	
Carbonated	X							
Radioactive	X		X				X	
Natural Peloid		X						
Mud Volcano		X						
Carbonate		X			X			
Sun-heated			X					
Cave							X	
Alluvial				X	X			
Paleo volcanism					X			
Kaolin, Smectite, and Bentonite (deposits)						X		
Any landscape (except desert)								X

3.4.4.1. Healing Through Water

Healing through water, also called spa or balneotherapy, is a well-known therapy. It is bathing in thermal or mineral waters. During bathing, minerals penetrate skin pores or absorb toxins through skin pores. It is usually combined with other treatments, such as physical exercise, hydrotherapy, and mud packs. The positive effects of spa are the effect on skin, musculoskeletal disorders, and psychological disorders. Therapeutic effects of water are associated with geothermal, brine, radioactivity, or richly carbonated water. In fact, the water origin might be mixed, such as geothermal that contains a radioactive element.

3.4.4.1.1. Bathing in Water

Bathing in geothermal heated water is the most common direct use of geothermal energy. If geothermal waters have at least one of the criteria—that is temperature, radioactivity, or chemical composition—then it is therapeutic water. Some well-known geothermal sites for natural baths are Kangal hot springs in Turkey, Santorini volcanic hot spring in Greece, highland pools in Landmannalaugar and Hveravellir in Iceland, and Hell's Gate in New Zealand. Examples of touristic geothermal spots that are also connected to radioactivity are Radium Hot Spring in Canada and Misasa Hot Spring in Japan.

Higher content of salt in lakes or the sea, which exceeds the normal content of the sea, is also a common use for therapeutic bathing. For instance, the Dead Sea has salt content ten times that of an ordinary sea. Moreover, it is more abundant in potassium, calcium, bromide, and magnesium; and lower in sodium, sulfate, and carbonate. Other well-known tourist destinations for brine-water therapeutic baths include the Pink salt lakes of Torrevieja in Spain, Lake Techirghiol in Romania, and the Red Sea coast in Safaga in Egypt.

Carbonated water bath is a method used for the prevention and treatment of cardiovascular diseases, as in the Baile Tusnad Spa Resort in Romania. Carbonated mineral waters are the result of the filtration of depth waters through volcanic soils that contain carbon dioxide. The carbon dioxide obtained in this way will favor the dissolution of other elements in the soil layers through which water passes. Eventually, carbonated mineral waters will have a complex composition (Gabriela and Alexandru, 2015, p. 36).

For most people, being exposed to a radioactive element is absolutely the worst idea. However, taking a bath in radium-dissolved water apparently is a common practice, as in Jachymov Spa in the Czech Republic, Milk River Mineral Bath in Jamaica, Rudas Bath in Hungary, Ramsar in Iran, Ikaria in Greece, and Ladek Zdroj in Poland. Among the conditions that have been treated in radioactive spas with greatest success are rheumatoid arthritis, bronchial asthma, and psoriasis (Zdrojewicz and Strzelczyk, 2006, p. 113).

3.4.4.1.2. Drinking Mineral Water

Drinking mineral water is an important way to input an important mineral supply to our body. Gomes (2013, p. 8) stated that mineral water drinking cure is principally water ingestion aimed at modification of gastrointestinal, metabolic, renal, and urodynamic functions. The practice of drinking mineral water for therapeutic purposes has existed since the historical periods. Water from underground has a high mineral content, because it absorbs minerals during its subsurface trip to the reservoir. There are many minerals present in mineral water, such as calcium, magnesium, potassium, Sulphur, and sodium. Many spa resorts offer this therapy, such as Rogaška Medical Centre of Slovenia, Therme Maris (thermal and spa resort) of Turkey, and Terme di Pejo of Italy.

3.4.4.2. Healing Through Mud, Sand, Stone, Minerals, and Clay

Using mud, sand, and stone for therapeutic purposes is a common practice, either in its natural environment or in a built environment. The mud might refer to geothermal / volcanic, brine water, mud volcano, or carbonate. The sand might be associated with radioactivity, geothermal / volcanic, or as an intrinsic part of climate. The stone used for therapeutic purposes is river sediment of rounded pebble size.

3.4.4.2.1. Healing through Mud

Mud for healing is usually called peloid, and the therapy is called mud therapy or pelotherapy. Peloids are being used in the treatment of rheumatoid arthritis, osteoarthritis (a condition that causes joints to feel sore, stiff, and swollen), gynecological disorders, sciatica (pain caused by nerves damaged or pinched), skin diseases, and skin care. Gomes et al. (2013, p. 32) defines peloid as:

> maturated mud or muddy dispersion with healing and/or cosmetic properties, composed of a complex mixture of fine-grained natural materials of geologic and/or biologic origins, mineral water or sea water and commonly organic compounds from biological metabolic activity.

The term "peloid" includes natural peloid and peloid s.s. (strict sense). Natural peloid means healing mud that matured in the natural environment where it occurs. On the other hand, peloid s.s. means healing mud dressed and matured in tanks with mineral water. In this work, description is focused on natural peloid.

There are various geologic environments of natural peloid already well known by tourists where they are taking a bath, as follows.

- Peloid linked to geothermal or volcanic action: Dalyan in Turkey and Laghetto di Fanghi of Vulcano Island in Italy.

- Peloid related to brine water: Dead Sea in Israel and Jordan, Wadden Sea in the North Sea, and Lake Techirghiol in Romania.

- Peloid refers to mud volcano: Tiga Island in Malaysia, El Totumoin in Colombia, and mud volcanoes of Azerbaijan.

- Peloid connected to white carbonate mud: the base of Milky Way Lagoon, Palau, Micronesia.

3.4.4.2.2. Healing through Sand

Psammotherapy is therapy by sand in the form of a sand bath, where muscular-skeletal diseases are the most common treatment target. Three sand types that have healing power are described, as follows.

1. Radioactive sand, such as on the Atlantic coast of Brazil, particularly on the beaches of Guarapari, state of Espirito Santo. The healing

efficacy originates from radioactive black sand beaches composed of monazite sand as a mineral naturally high in radioactive elements (Caufield, 1989, p. 195).

2. Sand heated geothermally, such as in Ibusuki Beach and Beppu Beach in Japan. Visitors are buried by a volcanic sand bath heated geothermally. At a resort in southern Bandung, Western Java province, Indonesia, sand bath therapy uses iron sand heated artificially, mimicking a geothermal system.

3. Sand heated by the sun. I expect the sand is strongly connected to the sun's heat as an intrinsic part of sand bathing in beach sand or desert sand. The sand might be composed of biogenic, volcanogenic, or quartz-rich materials. The efficacy of sand baths heated by the sun originates from the ability of sand grain, which is characterized by low heat conductivity, to release heat absorbed from the sun to the body slowly, without causing burns (Gomes, 2013, p. 6). This type of sand bath is common practice all around the world, such as in Porto Santo Island beach, archipelago of Madeira; Bile sayak beach in Lombok of Indonesia; Siwa sand beach near Dakrour Mountain in Egypt; and Merzouga desert dunes in Morocco.

The sand is also used as an ingredient of massage therapy. A massage practice in Bali uses volcanic sand combined with other ingredient such as bamboo ash, cinnamon powder, and reviving oil.

3.4.4.2.3. Hot Stone Therapy

Another massage therapy uses stone, called hot stone therapy. Someone might call it geo-thermo therapy. The stone used is pebble size (4 - 64 mm), rounded, and has a flat surface. It is usually found in alluvial soil. Basalt is the rock type used, since it retains heat longer. The longer the heat is retained, the longer the massage. A stone is heated by boiling water usually between 127°F and 130°F, but others use 130°F to 145°F. After heating, it may be placed on the spine, chest, stomach, face, palms, toes, and feet. The other stones are held by the massage therapist and used to work on the muscles. The stone heats the skin, opens the pores, better absorbs massage oils, and helps blood circulation. Other benefits are to relieve muscle tension and pain, reduce stress, and possibly boost immunity.

Sometimes a colder stone is used after the hot stone one. Switching between hot and cold stones helps increase blood circulation. The rock type used usually is limestone or marble (commonly handcrafted) because it retains cold longer. It is cooled in a bowl of ice at about 30°F. Marble, which stays cool longer and draws heat out of the body, is the best stone for cold stone therapy. The cold stone causes the blood vessels to narrow. The blood vessels widen when the stone is removed, which increases circulation. Other benefits are to reduce inflammation, decrease soreness, decrease high blood pressure, and relax muscle spasms.

3.4.4.2.4. Gemstone Healing

Healing through minerals is another therapeutic practice. It is also called crystal healing, gemstone healing, or gemstone treatment. However, this alternative treatment is not a popular treatment that would be recommended by most doctors. Despite lack of scientific support, the practice of healing through minerals is the attraction in several destinations such as Saxon Hotel, Villas and Spa of Johannesburg; Kimpton Seafire Resort and Spa of the Cayman Islands; and the Four Seasons Hotel Spa of Florence.

In practice, such treatment is integrated with facial treatment, massage, or other therapy methods where the mineral is put on the particular point such as on the forehead, throat, chest, stomach, or genital area. Each mineral has particular properties. For instance, Amethyst boosts the brain and nerves and relieves tension; Calcite stimulates excretion and provides relief from diarrhea and constipation; Emerald strengthens the immune system; and Rose Quartz helps improve blood flow.

3.4.4.2.5. Clay-Eating Therapy

In this work, Geophagy or Geophagia refers to healing through eating clay mineral. A person who practices it is called a clay eater. Such practices are common in many cultures such as in Haiti, Cameroon, Nigeria, India, Mexico, and among Native Americans. Typically, older generation of those cultures are clay eaters. However, modern society considers eating clay as related to pica, an eating disorder characterized by eating items that are considered to have little nutritional value such as hair, soap, string, wood, ash, talcum powder, and dirt.

The cause of geophagy remains a mystery. Young (2007, p. 21) organized hypotheses from many scientists on geophagy motivation. The outcome is composed of eight categories: nutrient craving, sensory disturbance, gastrointestinal malaise, detoxification, hunger, stress, mental illness, and cultural expectations. Possibly, two of those hypotheses might be used to increase geophagy popularity—that is, gastrointestinal malaise, where kaolin has a soothing effect (Young 2007, p. 23); and as a detoxification agent where kaolin, smectite (Gomes 2013, p. 4), and bentonite contribute. In our modern world, almost all people need detox.

Smectite, kaolin, and bentonite are clay mineral types, not "just" clay. The terms "clay mineral" and "clay" are differ. Clay mineral is hydrous aluminum phyllosilicates with a layered sheet-like structure, very fine grain size (smaller than 1/256 mm in diameter), and that may contain iron, magnesium, alkali metal, or other in varying quantities. Clay mineral is composed of four groups: kaolinite, montmorillonite / smectite, illite, and chlorite groups.

On the other hand, clay is a term for grain size smaller than $1/_{256}$ mm in diameter (Wentworth Scale). Clay size is the finest grain size. It will feel smooth on your teeth. If you rub a piece of clay with a drop of water, it will feel slippery. A clay sample might consist of one or more clay minerals and other minerals as well, such as calcite, quartz, and feldspar. Within a clay sample, all of those mineral sizes are clay size.

Several example of geophagic products sold on the market are Terramin, a Californian product composed of calcium montmorillonite for detoxification; Calabaa Chalk from Nigeria; and Ampo, a traditional snack from Tuban of Indonesia. I was curious to know the composition of Ampo, so I took a sample of Ampo and sent it to a laboratory to be analyzed by X-ray diffraction. It is interesting to know that the outcome of its composition was Kaolinite 68%, Quartz 25%, Muscovite 5%, and Chlorite 2%. In addition, local people have never reported any side effects after eating Ampo.

In relation to tourism, it is rare a restaurant that offers earth material as part of its cuisine. A French restaurant in Tokyo, Ne Quittez Pas, offer soil as one of menu items. The soil is processed to be part of various dishes such as dirt ice cream, dirt soup, dirt dressing on salad, dirt risotto, and others. Absolutely, the soil had been processed to remove hazardous things and also bacteria. Based on Google Review, most of the customers like it. The point is an earth material is able to be an attractive dish if it is well processed.

When earth material is able to be processed as attractive cuisine, then the dishes will act both as an attractive local cuisine and therapeutic agent. For instance, kaolin deposits in Bangka and the Belitung Islands of Indonesia, where those granitic region islands are rich in kaolin, have the potential to be developed as local dishes and medicationd. Similarly, bentonite, derived from weathered volcanic ash in the volcanic region that spreads across the Ring of Fire Zone, is fascinating when be prepared as attractive menu items in restaurants and as a detox method of a health resort.

3.4.4.3. Healing Through Gas, Aerosol, and Geomicro Climate

Apparently, man-made and natural cave environments contain health benefits, whether it is a tunnel of salt mine, ore mine, or cave in karst environment. Speleotherapy is therapy in a cave environment. It is basically respiratory therapy to cure respiratory disease such as asthma. Several components of the subterranean environment in the caves and mines, which have been thought relevant in asthma treatment, are due to the low level or absence of dust, gas pollutants, pollen and bacteria or bioaerosol contamination; and good air purity and stable humidity, temperature, and air pressure (Beamon et al., 2001, p. 2).

3.4.4.3.1. Salt Mine Tunnel and Dry Saline Aerosol

Dry saline aerosol in the salt mine tunnel is the main curative attraction. For instance, Resort "Golden Mountain" in the Czech Republic, where 2,000 patients are treated annually; Wieliczka salt mine tunnel in southern Poland, as the oldest of European speleotherapy centers; and Republican Speleotherapeutical Hospital in Armenia, where the room is situated 235 meters below the ground.

3.4.4.3.2. Geomicro Climate of Cave in Karst

In a karst environment, the essential curative attraction is actually the cave climate itself, as in Beke, Tapolca Hospital, and Abaliget caves in Hungary (Katalin et al., 2008, p. 222) and Jasovska Cave in Slovakia (Fig. 3.6). Natural steam inside the cave, such as inside the Yampah vapor cave in Colorado, is a major curative attraction where a deep, underground mineral-rich steam emits from the Yampah spring, offering therapeutic effects.

Figure 3.6. Jasovska Cave of Slovakia, well known for speleotherapy. Image courtesy of Spa Štos.

3.4.4.3.3. Ore Mine Tunnel and Radon Gas

In ore mine tunnel, the main curative attraction is radon gas, a daughter-product of uranium. Such gas apparently also presents in salt mine tunnel and cave of karst in different level. Despite long traditions for few countries, treatments using radon-rich air or water have not been unequivocally embraced by modern medicine (Zdrojewicz and Strzelczyk, 2006, p.106). Many health conditions are treated at the health centers. For instance, therapy in Bad Gastein, Austria, and a uranium mine in Montana in the United States, to cure inflammatory rheumatic illnesses, chronic polyarthritis (a condition in which pain and inflammation occur in several joints at once), scleroderma (a disease that involves hardening and tightening of the skin and connective tissue), rheumatoid arthritis (chronic inflammation in the joints), and degenerative and deforming joint infections (Zdrojewicz and Strzelczyk, 2006, p. 112).

Considering radon gas, radium water, or other healing methods related to radioactivity, it is interesting to remember what Paracelsus (1493–

1541, the founder of toxicology, stated: *"All substances are poisons; there is none which is not a poison. The right dose differentiates a poison and a remedy."*

3.4.4.4. Healing through the Earth itself (Earthing)

When was your last time to walk barefoot or lie on the ground? You should do it soon, because it has a positive impact on your health. Many studies suggest that direct contact with the Earth improves our health. It is called Earthing.

What does actually occur to our body when we made direct contact with the Earth? Evidently, the electrical potential in our body becomes equalized with the Earth's electrical potential through electron transfer from the Earth to the body (Chevalier et al., 2012, p. 3). In fact, the surface of the planet is electrically conductive (except in limited ultra-dry areas such as deserts), and its negative potential is maintained (i.e., its electron supply replenished) by the global atmospheric electrical circuit (Chevalier et al., 2012, p. 1).

Those transferred electrons scientifically provide a positive health impact. Chevalier et al. (2012, pp. 2-6) summarized many impacts such as improved sleep, decreased pain, cortisol normalizing effect, stress reduction, osteoporosis reduction, improved glucose regulation, improved immune response, and better blood fluidity. Moreover, other studies suggest that even one hour of contact with the earth promotes blood flow increase to the head and body (torso), which enhances skin tissue repair, health, and vitality, and optimizes facial appearance (Chevalier et al., 2015, p. 1054).

Fortunately, natural destinations are a place when we easily do the Earthing thing. Whether the ground is composed of sand, dirt, soil, gravel, rock, grass, plants, and living trees, what you need to do is take off your shoes and walk barefoot.

3.4.4.5. Toxic Substances, Pathogens, and Parasites in Geologic Materials

Geologic materials used for therapeutic purposes, such as clay-water mixes used in spa, geothermal water, and natural peloid, have to be carefully examined before use. As stated by Carretero (2002, p. 159), Gomes et al. (2013, p. 33), and Andri Subandrio (personal communication, 2015), several toxic substances possibly contained in clay-water mixes and geothermal waters are Arsenic (As), Lead (Pb), Mercury (Hg), Cadmium (Cd), Selenium (Se), Antimony (Sb), Copper (Cu), and Zinc (Zn). Natural peloid on the site needs to be investigated due to high vulnerability to anthropogenic contamination. It might be very acidic (pH 2-3) and usually bears a high content of heavy metals if the mud was deposited by acidic volcanic waters (Gomes et al., 2016).

Furthermore, pathogen distribution in beaches also needs to be examined. Although biological in origin, it is contained in geological materials. Solo-Gabrielle et al. (2016, p. 102) stated that *"...transmission of infectious diseases in beach environments occur via direct exposure to microbes found in sand or through the flux of microbes from water to sand within the swash or intertidal zone."*

In addition, there are health risks to consuming clay mineral without careful analysis and the best processing of the clay itself. Clay mineral can be contaminated by pathogens and parasites, and have a high heavy-metal or other toxic element content.

3.4.5. Art-related Stone and Mineral Attraction

This attraction is composed of two geological material types. The first is mostly characterized by natural external stone characteristics or the natural stone shape which might suggest natural scenes, human or animal. It refers to aesthetic appreciation of Asian Stone, such as Gongshi of Chinese Scholars, Suiseki in Japanese tradition, or Suseok of Korean culture. The stone was selected from nature, collected, prepared, and displayed for aesthetic purposes as art objects in the room or garden, like a painting or statue. In this work, let's call it the viewing stone.

The second is typified by physical properties such as color, luster, transparency, and durability. It refers to gemstones, which are mostly used as jewelry. Most of the gems are rock and mineral. However, not all gems are stone. For instance, pearl and coral—biogenic origin—are also gemstones.

I call this attraction art-related stones and minerals because the way to appreciate those stones and minerals differ among people. It is personal appreciation, which might differ from one point-of-view to another. I put this attraction in tourism geology concern because there are activities to go to nature to seek the viewing stone or gemstone for pleasure. In fact, there are particular destinations that offer such activities, such as gemstone hunting tours and suiseki hunting tours.

The scope of this attraction is the stone and mineral in its natural form (raw form), which is found in any geological or geomorphological environment. Hence, further fashioning of the stone and mineral, such as being cut, polished, and displayed in a room or used as jewelry, is beyond the scope of tourism geology.

The viewing stone is formed through natural processes. In brief, it has disintegrated from the rock and then been transported downslope to make it smaller in size and have a unique shape. Generally, the stone size is pebble (4 - 64 mm of width) to cobble size (64 – 256 mm of diameter). In some cases, the stone size might be half as big as a human. Some areas well known for the stone hunting are Eel River (Fig. 3.7) and the Mojave Desert of California, Sado Island of Japan, and the Gobi Desert of China.

The stone-hunting area might be on a hill slope, river bank, beach usually near estuary, or in a desert environment where wind blows the sand to abrade the stone and rock. It is mostly found by picking from the ground. The viewing stone provenance in an upstream area is any rock type, whether igneous, sedimentary, or metamorphic rocks (Andri Subandrio, 2015, personal communication). In addition, some of the viewing stone is basically petrified wood, meteorite and coral.

On other hand, the term "gem" is hard to define. It actually covers a large range of products: single crystals, amorphous minerals, organics, rocks, imitations, synthetics, treated stones, faceted or rough objects, and even assemblages of various materials (Fritsch and Rondeau, 2009, p. 148). It is not the mineral itself that makes a gemstone; but it is the characteristics of a specific sample (Groat and Laurs, 2009, p. 153). For instance, a quartz crystal is not a gemstone unless it was formed in an environment that allowed it to reach a perfect size, color, and transparency. In rough form, a gem might be encased in a stone. It may resemble translucent lumps or a defined shape. Generally, a gemstone size is pebble size (4 – 64 mm of diameter).

Gemstone hardness is a minimum of 5.5 of 10 on the Mohs scale. Generally, it falls in range of 6.5 to 7.5. In practice, if a mineral/stone cannot be scratched by your nail, then it is higher than 4 on the scale. If a knife can scratch a mineral/stone, then it means the mineral/stone hardness falls between 5 and 6.5. If a steel nail cannot scratched a mineral/stone, then the hardness is higher than 7.

In this context, there are two ways of gemstone hunting in nature: hiking and digging. Hiking means walking into the wild and exploring what you can find on the surface, just like traditional prospecting. Most likely a little bit of digging or chiseling is needed. A gem can be found on the surface because it was eroded and transported by rivers as placer deposit, the same as the viewing stone. The provenance of a gemstone might be metamorphic rock, a (paleo)volcanism rock where mineralization occurred, or the shear zones filled by veins.

Figure 3.7. (Top) Viewing stone hunting in Eel river, California. The river landscape for hunting is generally in an upstream area, where river sediment is dominated by pebbles to boulder sizes. (Bottom) The outcome is displayed to be presented. Image courtesy of Samuel Edge, 2012.

The second way, which is more popular, is to hunt a gemstone by searching in a mine dump, a disused area of a gem or gold quarry, or by visiting a location that is open for recreational mining. Some popular destinations for recreational mining in the United States are Crater of Diamonds State Park in Arkansas, and Cherokee Ruby Mine and Emerald Hollow Mine in North Carolina. Their motto is *"All of what you find during excavation is all yours to keep."*

3.4.6. Particular Feature Attraction

I consider this attraction as a particular feature for several reasons. It is due to accident-related factors, which requires a particular time to observe and is situated at a certain location. Few sites are ready to be visited. Others require advanced technology support.

This subchapter discusses those attractions. It is composed of drilling-related accidents, giant crystal caves, geological sites on the Moon and Mars, and powerful geologic processes and hydrothermal vents in the deep ocean floor.

3.4.6.1. Drilling-Related Accident Attractions

In petroleum or geothermal businesses, an exploration well is drilled to discover hydrocarbon deposits or geothermal energy sources in the subsurface. It is a risky business, because of the many uncertainties that lie in the subsurface environment in consequence of drilling operations. Hence, an accident sometimes occurs, whether it is related to human or natural causes. An example of a human cause is misinterpretation due to limitation of data quality and/or quantity. Examples of natural causes are earthquakes and hurricanes.

Whatever the main cause, there are sites that occurred due to drilling accident but later turned out to be tourist attractions. The main attraction of this type is the aftermath, not the history of the site. Thus the site should have unique evidence to be observed. The evidence supports the fact that without the accident, it would have been difficult for the site to occur.

There are at least three examples of drilling accidents that eventually turned out to be tourist attractions. They are Fly Geyser in Nevada, Darvaza Gas Crater of Turkmenistan, and Sidoarjo Mud Volcano or LUSI of Indonesia.

3.4.6.1.1. Fly Geyser of Nevada

Fly Geyser, also called Fly Ranch Geyser, is a small geothermal geyser in Washoe County, Nevada, in the United States. It is hard to find published reports or scientific papers that discuss the history of the site. What will be discussed here is based on news found from internet sources.

An accident formed the geyser when a ranch owner drilled looking for water for irrigation in the early 1900s. But he found the water was too hot for agricultural use. In 1964, a company explored geothermal energy. Unfortunately, they found the water was not hot enough. Apparently, the well was not plugged properly when they left it. As a consequence, the water has flowed to the surface, which also brings the mineral contained. Eventually, minerals deposited surrounding the well created the travertine mound and several terraces. Moreover, the thermophilic algae contained in the water color the mound and make it more attractive. The geyser is on private land that is not open to the public. Fortunately, it can be seen from a distance.

The closest geyser to the Fly Geyser is located 370 km to the west: Old Faithful in Calistoga, California. The geyser erupts from a well that also formed accidentally, when drilling for water in late 19th century. However, it does not show attractive features like the Fly Geyser. The closest naturally occurring geyser from the Fly Geyser is Yellowstone National Park in Wyoming, located 850 km to the northeast.

3.4.6.1.2. Darvaza Gas Crater of Turkmenistan

This crater is located on the Karakum Desert, Turkmenistan, which is about a three-hour drive from Ashgabat. In petroleum geology, the crater is part of the Zeagli-Darvaza gas field, discovered in 1959. It was outlined from 1960 to 1962, when Turkmenistan was one of the constituent republics of the Soviet Union (Gabrielyants et al., 1962, p. 671). The field is on small uplifts, about 10 km length (Clarke, 1988, p. 31).

It is hard to find reliable documents of what happened during drilling operations. As told by many internet sources, while drilling operations were conducted in 1971, geologists unexpectedly discovered a large, cavernous space. This probably occurred because of poor-quality geophysical data, which causes misinterpretations.

Whatever the cause, the drilling rig and camp were soon sunk into a wide crater during drilling operations. Large quantities of methane gas were released, posing a potential danger to the people of the nearby villages. Eventually the engineers decided to burn it off, which they thought would be safer. They expected the gas would burn within days. It is still burning, however, over five decades later.

There are three artificial craters. Two craters contain bubbling mud and water. One crater is called the Door to Hell. It has a dancing flame on its floor. The crater has a diameter of 70 meters (230 ft) to a depth of about 30 meters (100 ft). It is almost the size of an American football field.

In the winter of 2013, George Kourounis, a Canadian adventurer who specializes in documenting extreme weather and worldwide natural disasters, became the first person to ever set foot at the bottom. He collected rock samples, which later revealed bacteria, despite the hot, methane-rich environment.

3.4.6.1.3. Sidoarjo Mud Volcano of Indonesia

The world noted what happened on May 29, 2006, when a violent mud volcano was born in Sidoarjo, Indonesia. It is called Lumpur Sidoarjo, or LUSI, whereas the word "lumpur" means mud.

Geologically, Sidoarjo is onshore of the North East Java Basin, one of the most prolific petroleum basins in Indonesia. Today, within the basin, there are hundreds of exploration wells, of which the Banjar Panji (BPJ)-1 well is one. It was spudded in March 2006. Target objective was the Oligo-Miocene carbonates of the Kujung Formation, buried by over 2,500 meters of rocks.

On May 29, while drilling was still continuing, something occurred just 200 meters away from the drilling site. A mix of hot mud, water, and gas burst out unexpectedly. Unfortunately, it flooded the densely populated surrounding area, leading to evacuation of 24,000 people. They left their villages, housing estates, schools, paddy fields, farmlands, factories, mosques, shops, and offices.

Meanwhile, on May 27, 2006, two days before the birth of LUSI, an earthquake of 6.3 magnitude struke Jogjakarta, 250 km to the southwest from the BPJ-1 well. The earthquake soon became one of the major reasons.

Eventually, there are two main opinions among geoscientists to explain the cause. The first was a man-made cause due to BPJ-1 well drilling. The second was a natural disaster due to Jogjakarta earthquake. Soon, scientific debates continued at an international level, such as in the AAPG International Convention in Cape Town in October 2008. After arguments were presented, the majority of the audience voted that drilling was responsible.

LUSI is a feature that has attracts international media for years. In an attraction context, where should I put the attraction category? If there was no drilling of the BPJ-1 well, then would LUSI have occurred? It is hard to say yes. For that reason, I put LUSI as a drilling-accident-related feature, regardless how much contribution there was of the BPJ-1 well drilling to the existence of LUSI.

In December 2006, the initial eruption marked by boiling water, mud, and gas composed of methane, carbon dioxide, and a trace of sulfuric acid, occurred at a rate escalating from 5,000 m^3/d to 120,000 m^3/d during the first weeks, and reaching almost 180,000 m^3/d (Mazzini et al., 2007, p. 375). The mud was believed to originate from the Plio-Pleistocene shallow marine clay of the Upper Kalibeng Formation (personal communication with Darwin Kadar, 2015).

From 2006 to 2009, the government tried to stop the eruption. The effort ranged from a re-entry well with snubbing unit, side tracking, a relief well, and putting a high-density chained ball at the eruption center from the surface. Unfortunately, none of the measures successfully stopped the flow. In fact, the flow rate remained 100,000 m^3/d at that time (Agustawijaya, 2010).

Sidoarjo Mud Mitigation Agency, or BPLS following Indonesian terminology, an ad hoc agency formed by the government in April 2007 until 2017, had tried to control the mud to flow to a wider surrounding area. They built several dykes and diverted the mud to Porong River, the nearest river where it could be sedimented to Madura Strait. However, ground deformations such as subsidence, uplift, and lateral ground movement make it hard to control mud flows. The dykes often collapsed during the early years and also destroyed destruct other infrastructures.

Until 2016, mudflow had affected an area of about 1200 hectare (Fig. 3.8), equal to 1,494 soccer fields (Soffian Hadi, 2016, personal communication). He also mentioned that the mudflow rate was smaller, from 20,000 – 80,000 m^3/d erupting in geyser style. Moreover, he stated as a consequence of a smaller flow rate, a smaller subsidence rate of several millimeters per month compared to several centimeters per month during the early years. Bubble gas sites also decreased to 17 locations from 247 locations. Today, most of the mud has dried up to be hard surface, except near and in the crater. The crater acreage is about 42 hectares (BPLS, 2016a), equal to 52 soccer fields.

Figure 3.8. Sidoarjo mud or LUSI, as seen from a Google Earth image, bounded by dykes to prevent wider distribution to the city. Image was taken on 15 August 2016.

Mudflow temperature near the ponds was warmer, in the range of 33.7°C to 55.2°C (BPLS, 2016b), compared to the hot mud during initial eruption, which was more than 100°C. Vanderkluysen et al. (2014, pp. 2943-2944) analyzed gas released during explosion as observed in May and October 2011, where the outcome showed gas was composed of 98 mol % water vapor, 1.5 mol % carbon dioxide, and 0.5 mol % methane. LUSI had five mud eruption vents, initially, but only one remains active (Soffian Hadi, 2016, personal communication). It suggests that LUSI is entering a new phase, which is more stable and has fewer active phases.

As a preliminary study of mud composition, USGS scientists analyzed the mud, which was collected directly from the main eruption crater by backhoe in late 2007. The several outcomes show the water has pH 7.42 with highly dissolved solids, where sodium is the dominant cation; clay minerals are predominantly smectite, illite, and mixed illite/smectite; and inorganic sulfur indicates total sulfur content around 0.5 weight% (Plumlee et al., 2008, pp. 5,6,8). Krisnayanti and Agustawijaya (2014, p. 207) analyzed mud composition in 2009, which showed heavy metal concentrations were below environmental soil quality guidelines. However, the physical and chemical composition of mud-water was above the environmental standard.

How long will LUSI last? Three scientists have different estimates. Istadi et al. (2009, p. 1732) estimate from 23 to 35 years. Davies et al. (2011, p. 517) expects LUSI will develop for 26 years. Rudolph et al. (2011, p. 128) predict LUSI has a 33% chance of lasting less than 21 years and a 67% chance of lasting less than 84 years. If LUSI will last for 26 years, then in 2037 the eruption will disappear.

In the scientific context, there is no doubt: LUSI is absolutely attractive. LUSI represents a unique opportunity to adore and study the evolution of geological process of a mud volcano since its birth.

Tourism has been working in LUSI since its birth, managed by local people. News broadcasts by local and international media indirectly promote the area as a destination. Curiosity about what happened and the current situation are the main theme. Today, according to local information, LUSI attracts tens of visitors daily, both international and domestic tourists. If we assume 20 visitors per day on weekdays and 50 visitors per day on the weekend, then it will be fewer than 11,000 visitors per year to LUSI.

LUSI has natural and man-made attractions. The main LUSI attraction is mud eruption, bubbling gas on gryphon structures, warm mudflows to the ponds and to the Porong river, and smaller mud fan on the ponds. In addition, man-made attractions are the destroyed buildings buried by a couple meters of mud.

To improve LUSI as a destination, other attractions should be created, so that tourists have more experience and get their own sense of place. For instance, mud composition should be analyzed for pelotherapy use and a health spa resort could be built nearby. There could be mud handicraft as souvenirs and local modern dance to depict the tragedy. If the tourism-based economic attraction successfully grew, how long would it last? Most likely, the longevity of eruption is the time span of the main tourist attraction.

LUSI is indeed a Pompeii of Indonesia in which tragedy in the past is the main theme. Yet, the real Pompeii in Italy attracts millions of visitors per year. Tourism should be developed at best to reveal the charm of the Indonesian Pompeii. The main spirit: giving back the life of the displaced people.

3.4.6.2. Giant Crystal Cave Attraction

A particular cave type, called a cave mine, is found during mining works where the cave has no connection to the surface. The floor, wall, and ceiling of the cave mine might be decorated by crystals, which is the topic in this subchapter. The crystals are the main attraction of the cave mine, where it has unique three-dimension shape, extraordinary size, and is rare in the world. I call this particular interest giant crystal cave. In this context, this description excludes the usual speleothem found in limestone or dolostone caves.

An ideal subsurface environment allows the crystal to grow in perfect shape and to a breathtaking size. Visiting those caves will be like visiting another planet, where giant crystals grow over one meter in length. More surprisingly, those unique cave crystals were found fortuitously, mostly during ore exploitation. I believe many other giant crystal caves are still undiscovered.

Dr. Ing. Thomas Krassmann, a German geologist and mineral collector with over 20 years of experience, collects information particularly about the giant crystals of the world. His project was called "The Giant Crystal Project Site" and was presented on in his website, http://giantcrystals.strahlen.org, since 2004; but unfortunately the host closed down the site a couple of years ago.

A giant crystal is defined by a size that is at least one meter in at least one dimension. His information on the world of giant crystals is from crystals found during mining at the surface and during underground mining. Based on his information, I chose eleven giant crystal caves (Table 3.5).

Four caves in Table 3.5 (nos. 1 to 4) have an unknown current status on whether the crystals or crystal aggregates are still there and/or available for visitation. Another four caves (nos. 5 to 8) are prohibited to visit. Only three caves (nos. 9 to 11) allow for tourist visitation.

Table 3.5 The giant crystal caves in the world. Adapted with permission, based on works of Krassmann, 2007.

No.	Mineral Type, Crystal Size and Form	Location and Year Found	Status
1	**Rhodochrosite** (manganese carbonate?) Stalactitic aggregates may however reach several meter in length.	Not available information	The actual mining of lead and zinc sulphides stopped decades ago.
2	**Calcite, Dannemorite, Fluorite, and Hedenbergite** Crystals may all reach sizes of up to 1 m.	Dalnegorsk ore field, Primorskiy Kraj, Far Eastern Region, Russia. Found in 1960 (?)	Ongoing mining activity in both the sulphide and boron deposits
3	**Feldspar** 1 meter large crystals are visible in the walls of the 'underground lake'.	Quarzbruch Hennenkobel (Hühnerkobel), Kiesau, Rabenstein, Zwiesel, Bavarian Forest, Bavaria, Germany. Found in 1877 (?)	The partly drowned underground workings with the large feldspar crystals are gated.
4	**Halite** Maximum size of crystals is about 1 m.	Eddy Potash Mine, Carlsbad, Eddy Co., New Mexico, USA. Found in 1962.	It is not exactly known, possibly the crystal still in place. The mine itself was closed at the end of 1997.
5	**Aragonite, Gypsum,** and **Calcite** Several meter long speleothems of aragonite and gypsum, often in chandelier or tree like shapes. The aragonite and gypsum form large chandeliers and crystal aggregates which may reach a length of 4 meter and more.	Kap-kutan cave system, Kugitangau mountains, Tienshan, Turkmenistan,	Protected cave system. Access is restricted to scientific research parties only
6	**Aragonite** and **Gypsum** Crystal 'chandeliers' up to 3 meter size, though the individual crystals are much smaller.	Lechuguilla cave, Carlsbad, Eddy Co., New Mexico, USA	Protected, access to the cave is restricted to scientific caving expeditions
7	**Gypsum inside geode**. Medium size of 0.5 m, whereas the maximum recorded crystal size is two meters. Geode dimension: inner length 8 m, width 1.8 m, medium height 1.7 m.	Mina Rica (Quien Tal Pensara mine), Pilar de Jaravia, Sierra del Aguilon, Almeria Province, Spain. Found in 1999.	The site is protected and access is restricted to scientific parties only.

No.	Mineral Type, Crystal Size and Form	Location and Year Found	Status
8	**Gypsum (Selenite)**, possibly some sulfide minerals. It is mostly freestanding prismatic crystals up to 11.4 m length.	Naica Mine, Chihuahua, Mexico. In 1910 found Cave of the Swords at 120 m deep where crystal size is up to 2 m lenght. In 2000 found Caves of the Crystals at 300 m deep with more gigantic crystal size.	Active mine and access is restricted to scientific parties only.
9	**Celestite** Though the maximum size of the crystals is given with 18 inches, it is expected that some of the crystals may well reach about 1 m size.	Crystal Cave, Put-in-Bay, South Bass Island, Ottawa Co., Ohio, USA. Found in 1897.	A very popular show cave, which is open to the general public.
10	**Halite** Crystal with 1.10 m of cubes is confirmed.	Merkers potash mine, Wartburgkreis, Thuringia, Germany. Found prior 1990	Museum mine, tourists are welcome to visit the crystal cave
11	**Gypsum** Average crystal size was about 3 m with the largest crystals being up to 7 m length.	Debar, Western Macedonia. Found prior 1985.	Dormant underground mine, partly flooded, but still acessible for tourist.

3.4.6.2.1. Naica Cave Mine

Among those caves in the list, in the context of size, the cave of Naica mine is the most interesting cave. The mine is one of the most important silver mines in the world. It is in the state of Chihuahua, northern Mexico, and operated by a Mexican private company, Industrias Penoles. There are important caves intercepted during underground mining. The first cave, found in 1910, was *Cueva de las Espadas,* or Swords Cave, at 120 m depth. The cave mouth was completely covered by selenite crystals, one of the four gypsum varieties, some up to two meters in length. The second cave was found in 2000, at 290 m depth, filled by giant selenite crystals. It is comprised of several caves: *Ojo de la Reina* or Queen's Eye Cave; *Cueva de las Velas,* also called Sails Cave or Candles Cave; and *Cueva de los Cristales* or Crystal Cave.

Cueva de los Cristales is the most amazing underground wonder of the Earth (Fig. 3.9). It contains 162 crystals, mostly around four to six meters in length (Badino et al., 2009, p.1767). The cave also has the most giant crystals. The largest crystal size is 11.4 meters in length, about 5 m³ in volume, and with an estimated mass of 12 tons (Badino et al., 2009, p. 1768). It is called Cin Crystal to honor the deceased of Francesco Dal Cin, a prominent Italian caver and a member of the La Venta team. This is the team that organizes and runs various geographical-speleological and environmental exploration projects in remote areas with difficult access.

Figure 3.9. Giant gypsum crystals criss-crossing at the *Cueva de los Cristales*, at 290 m depth, Naica cave mine, Mexico. Note a person in the bottom right for scale. Image courtesy of Alexander Van Driessche, 2010, CC BY 3.0.

Garcia-Ruiz et al. (2007, p. 330) predict that other caves with similar or even larger selenite crystals exist among the tangle of underground galleries in the Naica mine area, which might make up one of the oddest locations of the mineral world.

The Naica's crystal was formed at least 191,000 years ago (Sanna et al., 2011, p. 24) at a temperature around 58°C (Garcia-Ruiz et al., 2007, p. 329). It occurred when the crystals immersed in hot and mineral-rich underground water grew until dewatering since 1985 (Sanna et al., 2011, p. 24). In an aerated condition, the cave temperature falls to 45.5°C with 92% - 94% humidity (Badino, 2009, p. 1408). Such an environment is a deadly environment for cave investigation.

Ptolomea, a dedicated design of an all-covered suit, was constructed. It was integrated with cooling and respiration systems along with friendly crystal boots. It allows the scientist to observe the cave for over one and a half hours instead of one and a half minutes without using the suit.

As a natural response of dewatering, gypsum condensation and dissolution occurred. Examples include saw marks, corrosion features and dissolution-recrystallization of the gypsum edge (Gazquez et al., 2016, p.159). Moreover, Bernabei et al. (2007, p. 23) reported a new gypsum speleothem, whose genesis is related to the environmental condition inside the cave after its artificial dewatering. The new speleothem is called "sails" and has only been observed in *Cueva de las Velas*.

Visiting the caves allows for scientific investigation only. In the near future, the mine will be unprofitable for mining. Hence, dewatering will be unnecessary. As a consequence, the groundwater level will go back to 120 m of depth, flooding the caves and then gypsum will keep precipitating for eternity.

I imagine that in the near future there will be a company willing to make the Naica cave mine into an underground world-class destination. It will be high risk, but might also be high reward. The challenges ahead are as follows:

- The crystals need to grow normally to conserve their physical state. This means the cave mine needs to be flooded by hot water as in its original condition.

- In such a situation, the tourist should be able to adore the crystals through transparent large and thick windows able to hold hundreds of pounds of water pressure, derived from 170 m of hot-water column.

- The tourist should possibly wear a special all-covered suit.

- The crystals inside the cave should be illuminated by a specially designed lighting system, probably energized by the hot underground water.

- Excellent cave cooling systems will be needed for tourist visitation.

- The cave mine will be more interesting if integrated with a speleotherapy health resort.

Hence, the crystals might still grow, while at the same time, underground tourism is taking place. For those who visit, staring at the giant crystals will be an unforgettable experience for everyone, even though for only a couple of minutes.

3.4.6.3. Moon and Mars Attraction

The space age commenced in 1957, when the Soviet Union (now Russia) launched Sputnik 1, the world's first artificial satellite. Since then, the effort to conquer outer space has increased, to extend human occupation in this universe. Early motivation was to explore extraterrestrial objects in search of life. In this century, travel to outer space for leisure purposes becomes more familiar.

Two extraterrestrial objects are the most discussed to be visited: Mars and the Moon. Besides, among many extraterrestrial objects, those two objects have the most completed missions (Greeley, 2013, p. 11). Some companies estimate that tourism on the Moon or Mars will be a reality within the next decades.

NASA, a United States government agency, through their website on September 15, 2015 has a plan to send humans to Mars in the

2030s. In addition, Moon tourism might be just a couple years ahead. Assume that in those years the schedule to visit Mars or the Moon will be on time, where is our destination for pleasure activities? The Moon and Mars are vast in area. A particular location is needed where the site will be visited.

Geological understanding of the extraterrestrial objects is mostly derived from remote sensing data, from pictures taken from the spacecraft. Thus, most of the identification of possible attractions refers to scenic beauty attractions. The landscape types on the Moon and Mars related to scenic beauty attraction are impact craters, particularly on the Moon; volcanos; deserts; and structurally related attractions. Geologic attractions—which are the geologic history of a site—are always inherent in the attraction, off course.

To assess the potential scenic beauty on the Moon and Mars, the scenic beauty perception based on Earth features might be applied to extraterrestrial objects. Thus, geologists should predict similar geologic character on earth by observing planetary maps or extraterrestrial images of the Moon and Mars. In this book, the interest in extraterrestrial sites is described based on geomorphic features as seen in images taken from spacecraft.

3.4.6.3.1. Possible Natural Attractions on the Moon

Scrutinizing the surface character from remote sensing images, it seems all impact crater types are on the Moon. An impact crater is a result of a solid object hitting the surface. Moon volcanism ceased at about 1.2 giga-years ago (Greeley, 2013, p. 78), and the Moon has no atmosphere, no plants, no water, no weathering, and no plate tectonics. This means that once the crater is formed, it will last forever until another impact destroys it.

The Moon has craters in various sizes, forms, ages, and other associated features. The craters range in size from less than 100 meters across to hundreds of kilometers in diameter, called a basin. Various craters formed range from perfectly bowl-shaped to oval-shaped. There is a crater chain called "catena." The crater floor has many characteristics such as fractured, mounded, benched, or with the peak in the floor. A new one formed might show fresh impact ejecta. For an older one, it might superimpose with the newer one. "Craters in craters" are common, where the smaller and younger one is inside an older and larger one. Many craters have named been, especially the larger ones. Many of smaller ones, however, still have no name.

Volcanic processes exist in the Moon as the outcome of impact processes. The volcanic source might have formed domes a few kilometers across and several hundred meters high. The eruption volcanic material produces lava terrain, called *maria* or *mare*. It accumulated in topographically low areas, and might cover about 17% of the Moon's surface (Greeley, 2013, p. 77). Lava terrain also forms distinctive surface feature such as rille, also called vallis; and mare ridge, also called wrinkle ridge.

An example of a typical Moon crater to be visited is Crater Mendeleev, 313 km in diameter. It is a superimposed crater in the middle and in its edge. An interesting feature is Catena Mendeleev in Crater Mendeleev, which is the chain of about 28 craters forming a straight line.

Another beautiful crater complex and its associated features to be visited is Sinus Iridium (Fig. 3.10). It is an impact crater that superposes the larger crater, Imbrium basin. Unlike most craters, this crater forms a bay bounded by the Montes Jura Range as the crater wall and the two protruding parts, Promontorium Laplace and Promontorium Heraclides, which are 236 km apart. The crater floor is filled by Mare Imbrium, a lava terrain originated during impact, forming of Imbrium basin. The Mare Imbrium decorated by wrinkles ridges and smaller craters.

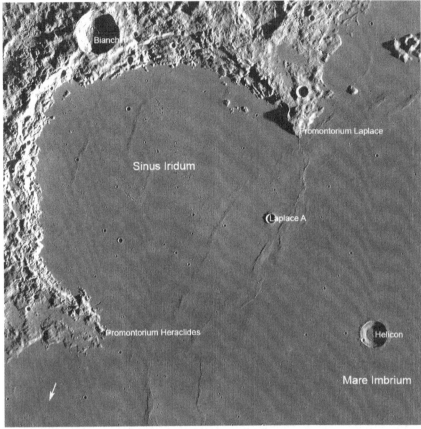

Figure 3.10. Sinus Iridum, also called "Bay of Rainbows" area of the Moon. Arrow on the left bottom corner shows the location of Soviet Lunokhod 1 Rover. The LROC WAC mosaic is 360 km wide (Robinson, 2013). Image courtesy of NASA/GSFC/Arizona State University.

Like on Earth, a volcanic process on the Moon produces lava flow on the surface. The flow might produce a cave, called a lava tube. The cave occurred when the lava flow froze on the surface, produce a hard surface while the inside part still flowed. The outcome is a long cave. The surface sometimes collapses, producing a pit that can be used as cave entrance (Fig. 3.11). Such pit features are investigated using special cameras such as the Lunar Reconnaissance Orbiter Camera (LROC) and Narrow Angle Camera (NAC). The imaging outcome revealed more than 140 negative relief features formed in impact melt deposits, some of which are likely to be the result of collapse into subsurface void spaces (Ashley et al., 2011). Such investigations are needed, since the cave provides protection from surface hazards such as radiation and micrometeorites.

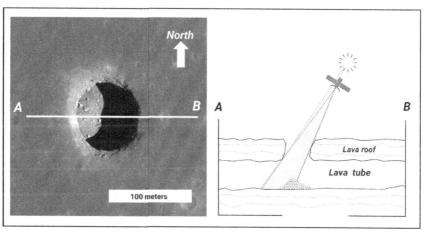

Figure 3.11. Left: Spectacular high Sun view of the Mare Tranquillitatis pit crater, revealing boulders on an otherwise smooth floor. NAC M126710873R. Image Courtesy of NASA/GSFC/Arizona State University. Right: Cartoon shows a general cross-section of A-B in the left figure (not to scale), suggesting internal lava tube structure. Cartoon was drawn by the author.

3.4.6.3.2. Possible Natural Attractions on Mars

Among many planets in the Solar System, other than Earth, Mars is the most popular. It becomes the subject in movies and novels. Mars is a symbol of human hope and also human fear. In many stories, Mars creatures with their advanced civilization strike to occupy the Earth. In reality, however, humans will occupy the red planet.

As a symbol of human hope, the nature of this red planet is like Earth. It has the same geologic processes that shaped our planet, such as impact cratering, volcanism, tectonics, and gradation. Gradation processes are surface processes involving weathering, erosion, transportation of the weathered debris, and material deposition.

The processes redecorated the landscapes. For instance, a crater is formed due to impact marks on its surface, whereas volcanism produces large and broad shield volcanoes with its lava flows and deep valleys that mark the existence of tectonics. Hence, it has more features to be visited and provides more playgrounds. Some of the Mars features are described briefly, to be further investigated for future visitation.

There are many outcrops on Mars that resemble sedimentary processes in the past. One is called Link, a conglomerate outcrop encountered by Curiosity Rover. The outcrop has been interpreted as deposited in a fluvial environment, the same interpretation as when a similar outcrop is observed on earth (Fig. 3.12). It is one of the geologic attractions on Mars.

Figure 3.12. Comparison of conglomerate outcrop on Mars (left) with similar outcrop on Earth (right). Erosion in outcrops causes gravel to fall to the ground, creating a pebble pile (circle on left photo). Image courtesy of NASA/JPL-Caltech/MSSS and PSI.

Craters on Mars have similar character to the Moon's craters. What makes them differ in appearance are the surface conditions during impact and the surface processes modification after impact. For instance, ejecta deposits show flow-like patterns, suggesting the terrain was wet (e.g., a crater in Hephaestus Fossae). On the other hand, many craters show mesa-like platforms, called pedestal craters, where the ejecta deposits are more resistant to erosion.

Among many unique craters on Mars, there is a crater that has the internal structure mimicking a happy face. It is one of the unique craters as shown in the image captured by the Mars Reconnaissance Orbiter (MRO) Context Camera (CTX, Fig. 3.13). It is 3 km across and located among the Nereidum Montes, north of the Argyre basin. When we stand on the peak of the crater wall, we can see the happy face-like feature with our own eyes.

Unlike the Moon, Mars volcanoes have distinct topographic features. Olympus Mons is the largest volcano on Mars and also in the Solar System. A shield volcano, it has impressive dimensions, being 624 kilometers in diameter and 25 kilometers in height (16 miles) from its floor, and it has a summit caldera 80 km across in diameter. Compared to Mount Everest, Olympus Mons stands about two-and-a-half times its size.

Another three smaller shield volcanoes are located nearby to the southeast: Arsia Mons, Tharsis Mons, and Ascraeous Mons, where their position forms a NE-SW straight line. Although smaller than Olympus Mons, their dimensions are still impressive where diameter range from 375 to 480 km, 14 to 20 km high, and 15 to 72 km caldera diameter. Despite the facts that these four volcanoes are higher and bigger compared to the earth's mountains, the slopes are gentle. It is estimated the slope is about 4° to 5°.

Figure 3.13. An unnamed crater, 3 km across, mimicking a "happy face," taken by the Mars Reconnaissance Orbiter (MRO) Context Camera (CTX; Malin et al., 2008). Image courtesy of NASA/JPL/Malin Space Science Systems.

Mars also has the deepest, longest, and widest canyon in the Solar System. It is the Valles Marineris, also called the Grand Canyon of Mars. It stretches 3,000 km long, up to 200 km wide, and up to 8 km deep. Compared to the Grand Canyon in Arizona, it is approximately nine times longer, seven times wider, and four times deeper. The Grand Canyon has dimensions of about 446 km length, up to 29 km wide, and up to 1.83 km deep. Valles Marineris might reflect huge fracturing through the lithosphere.

The cave in Mars is important. It particularly provides protection from ionizing and ultraviolet radiation for humans, insulation from thermal oscillations, impacting object protection, sealing ability to contain a higher-than-ambient atmospheric pressure and access to potentially important subsurface resources (Boston et al., 2002, p. 7). So that going to Mars will most likely mean visiting the cave as well.

However, until now the dissolution cave type is unknown. The cave type known on Mars is suspected lava tubes, the same cave type as on the Moon. Scientists have been observing the cave entrance of Mars using CTX (Context Camera, a high-resolution camera). Cushing and Okubo (2015) identified a total about 1200 candidates for cave entrance locations.

The theme "follows the water" always becomes the main important theme in Mars exploration. Although no ocean, lake, or river flows have been observed on the present-day surface, geomorphic features relate to existence of water in the past. For instance, Ma'adim Vallis is one of the largest outflow channels on Mars, about 700 km long and over 20 km wide. It probably carried water or water and ice into Gusev crater, which was an impact crater filled by water to become a lake crater.

Among many geomorphic features related to water evidence on Mars, perhaps the most beautiful feature is a fossil delta in Eberswalde Crater, a 65-km-diameter crater. It is called Eberswalde Delta, covers 115 km sq (Fig. 3.14), and was formed in the rim of a lake, Eberswalde lake crater. The presences of meandering channels and distributaries of the delta are clear, similar to the Lena Delta in Russia, where the channels overlap each other representing different phases of deltaic deposition. It also becomes evident that a long time ago Mars was wet.

Figure 3.14. The amazing Eberswalde Delta—a fossil delta—with clear meandering channels and distributaries. It is in the rim of Eberswalde Crater (Malin and Edget, 2003). Image courtesy of NASA/JPL/Malin Space Science Systems.

3.4.6.4. The Potential Attraction of Powerful Geologic Processes

Everyone knows the power of geologic processes such as landslides, earthquakes, tsunamis, or volcanic eruptions. If those processes appear in front of our eyes, then our first perception is they are hazards and we should evacuate the area. It is a normal attitude, since we do not know how big the magnitude and its intensity.

A natural process is called a disaster when it causes property damage, injury, or fatality. However, should we call it a disaster when no injury or no fatality and minimum to no property damage occurred? Is it possible for such processes to be perceived as tourist attractions?

What was considered as dangerous phenomena in the past and present might be considered a tourist attraction in the future, or even in the present day for some people. For instance, the traditional perception of a storm is a dangerous phenomenon that should be avoided. Nowadays, however, storm-chasing tours for five to six days are offered by several tour agencies in United States. The attraction is the process itself, not the aftermath, nor the local people who suffer. Call it anything for this tourism type: landslide tourism, volcano eruption tourism, earthquake tourism, or tsunami tourism. It will be time for the Earth shows!

The geological processes as attractions rely on prediction accuracy on when, where, and how big such natural wonder will occur. If possible, the prediction results are a few days or weeks before the process occurs. Firstly, the local people should be first warned and evacuated (if needed), so that no one feels disadvantaged by this type of tourism. Secondly, to allow a longer time for tour operators to arrange and promote the tour itself. Tourist motivation may satisfy their curiosity, having a new experience or even learning about the process from a safe distance.

Today's typical time of notice before those processes occur are on the order of seconds to tens of seconds for earthquakes, minutes to hours for tsunamis, and possibly hours to days for landslides and volcanic eruption. Thus, for this time being, this attraction type is only suitable for tourists who are ready to go at any time.

The geologic process proposed as a tourist attraction is not at a catastrophic level. On the catastrophic scale, those processes will have many consequences to aspects of life such as damaging the infrastructure. Thus the scale suggests those processes to be a potential tourist attraction is as follows:

- Landslide attraction, in terms of movement, is proposed to move within seconds to hours.

- Earthquake attraction is proposed at 4.0 to 5.5 magnitude on the Richter Scale, while earthquake hazard is bigger than 6.5 magnitude. Potential attraction worldwide on those scales is about ±1,150 to ±32,000 potential earthquakes annually (USGS, 2016a).

- Tsunami attraction is proposed within scale IV (largely observed) to V (strong) of Papadopoulos–Imamura scale, when on the scale VI or more is hazard. Unfortunately, the tsunami frequency on the scale suggested is unknown as yet.

- Volcano eruption attraction is proposed at Volcanic Explosivity Index (VEI) 0 to a maximum of 4, whereas VEI 5 or more is disaster. On this scale, there are total 70 eruptions annually (Siebert et al., 2010, p. 42).

When prediction goes accurately along with the readiness of the people, then what will we do when those geologic processes come? My belief: the media will report the increase rate of tourist visitations rather than how many people suffered because of lost business opportunities due to travel bans. Maybe the media will reveal the amount of economic gain because of tourists staying longer to wait for upcoming powerful geological processes, instead of how long is needed to recover the local economy. When the people accept this idea, and when scientists are able to predict accurately, then it is when the processes come will be the most wanted moment rather than the moment to avoid.

Nevertheless, we should careful when marketing this attraction type. It might be sensitive for some people because of past events, such as losing a relative or their belongings. If so, postponing the marketing is better. In the next section, we will discuss the character of powerful geological process as attractions.

It needs to be emphasized that a powerful geologic process will be called an attraction when predictions can be made of when, where, and how big the magnitude. However, for the time being, those processes are still considered as hazards until accurately prediction methods are formulated.

3.4.6.4.1. Landslide Attraction

Landslide is a general name for or any downslope movement of a mass of regolith, bedrock, or a mixture of rock and soil under gravity force. It is used to show any mass-wasting process. Landslides contribute to reshaping the landscape and transforming local topography by transporting the material.

There are three types of how landslides move:
- Slides moves that move several inches per year (e.g., slumps, creep, rock slides).
- Flows (e.g. mudflows, lahar, debris flows, debris avalanches).
- Falls (e.g., rock falls, debris falls).

The processes such as creep move only one inch per year. Others, such as debris avalanches, might move at hundreds of kilometers per hour.

The most prone area for landslide attraction is basically the steep slope area, steeper than 30° to 35°, whether on mountain slopes or under the sea. Deforestation, earthquakes, and long rain periods may trigger landslides. Rainwater will fully saturate the pore space among grains, reducing friction and internal cohesion of slope material. Earthquakes cause shaking of the ground, loosening boulders, and starting landslides.

Cold laharic flows through the river valley. It is a re-sedimentation of previous volcanic deposits, which is not related to volcanic eruption. It is occurred particularly after or during heavy rain. The flow is a fast-moving muddy flow with rolling boulders in river valleys.

For tourist attraction context, a landslide process is considered interesting if it occurred during seconds to minutes or hours, but less likely if it occurred in days or longer. Seeing landslides such as mudflow, debris flow, lahars, and rock falls from safe distance is a must.

In countries where large snow accumulation often occurs, the snow on the mountain slope is periodically controlled by local agencies, such as transportation departments. It is needed to avoid hazard on the highway crossing the mountain valley. Their main task is to make smaller snow avalanches, and to avoid dangerous bigger ones by method such as shooting with heavy artillery. Their work makes it possible to enjoy snow avalanche attraction since it is controlled.

Although snow avalanche is a domain of snow science, the mountain slope supports the avalanche. Hence, geological feature are responsible to the existence of the avalanche. It is interesting to discuss where the avalanche closely relates to landslide attraction.

Their work is scheduled by weather situation. Yet, more are done with very short notice. Although the work is frequently conducted, due to safety reasons, they disallowed people outside when they were shooting. In addition, most of their work was done in the dark during storms when there is nothing to see (Harry Nelson and Matt McKee, 2016, personal communication).

Despite natural obstacles and their ban, it is still desirable to observe snow avalanches during their work from a specific point of view in a different place where there are many tourist resorts, such as told by Matt McKee, supervisor for avalanche safety for the state highway in Little Cottonwood Canyon, in the United States. He noticed during his works that the snow avalanche might be observed from inside the resort, because of a different point of view, although it was a rare event (personal communication, 2016). Thus, it is still possible for us to watch the beauty of a snow avalanche process moving down the slope from inside a resort. What we should know is when the avalanche control will be conducted and what resort we need to stay in.

3.4.6.4.2. Earthquake Attraction

Earthquakes are basically a sudden shaking of the ground. Most result from plate movement while the rest are a result of volcanic action or man-made explosions.

The power of an earthquake is measured by its magnitude and its intensity. Magnitude is a quantitative measure of the earthquake size at its source in the subsurface, also known as the focus or hypocenter. The scale is measured according to the Richter Magnitude Scale, from 1 as the lowest to 10 as the highest on a logarithmic scale (Table 3.6). This means that 6 on the scale is ten times stronger than 5, and a hundred times stronger than 4. Usually, ground shaking itself occurs only for seconds.

The second measurement is intensity as the earthquake shaking severity in the surface, also known as epicenter. The scale is measured according to Modified Mercalli Intensity (MMI) scale, using roman numerals ranging from I to XII (Table 3.7). The intensity is used by engineers to describe building effects.

Table 3.6. Earthquake magnitude (Richter scale) and average annual number of earthquakes of each magnitude (USGS, 2016a).

Magnitude	Description	Average Annually
2.0 – 2.9	Minor	1,300,00 (estimated)
3.0 – 3.9	Minor	130,000 (estimated)
4.0 – 4.9	Light	13,000 (estimated)
5.0 – 5.9	Moderate	1319 (a)
6.0 – 6.9	Strong	134 (a)
7.0 – 7.9	Major	17 (b)
8.0 and higher	Great	1 (b)

(a): based on observations since 1990
(b): based on observations since 1900

Table 3.7. Modified Mercalli Intensity (MMI) scale. Simplified from USGS, 2016b.

Scale	Description of MMI
I	Not felt except by a very few under especially favorable conditions
II	Felt only by a few persons at rest
III	Felt quite noticeably by persons indoors
IV	Felt indoors by many, outdoors by few during the day
V	Felt by nearly everyone; many awakened. Some dishes, windows broken
VI	Felt by all, many frightened. Some heavy furniture moved; Damage slight
VII	Damage negligible in buildings of good design and construction
VIII	Damage slight in specially designed structures. Damage great in poorly built structures
IX	Damage considerable in specially designed structures. Damage great in substantial buildings, with partial collapse
X	Some well-built wooden structures destroyed. Rails bent
XI	Few, if any (masonry) structures remain standing. Bridges destroyed. Rails bent greatly
XII	Damage total. Objects thrown into the air

The relationship of magnitude and intensity is similar to a cellphone and its signal. Magnitude is similar to the signal sent out from a base transceiver station. Intensity is analogue of how well the cellphone receives signals. Table 3.8 the shows relation of magnitude and intensity.

Stein and Wysession (2003, p. 11) mentioned that earthquake hazard is due primarily to large earthquakes, typically with a magnitude greater than 6.5 on the Richter Scale. Fortunately, they also mentioned that the largest earthquakes are expected only about every 200 years (p. 21).

Table 3.8. Comparison of earthquake magnitude and intensity (USGS, 2016b).

Magnitude	Typical Maximum Modified Mercalli Intensity
1.0 – 3.0	I
3.0 – 3.9	II – III
4.0 – 4.9	IV – V
5.0 – 5.9	VI – VII
6.0 – 6.9	VII – VIII
7.0 and higher	IX or higher

Usually after the earthquake strikes with strong and greater magnitudes, it might be followed by landslide, liquefaction, sand blows, or even tsunami. Loose sediments and other weak rocks at the surface might enhance ground motion compared to the solid bedrock sites.

Earthquakes primarily occur at the plate boundaries where the tectonic plates converge, diverge, or slide past each other. Based on earthquake focus distribution with magnitudes 4 and greater since 1897 to 1990, the earthquake majority is distributed where the Pacific, Phillipine, and Indian Plates subduct below the Eurasian Plate (Simkin et al., 1994). It includes the region of New Zealand, Tonga, Solomon Islands, Indonesia, Japan, Taiwan, the Philippines, the southeastern coast of Russia, the Aleutian Islands of Alaska, and the western coast of the United States and Southern America (Fig. 3.15). To understand the history of earthquakes all around the world, accessed the USGS earthquake database (earthquake.usgs.gov/earthquakes/search or go to tinyurl.com/y7dkdoqo).

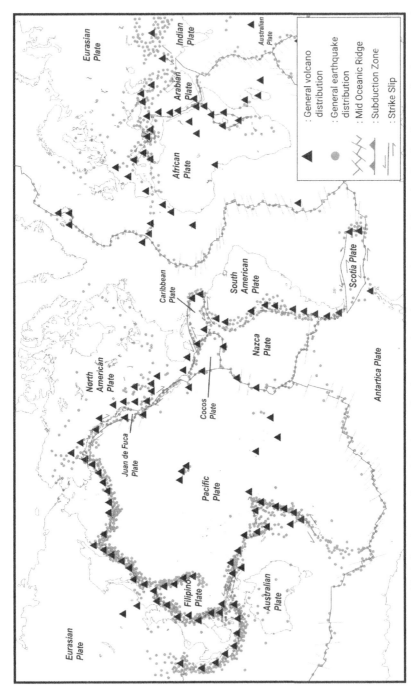

Figure 3.15. Simplified distribution of earthquakes and volcanoes, based on Simkin et al. (1994). The distribution of volcanos and earthquakes is also called the Ring of Fire.

The earthquake power suitable for a tourist attraction is probably at best 4.0 to 5.5 magnitude, while an earthquake hazard would have to be greater than 6.5 magnitude. In the scale, 4.0 to 4.9 magnitudes, which are identical to IV to V MMI, most people feel a light quake. Everyone feels it as a moderate quake at 5.0 to 5.5 magnitudes, which possibly corresponds with VI on the MMI Scale. At those magnitudes, there are estimated to be about ±1,150 to ±32,000 potential earthquake attraction sites annually in the whole world (Fig. 3.16).

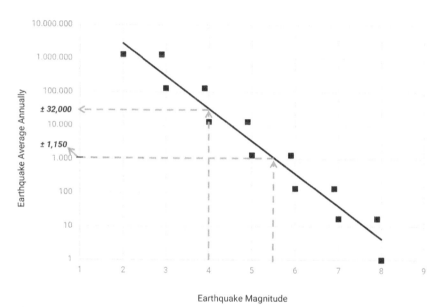

Figure 3.16. Graph shows the relation of earthquake magnitude (normal scale) and earthquake average annually (logarithmic scale), where the value is based on Table 3.6. An exponential trend line is drawn (solid black line) to estimate earthquake average annually at 4 and 5.5 magnitudes.

One of the major challenges for scientists, which is hard to resolve today, is to accurately predict the earthquake. Many attempts to predict earthquakes have searched for precursors, an observable behavior that precedes earthquakes. However, the warning time is short, typically only seconds to tens of seconds, which makes it hard to arrange a tour.

The true attraction for tourists is experiencing the ground-shaking sensation in nature, although generally less than one minute. The people who live in plate boundaries have more opportunity to have earthquake experience. A relatively flat area, far from buildings or steep slopes, is most likely the best place to be entertained by the quake sensation. Let me remind the reader about one important quote on earthquakes: *"Earthquakes don't kill people, but weak structure does."*

In the Tokyo earthquake simulation center, we can have an experience of earthquakes by a computer-controlled earthquake for the public. To enhance Tokyo's resident preparedness, they should attend the course; Japan is one of the most earthquake-prone regions.

3.4.6.4.3. Tsunami Attraction

Tsu-nami' is a Japanese term for "harbor-wave," referring to a huge and fast sea wave on the coast. The tsunami formation is primarily related to an earthquake on the seafloor with sharp vertical displacement, generally about 7.5 magnitude or larger (Pugh and Woodworth, 2014, p. 195). A minority are because of underwater volcanic eruptions, meteorological causes, or landslides into the sea or lake.

In deep water (e.g., 4000 m), the wave crest of a tsunami is limited to tens of centimeters. But the wave will travel at the speed of a jet plane. Before the tsunami wave arrives at the coast, the sea level unusually recedes faster, exposing a vast seabed area as if the coast was drained of water. When a tsunami wave approaches the coast, the amplitude increases where in the case of catastrophic tsunamis, the run-up height reaches several tens of meters. The wave is capable of flooding the inland several kilometers away from the coastline. Wave run-up occurs in seconds, but flooding to the flat-lying coastal dry land might take hours.

Tsunamis are also capable of crossing the entire ocean and hitting the opposite coastline areas. For instance, in 1960, an earthquake with a 9.5 magnitude in Chile caused a tsunami to hit Hawaii, Japan, the Philippines, eastern New Zealand, southeastern Australia, and the Aleutian Islands. In 2015, an earthquake with lower magnitude, 8.3, occurred in Chile and caused three tsunami waves of at least 4 meters in height. But a smaller tsunami wave of about less than 1 meter hit Japan, Hawaii, the western coast of the United States, and Alaska within hours after the earthquake.

To depict tsunami power, Papadopoulos and Imamura (2001, pp. 573-575) present tsunami intensity in 12 scales (Table 3.9), from Scale I, which is not felt; to Scale XII, for completely devastating. The scale is organized in accordance to its influence on people, and its impact on natural and artificial objects, including boats of different sizes and damage caused to buildings.

The coast that has the most tsunami attraction is the coast facing the Pacific Ocean and facing the Indian Ocean. It includes the western coast of South America, eastern coast of the United States and Canada, Aleutian Islands, Japan, the Philippines, Indonesia, Myanmar, Bangladesh, India, and Sri Lanka. It also includes isolated island likes Polynesian Islands, Cocos Islands, and Christmas Island.

In addition, the lakeshore, such as Singkarak Lake in Western Sumatra, that formed by tectonic process (transtensional lake) along the Sumatran Fault System (also called the Great Sumatran Fault or Semangko Fault), also has tsunami potential attractions such as earthquakes in 2004 and 2007 (personal communication with local people of Singkarak Area, 2013). The earthquake in 2004 occurred at 9.1 to 9.3 magnitude in the Indian Ocean, close to the northwestern coast of Sumatra, where a tsunami struck the area. The earthquake in September 2007 that hit offshore from western Sumatra occurred at 8.4 magnitude.

Thus almost all of the living community, whether on the coast or in the tectonic lakeshore, has a tsunami attraction to a varying degree. To understand the history of tsunamis all around the world, visit the NOAA tsunami data and information database (ngdc.noaa.gov/hazard/tsu. shtml or go to tinyurl.com/rvb6u5w).

Table 3.9. Simplified Tsunami Intensity Scale and its possible correlation with tsunami/ wave height. Based on Papadopoulos and Imamura, 2001, with permission.

Scale	Description	Wave Height (m)
I	Not felt	
II	Scarcely felt; felt by some people in light boats. No tsunami run-up observed on the shore	
III	Weak; felt by most people in light boats, observed by some people on the shore	≤ 1
IV	Largely observed; felt by all people in light ships and some on large vessels, tsunami observed by most people on the shore.	
V	Strong; felt by all people on large vessels, observed by all people onshore, some people are frightened because of runup elevations, limited flooding along the coast	
VI	Slightly damaging; many people are frightened because of run-up elevation, most light vessels are carried inland over significant distances	2
VII	Damaging; most people are frightened and try to run away onto higher elevations, most light vessels are damaged.	4
VIII	Heavily damaging; all people frightened because of run-up elevations, some are carried out to sea by the wave, large objects are washed away, widespread flooding inland.	
IX	Destructive; many people are carried away by the wave, most floating structures are carried away	8
X	Very destructive; general panic, most large vessels are carried inland over large distances	
XI	Devastating; vital communications destroyed, large rocks of different kinds are carried onshore from the seafloor	16
XII	Completely devastating; practically all brick buildings are wiped out	32

Our knowledge about earthquakes can tell us how often earthquakes occur each year on average, at a given magnitude. Unfortunately, it is hard to find similar information for the tsunamis. The available information is on historical tsunamis and their destructive intensity.

Probably, tsunami attraction best falls within scale IV (largely observed) to V (strong), where scale VI or more is the hazard. Within scale IV to V, the tsunami wave height generated is up to 1 meter (Table 3.9). At scale IV, tsunamis are largely observed by most people on the shore, felt by all people in small boats and some on large vessels, some light boats are slightly carried onto the shore, but there is no damage to buildings. At scale V, tsunamis are observed by all people on the shore because of high run-up elevations; many light vessels are carried inland over significant distances; there is limited flooding along the coast; and limited flooding of coastal structures, building, and territories.

In relation of tsunami wave height to earthquake magnitude, Morner (2017, p. 90) found a correlation of known earthquake magnitude and known tsunami wave height from 2004 to 2011. His focus was on relation of major earthquakes and destructive tsunamis. Using his idea, it is predicted that 1 meter tsunami height—scale IV to V—might be generated by a maximum of about 6.7 earthquake magnitude (Fig. 3.17). When an earthquake magnitude lowers, it most likely means that a more frequent tsunami wave might occur with a smaller intensity. But tsunami generation also depends on the earthquake type, its location to the coast, and coastal topography.

The attraction is the process of receding of the sea, run-up of the tsunami wave, and flooding the low-lying flat, dry land. Geologists should assess how far the flood of the tsunami wave inundated the area. Seeing such a powerful process should be from safe area such as a high building with strong structures, the peak of the hill, or from a helicopter. Even with tsunami floods less than 0.5 meter in height, they can still cause fatalities—due to the fast current—if we are not ready.

Tsunami prediction is as hard as earthquake prediction. Fortunately, tsunamis have a longer warning time than earthquakes. For instance, the Japan Meteorological Agency (JMA) issued a tsunami warning only 3 minutes after the earthquake onset. In 2011, the first strong wave reached the nearest coast in about 30 minutes. It is a challenge for the tour operator to promote a tour within minutes. Yet, warning time for transoceanic tsunami is in hours.

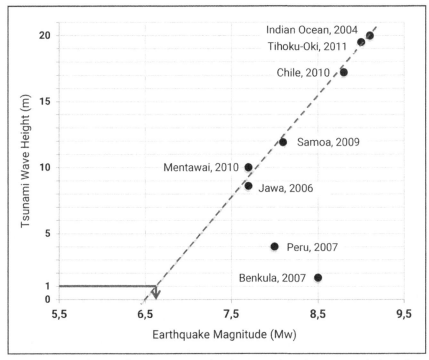

Figure 3.17. Relation of tsunami wave height to earthquake magnitude based on known tsunamis from 2004 to 2011. Tsunamis in Peru (2007) and Benkula (2007) obviously did not reach the largest wave height, and are not excluded in establishing line relation (Morner, 2017, p. 90). Therefore, it is predicted that a 1-meter tsunami might be generated by a maximum of about 6.7 earthquake magnitude.

3.4.6.4.4. Volcano Eruption Attraction

Volcano eruption is a process where magma comes out to the earth surface or seabed through a vent or fissure. When it occurs, the rising hot cloud might reach several kilometers into the atmosphere, throwing out hot blocks with a loud explosive sound, hot clouds rushing down to the downslope or the flowing of glowing-hot lava.

Volcanologists described magmatic eruption types in terms of character activity at particular volcanoes or volcanic regions. There are seven common magmatic eruption types:

- Hawaiian type, effusive eruption after typical eruption of Hawaiian volcanoes.

- Icelandic type, like Hawaiian type but from regional fissures.

- Strombolian type, explosion type with common low-viscosity lava fragments.

- Vulcan type, explosion also ejecting blocks, bombs, and tephra.

- Plinian type, the powerful explosion with convective eruption columns that ejects large volumes of ash to high altitudes.

- Pelean type, explosive eruptions accompanying collapse of summit lava domes producing pyroclastic flows, also called Merapi-type pyroclastic flows.

- Sursteyan type, shallow explosion under sea that ejects a column of ash, mud, and steam, with individual ejected blocks.

The power of volcano eruption is measured by the Volcanic Explosivity Index (VEI, Table 3.10). It was originally devised by Chris Newhall of the United States Geological Survey and Stephen Self at the University of Hawaii in 1982. It has eight scales of increasing explosivity, where each scale represents an increase of about a factor of ten. The VEI combines a total volume of explosive products, eruptive cloud height, descriptive terms, and other measurements. To understand the history of volcano eruption all around the world, visit volcano.si.edu, the Global Volcanism Program of the Smithsonian Institution.

Eruptions vary in duration, quiescent interval, majority eruption magnitude (VEI), and total eruptions per year. Volcano eruption data analyzed by Siebert et al. (2010, pp. 24, 37, 40, 42) showed the following:

- Eruption median duration about seven weeks.

- Majority of eruption magnitude falls to VEI 2.

- Median quiescent interval between successive eruptions from the same volcano is about 12 years.

- 70 total eruptions annually around the globe and one eruption per decade for larger-magnitude (VEI ≥4).

Table 3.10. Simplified Volcanic Explositivity Index. After Newhall and Self, 1982, p. 144.

VEI	Classification of Magmatic Eruption	Eruption Description, Qualitative Description, Duration of Continuous Blast	Eruption Column Height (Km)	Example
0	Hawaiian	Non-explosive, gentle & effusive, < 1 hour	< 0.1	Kilauea, Piton de la Fournaise, Erebus
1	Hawaiian / Strombolian	Small, gentle & effusive, < 1 hour	0.1 – 1	Nyiragongo (2002), Raoul Island (2006)
2	Hawaiian / Strombolian	Moderate, explosive, < 1-6 hours	1 – 5	Galeras (1993), Sinabung (2010)
3	Vulcanian	Moderate – large, explosive, 1-12 hours	3 – 15	Nevado del Ruiz (1985), Nabro (2011)
4	Vulcanian / Plinian	Large, cataclysmic, 1 - > 12 hours	10 – 25	Eyjafjallajokull (2010), Galunggung (1982)
5	Plinian / Ultra-Plinian	Very large, paroxysmal, 6 - > 12 hours	> 25	Vesuvius (79), St Helens (1980)
6	Plinian / Ultra-Plinian	Very large, colossal, > 12 hours	> 25	Krakatoa (1883), Pinatubo (1991)
7	Plinian / Ultra-Plinian	Very large, colossal, > 12 hours	> 25	Tambora (1815), Rinjani (1815)
8	Plinian / Ultra-Plinian	Very large, colossal, > 12 hours	> 25	Yellowstone (640,000 BC), Toba (74,000 BC)

It has been assessed that VEI 0 to a maximum of VEI 4 are considered the best eruption scale for tourist attractions, whereas VEI 5 or more is catastrophic. VEI 0 means eruptions like Hawaiian volcanoes with effusive eruption. VEI 4 is similar to Pelean / Plinian or Sub-Plinian eruption type, which has substantial eruptive injection to troposphere, the lowest part of the atmosphere. In a simple sense and putting aside the complexity of volcanic variables interaction, let's say the more frequently a volcano erupts, the eruption power is lower, and usually a safe distance for observation is closer to the eruption center. Whatever the VEI of a volcano, selecting the safest place to appreciate it is important.

At a minimum, there are about 70 eruptions per year in total potential volcano eruption attractions. Fortunately, the warning time before eruption ranges from hours to days, which is longer than an earthquake or tsunami warning. Longer warning times mean it is easier for a tour operator to promote the tour.

There have been 1,432 volcanoes with eruptions during the Holocene periods (approximately the last 10,000 years; Venzke, 2013). Those volcanoes form the volcano chain particularly around the Pacific Ocean margin, called "the Ring of Fire" (Fig. 3.15).

There is another volcano eruption type, other than the magmatic eruption type. It is the phreatomagmatic and phreatic eruption types. Those two types are also interesting to be appreciated. For instance, phreatic eruption (or steam eruption) of Merapi Volcano, Indonesia, occurred from May 11, 2018 to early June 2018. The eruption occurred for a couple of minutes, releasing fine-grained volcanic material forming an eruption plume of a white gigantic smoke ring 5,500 m above the peak. The eruption was interpreted to occur in VEI 3 (Global Volcanism Program, 2018).

Mild volcanic eruption was proved an interesting attraction. In early 2019, a mild eruption of Bromo volcano attracted tourists. The news of eruption apparently attracts people's curiosity to visit. Some tourists said that Bromo was more attractive during eruption since it formed gigantic white smoke. Moreover, it can be seen from a safe distance, more than about 1 km from the crater. The eruption continued from February to at least July 2019 with VEI 0.

There was an interesting personal experience of Nico Lumanauw (2007) when magmatic volcano eruption turns out to be an unexpected attraction. During the Krakatau Festival August 18, 2008, in Sumatra, 20 ambassadors were to tour the Anak Krakatau Volcano in Sunda Strait by ferryboat on August 24. In the meantime, the volcano was at a high to the highest alert level since October 2007, where the volcano erupted intermittently at about VEI 2. To avoid risk, the Volcanological Survey of Indonesia issued a warning for them to not tour to the volcano.

Yet Nico Lumanauw, as tour coordinator, argued that the small amount of volcanic smoke would make the tour more interesting. Despite the warning, the tour continued as scheduled and nobody knew exactly what would happen.

When the ferry was on the way fully loaded with ambassadors, the volcano suddenly erupted five times for two hours in VEI 2 (Fig. 3.18). It was an extraordinary attraction when everyone was amazed and moved to one side of the ship to see the eruption until the ship was a little bit tilted. It was a wonderful experience to be a witness of the eruption.

Figure 3.18. Anak Krakatau volcano eruption on August 24, 2008 in VEI 2. It was an amazing experience for twenty ambassadors during the ferry boat tour around the volcano on Krakatau Festival August 18, 2008. Image courtesy of Nico Lumanauw.

3.4.6.5. Hydrothermal Vent Attraction in the Deep Ocean Floor

Why does the deep sea receive special attention in this work? The ocean—which covers over 70% of the earth's surface, regulating temperature, and driving weather—is supporting all living organisms, including our lives. However, up to now, only a small fraction of the ocean has been explored.

My purpose in discussing the deep ocean floor is to get more public attention for deep marine research by reintroducing deep sea features to you, particularly tourism-related professionals. When they contribute their interest in deep sea features, they might support deep sea exploration. For tourists, in the simple motivation, it is another playground to have breath-taking experiences.

What lies beneath the deep and dark of the ocean floor? It is common to see a hot spring, geyser, or fumarole on the earth's surface. Yet once it is found on the seabed, it shows a spectacular character. It forms a natural tower structure that might reach 60 meter height, emitting clouds of tiny minerals. Most people called it a hydrothermal vent. It also called a sea vent, hydrothermal site, black smoker or white smoker, where the color depends on mineral emitted; or it is just called a vent.

A hydrothermal vent is a manifestation of heat transferred from the lithosphere to the sea floor. The vents are formed when cold seawater percolates through fractures or pores deeply into the lithosphere, which is a hot rocks environment since located near a magma reservoir or another heat source. The seawater then heated, reacts, becomes hotter and able to leach metals such as iron, zinc, copper, lead, and cobalt from the surrounding rocks. The hot fluid of heated seawaters, laden by rich minerals including metals, rises back to the sea floor through other opening fractures. When the hot fluid—which might reach 400°C or more—encounters colder seawater, firstly it spews out, forming clouds. Eventually, the minerals precipitate nearby to form metal-rich towers and mineral deposits on the ocean flo or (Fig. 3.19).

Figure 3.19. The "Can de labra" black smoker at a water depth of 3,300 meters in the Logatchev Hydrothermal Field on the Mid-Atlantic Ridge. Image courtesy of MARUM, Center for Marine Environmental Sciences, University of Bremen, CC-BY 4.0.

Hydrothermal vents are found in active plate boundary spreading centers, mostly observed in a water column range of 2,000 to 3,000 m (Beaulieu et al., 2013, p. 4899). However, the vent is also associated with other features such as fracture zones, back-arc spreading center, volcanic arc and intra-plate volcanoes (German et al., 1995, p. 3; Beaulieu et al., 2013, p. 4897; Fig. 3.20). Nowadays, a great work of Beaulieu (2015) that inventories hydrothermal vents, suggests 688 hydrothermal vents discovered from all around the oceans (see vents-data.interridge.org).

Considering the deep, the deepest active known vents are in Cayman Trough, 4.957 m deep in the Caribbean Sea, named Beebe Hydrothermal Vent Field. However, such vents do not belong to the deep alone. Vents are also observed on the beach just 1 to 2 meters deep, such as the hot beach in Mendeleev Volcano of Russia and in Sangeangapi Volcano of Indonesia.

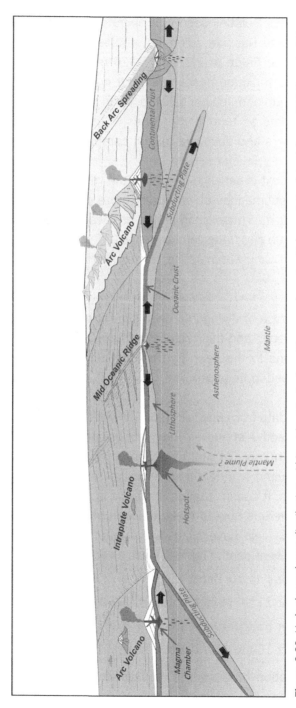

Figure 3.20. Hydrothermal vent distribution within various tectonic settings, such as Arc Volcano, Intraplate Volcano, Mid Oceanic Ridge, and Back-Arc Spreading. Figure is based on Simkin et al., 1994.

In summer 1999, a Seattle-based tour operator conducted a touristic excursion linked to Russian scientific studies at Rainbow vent site in the Mid-Atlantic Ridge at 2,270 to 2,320 m deep. They used the Mir, a submarine for three passengers, but it has not scheduled for another trip (Dando and Juniper, 2001, p. 8). In this book, I reintroduce hydrothermal vents as tourist attractions, which commonly interest marine researchers and deep sea mining companies.

Fortunately, our next experience to explore the vents might come soon, since there are submarines able to carry more passengers to dive to deeper than 500 m. Those submarines are available on the market, such as Cruise Sub and C-Researcher series (U-Boat Worx), 1000, 3000, and Ultra -Deep Diving Submersibles series (Triton) and Aurora series (SEAmagine).

Usually, the purpose of diving into deep sea for tourists by submarine is to see shipwrecks and their cultural heritage. I hope they will have more destinations to the deep by the idea of visiting hydrothermal vents as described in this book.

Using inventory data from Beaulieu (2015), I select 182 vents that have confirmed vent active status as future tourist destinations (Fig. 3.21, Table 3.11). The number of vent attractions might change whether due to new data acquired or different assessment methods during analysis of the same data. It doesn't matter whether it is more or less than 182 vents; what matters is how to make the vent an accessible attraction and to make the visit have a positive impact on our environment. Summary of the vent depth (Table 3.11) is as follow:

- Vents number 1 to 20: depth range of 3–200 m.
- Vents number 21 to 54: depth range 201–1,000 m.
- Vents number 55 to 179: depth range 1,001 m–4,000 m.
- Vents number 180 to 182: depth range 4.001 m–4,957 m.

Detailed description of the vents can be scrutinized at vents-data. interridge.org.

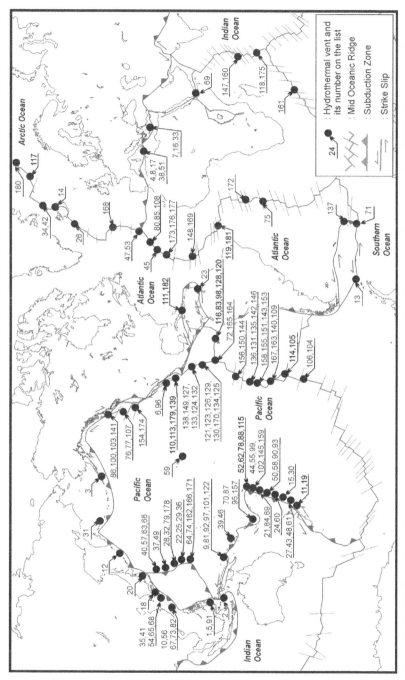

Figure 3.21. 182 hydrothermal vents as potential tourist attractions worldwide (selected data of Beaulieu, 2015). Vent data is listed in Table 3.11. Base map is redrawn from Simkin et al., 1994.

Amazingly, life in the sea is also found in the eternal darkness of the deep ocean with its crushing pressure. Because sunlight is unable to penetrate into the deep, no photosynthesis occurs. However, there is a process called chemosynthesis. It is a chemical process where special microorganisms are able to convert chemical fluid spewing out from the vent into usable substances, to be later used by other larger organisms. Such microorganism acts as primary producers, like plants do on land. Moreover, many larger organisms live in a symbiotic relationship with them.

There are many unique lives, which are not comparable to the life in the shallow sea. In fact, the knowledge of deep ocean life started in 1977. It was when researchers from Woods Hole Oceanographic Institution (WHOI) discovered life in the Galapagos Rift, 2,500 m deep, near Galapagos Island. Today, hundreds of new species have been identified. The chosen 182 vents are also reported to be inhabited by typical vent biota. Thus, those organisms absolutely add to the attractiveness of the deep.

Table 3.11. List of 182 hydrothermal vents as future tourist destinations, selected data of Beaulieu, 2015. The vent numbers on this table and on the map (Fig. 3.21) are the same. The vent position is shown in Figure 3.21.

No.	Name	Region or National Jurisdiction
1	Lembeh Strait	Indonesia
2	Banda Api	Indonesia
3	Kagamil Island	United States
4	Ischia Island, Gulf of Naples	Italy
5	Banua Wuhu submarine volcano	Indonesia
6	Bahia Concepcion	Mexico
7	Nisiros	Greece
8	Capo Miseno, Gulf of Naples	Italy
9	Matupi Harbour, Rabaul caldera, New Britain Island	Papua New Guinea
10	Kueishan Island	Taiwan

No.	Name	Region or National Jurisdiction
11	Whale Island	New Zealand
12	Kraternaya Bight, Ushishir Volcano	Russia
13	Deception Island	Antarctica
14	Kolbeinsey Field	Iceland
15	Giggenbach volcano	New Zealand
16	Milos	Greece
17	Panarea	Italy
18	Kagoshima Bay	Japan
19	Calypso Vents	New Zealand
20	Omuro Hole	Japan
21	Tonga Arc, Volcano 1	Tonga
22	Ruby	Northern Mariana Islands and Guam (United States)
23	Kick'em Jenny submarine volcano	Grenada
24	Hinepuia volcanic center	New Zealand
25	Esmeralda Bank	Northern Mariana Islands and Guam (United States)
26	Steinaholl Vent Field	Iceland
27	Rumble III volcano	New Zealand
28	Daikoku volcano	Northern Mariana Islands and Guam (United States)
29	East Diamante volcano	Northern Mariana Islands and Guam (United States)
30	Macauley Caldera	New Zealand
31	Piip Submarine Volcano	Russia
32	Kasuga 2 Seamount	Northern Mariana Islands and Guam (United States)
33	Kolumbo	Greece
34	Troll Wall	Jan Mayen (Norway)
35	Yoron Hole	Japan
36	Northwest Rota-1 volcano	Northern Mariana Islands and Guam (United States)
37	Nikko volcano	Japan

No.	Name	Region or National Jurisdiction
38	Enarete Seamount	Italy
39	Grover Seamount	Solomon Islands
40	Sumisu Caldera	Japan
41	Minami-Ensei Knoll	Japan
42	Soria Moria	Jan Mayen (Norway)
43	Rumble V volcano	New Zealand
44	Niua North	Tonga
45	Lost City	International Water
46	Stanton Seamount	Solomon Islands
47	Menez Gwen	Azores (Portugal)
48	Tangaroa volcano	New Zealand
49	Kaikata Seamount	Japan
50	Tonga Arc, Volcano 19	Tonga
51	Palinuro	Italy
52	Vailulu'u Seamount	American Samoa (United States)
53	Bubbylon	Azores (Portugal)
54	North Knoll, Iheya Ridge	Japan
55	Niua South	Tonga
56	Kueishan Island, offshore	Taiwan
57	Mokuyo Seamount	Japan
58	Tonga Arc, Volcano 18	Tonga
59	Loihi Seamount	Hawaii (United States)
60	Monowai Caldera	International Water
61	Brothers volcano	New Zealand
62	West Mata submarine volcano	Tonga
63	Myojin Knoll	Japan
64	Seamount X	Northern Mariana Islands and Guam (United States)
65	Izena Cauldron	Japan
66	Suiyo Seamount	Japan

No.	Name	Region or National Jurisdiction
67	SPOT, Yonaguni Knoll IV	Japan
68	Iheya Ridge	Japan
69	Aden	Djibouti
70	Temakons	Vanuatu
71	Kemp Caldera	South Georgia and the South Sandwich Islands (United Kingdom)
72	Precious Stone Mountain	International Water
73	SPOT, Hatoma Knoll	Japan
74	Forecast	Northern Mariana Islands and Guam (United States)
75	Lilliput	Ascension (United Kingdom)
76	Axial Seamount, International District	International Water
77	Axial Seamount, ASHES	International Water
78	Maka	Tonga
79	Northwest Eifuku	Northern Mariana Islands and Guam (United States)
80	Lucky Strike	Azores (Portugal)
81	PACMANUS field	Papua New Guinea
82	Irabu Knoll	Japan
83	Calyfield	Galapagos Islands (Ecuador)
84	Vai Lili	Tonga
85	Evan	Azores (Portugal)
86	Magic Mountain	Canada
87	Nifonea Ridge	Vanuatu
88	Mata Tolu	Tonga
89	Tu'i Malila	Tonga
90	Hine Hina	Tonga
91	Kawio Barat	Indonesia
92	NE Pual	Papua New Guinea
93	Mariner	Tonga
94	White Lady	Fiji

No.	Name	Region or National Jurisdiction
95	Sonne 99	Fiji
96	Guaymas Basin, Southern Trough	Mexico
97	DESMOS Cauldron	Papua New Guinea
98	Uka Pacha	Galapagos Islands (Ecuador)
99	ABE	Tonga
100	High-Rise Field	Canada
101	Vienna Woods, Hydrothermal Field 4	Papua New Guinea
102	CDE	Tonga
103	Main Endeavour Field	Canada
104	EPR, 37 48'S Axial Dome	International Water
105	Saguaro Field	International Water
106	EPR, 37 40'S Axial Dome	International Water
107	South Cleft	International Water
108	Rainbow	International Water
109	Pito Seamount	International Water
110	Alarcon Rise, Meyibo	Mexico
111	Von Damm	Cayman Islands (United Kingdom)
112	Teotihuacan	Mexico
113	Alarcon Rise, Ja Sit	Mexico
114	Nolan's Nook	International Water
115	Mata Ua	Tonga
116	Navidad	Galapagos Islands (Ecuador)
117	Loki's Castle	Svalbard (Norway)
118	Kairei Field	International Water
119	Semyenov	International Water
120	Rose Garden	International Water
121	EPR, 9 50'N	International Water
122	Vienna Woods	Papua New Guinea
123	EPR, 9 47'N	International Water
124	Feather Duster	International Water
125	EPR, 8 38'N	International Water

No.	Name	Region or National Jurisdiction
126	EPR, 9 40'N	International Water
127	EPR, 11 17'N	International Water
128	Tempus Fugit	International Water
129	EPR, 9 33'N	International Water
130	EPR, 9 30'N	International Water
131	Rehu-Marka	International Water
132	EPR, 10 44.6'N	International Water
133	EPR, 11 24'N	International Water
134	Medusa	International Water
135	EPR, 17 34'S	International Water
136	EPR, 17 12'S	International Water
137	ESR, E2	South Georgia and the South Sandwich Islands (United Kingdom)
138	EPR, 13 N	International Water
139	EPR, 21 N	Mexico
140	EPR, 23 30'S	International Water
141	Baby Bare Seamount	Canada
142	Stealth	International Water
143	EPR, 18 32'S	International Water
144	EPR, 14 S	International Water
145	Kilo Moana	Tonga
146	EPR, 17 44'S	International Water
147	Solitaire Field	Mauritius
148	Logatchev 2	International Water
149	EPR, 13 N, Marginal High	International Water
150	EPR, 11 18'S	International Water
151	EPR, 18 26'S	International Water
152	EPR, 23 50'S	International Water
153	Animal Farm	International Water
154	Sea Cliff	United States
155	EPR, 18 15'S	International Water

No.	Name	Region or National Jurisdiction
156	EPR, 7 25'S	International Water
157	Mussel Valley	Fiji
158	EPR, 18 10'S	International Water
159	Tow Cam	Tonga
160	Dodo Field	Mauritius
161	Dragon	International Water
162	Pika	Northern Mariana Islands and Guam (United States)
163	Rapa Nui	International Water
164	AHA Field	International Water
165	EPR, 3.9 N offset	International Water
166	Snail	Northern Mariana Islands and Guam (United States)
167	EPR, 20 06'S	International Water
168	Moytirra	International Water
169	Logatchev	International Water
170	Mounds and Microbes	International Water
171	TOTO Caldera	Northern Mariana Islands and Guam (United States)
172	MAR, 4 48'S	International Water
173	Broken Spur	International Water
174	NESCA	United States
175	Edmond Field	International Water
176	TAG	International Water
177	Snake Pit	International Water
178	Alice Springs Field	Northern Mariana Islands and Guam (United States)
179	Pescadero Basin, Auka	Mexico
180	Aurora	Greenland (Denmark)
181	Ashadze	International Water
182	Beebe	Cayman Islands (United Kingdom)

Let me recount some exotic biotas.

- Tube worms (Fig. 3.22) and palm worms able grow up to 2 meters long and 10 centimeters in diameter, rely on mutualistic symbiotic bacteria living in their tissues to produce the "cell food" needed to keep them alive.

- Mussels, limpets, clams, and barnacles nearly all have white or translucent shells and rely on symbiotic bacteria to help them get nutrients.

- Strange shrimp with eyes on their backs and sensitive spots on their heads used to detect heat.

- Zoarchid fish, eel-like with the two-foot long whitefish which eats everything but is slow and lethargic.

- Hydrothermal octopi, white, grow to about three feet long, with heads the size of an orange, live under colonies of sessile mollusks and feed on them.

- White scavenger crabs that eat bacteria and dead animals.

Figure 3.22. Tubeworm concentration in "Tempus Fugit Vent Field" at about 2,560 meters in the vicinity of Galapagos Island. Image courtesy of NOAA Okeanos Explorer Program, Galapagos Rift Expedition, 2011.

To make vent explorations for tourists more interesting, integrating them with a cruising tour might increase tourist satisfaction. For instance, there are at least five vents surrounding Naples, Italy (Fig. 3.23). While cruising from Barcelona to Naples, it would be a good idea to visit one or two vents for a couple of hours. Passengers might admire the vent through a huge screen, studio, or through virtual reality in the ship while the ROV observes the vent closely. It is more attractive when tourists encounter deep sea fish and the amazing fauna that live surrounding the vents. It might be a once-in-a-lifetime experience for passengers to appreciate what actually occurs there.

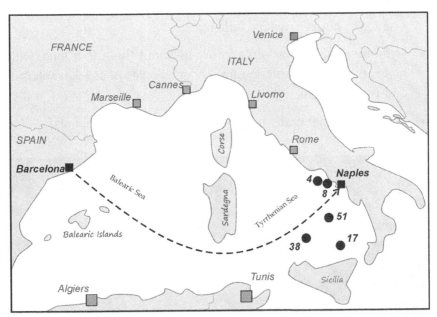

Figure 3.23. Cruise itinerary map from Barcelona to Naples where the nearest vents are numbers 38 (Enarete Seamount, max. depth 600 m), 17 (Panarea, max. death 200 m), 51 (Palinuro, max. depth 1000 m), 8 (Capo Miseno, max. depth 20 m), and 4 (Ischia Island, max. depth 10 m). Vent number is the same number as in Table 3.11.

3.4.7. Geologist's Tasks in the Context of Attraction

Geologists' tasks in the context of attraction are to explore geological features that potentially trigger tourist interest or potentially have attraction value. These may exist in an area, spot, or route defined from map, report, or publication from any media.

Geologist might use data and information, such as scientific publications, internet sources, or tourist guide books. Geologists also need to communicate with local geological agencies or local people to evaluate whether the site has the potential to fulfill an interest and other related issues. If a site had a core attraction, a geologist might explore other attractions as supporting attractions. For instance, an attraction on the route during traveling to the main attraction.

During geological assessment, it is necessary to express the uncertainty about whether or not the attraction exists and fulfills expectations or whether or not the activity can be conducted. The interpretation of attraction and activity is categorized into three level of status: proven, probable, and possible. The statuses are regardless of whether or not the destination is developed.

The three levels of status are described as follows.

- Proven: the attraction and activity confirm exist. It might be confirmed by tourist reports from various media types (e.g., social media, YouTube, Google Maps, local newspapers, blog), mentioned in a scientific report, or personal experience.

- Probable: the attraction and activity are probable because they have similar geological characteristics compared to nearest proven attractions. However, there is no tourist report found or there is a report, but no geographical points reported (e.g., points on Google Maps). Investigation might be needed to ensure whether the activity is able to be performed but in low urgency.

- Possible: the attraction is identified from an analysis of data and/

or information. There is no visitation recorded. Investigation is highly needed to ensure whether the activity could be performed, which is also related to safety issues (high urgency).

I list several ideas for attraction identifications such as what is needed to be done or in what geological environment the attraction exists. It is as follows.

- Geoscientific attraction: outcrop of type locality, fieldtrip stop site, determine the uniqueness of geological information on the spot, and describe its geological history.

- Scenic beauty attraction: describe why a geological feature has an interesting scenery or feature, and determine a particular spot, route, or zone to see and decide the best time to view it.

  It is easy to find a scenic beauty landscape. In fact, you do not have to be geologically educated. But the case will be different when you should identify or consider safety and impact factors of an activity on the site.

  Landscape that has beautiful scenery should be easy to search, because it is frequently reported by people through social media and local newspapers. Location on Google Maps with photos may be used for verification of the scenery.

  The cave(scape) is an interesting environment to visit. Every country should have their own database. I found interesting websites about cave database such as List of Caves (Wikipedia), world cave database (www-sop.inria.fr/agos/sis/DB/countries. html or go to tinyurl.com/rwlkczc), and wiki cave (en.wikicaves.org or grottocenter.org).

  To understand scenic beauty on the scape of the ocean floor, it can be scrutinized through the NOAA website (oceanexplorer. noaa.gov/gallery/maps/maps.html, or go to tinyurl.com/w33kku2), which offer many beautiful videos and images of the deep sea.

- Curative attraction: determine the healing potential of a geological material and/or geological environment on the site and how to use it for therapy. Also consult medical supervisors of the therapeutic effects or medical justification. The attraction might be related to volcanic/geothermal, mud diapir, karst, salt-mining tunnels, ore-mining tunnels (radon gas), natural (hot) springs, or any landform for Earthing (see Table 3.4).

- Particular landform attraction: describe what is the attraction and the activity at the attraction (see Table 3.3). The landform for outdoor activity is various, depend on activity type. It can range from fold and thrust belt mountain to coast; from karst to volcano.

- Art-related stone and mineral attraction: for viewing stone, it is found mostly in a river environment, where sediment of pebble to cobble sizes is deposited, whatever the rock provenance. It is also found in desert environments and hill slopes. It is bigger opportunity to find a gemstone in a river bank or area where it has provenance of metamorphic rock, (paleo)volcanism rock where mineralization occurred or the shear zone filled with veins. A mine dump or a disused area of a gems or gold quarry or a destination for recreational mining is also interesting to be visited for gem hunts.

- Giant crystal cave and drilling-related accidents: determine the uniqueness of geological information on the spot. It seems those two attractions are limited in existence. Giant crystal cave destinations from Krassmann (2007) in Table 3.5 can be used, or visit the Hudson Institute of Mineralogy (mindat.org).

- Powerful geologic process attractions: estimate when, where, and how big those processes of the next event are, and define the best and the safest spot to appreciate the attraction, are the main geologist tasks. It is conducted by literature study, communicating with local geological agencies, or consulting an expert, such as a volcanologist for volcanic eruption attraction or seismologist for earthquake attraction. Although the scale proposed for landslide, volcanic eruption, earthquake, and tsunami is relatively smaller, readiness is the key to staying safe.

- There are many websites open for the public to understand past powerful geologic processes:
    - USGS earthquake database: earthquake.usgs.gov/earthquakes/ search/, or go to tinyurl.com/y7dkdoqo.
    - NOAA tsunami data: ngdc.noaa.gov/hazard/tsu.shtml, or go to tinyurl.com/rvb6u5w.
    - Global volcanism program: volcano.si.edu.
- Moon and Mars attractions: visualize the scenic beauty area using a 3D model. There are sites that offer images and maps of the Moon and Mars as follows.
    - Malin Space Science Systems (msss.com).
    - Lunar Reconnaissance Orbiter Camera (lroc.sese.asu.edu or go to tinyurl.com/ko2pgr).
    - USGS Astrogeology Science Centre (usgs.gov/ centers/ astrogeosc/ or go to tinyurl.com/vvc436n).
    - Lunar and Planetary Institute (lpi.usra.edu or go to tinyurl.com/ ubz5kj7).
    - Images from NASA (nasa.gov).
- Hydrothermal vent attraction: decide which one is the most attractive vent based on available information. The most attractive vent might be based on vent dimension, its number on the spot, how active the smoke spewing out from the ventis, and also accessibility. If able, assess the biota living surround the vent, which absolutely adds to the attractiveness of the deep ocean. To know a nearest vent at a destination, please visit InterRidge Vents Database (vents-data.interridge.org), while (general) bathymetry data can be obtained at gebco.net.

Those ideas absolutely must be further investigated for more detailed requirements on each attraction. An attraction might satisfy more than one tourist interest. Hence, the degree of an attraction allows to be constructed based on how many interests are fulfilled. The result might be constructed in a scale such as high, moderate, or low. For example, the outcome is moderate if two to three interest values are fulfilled and low if only one interest.

I believe every geological site has attraction value. I admire the quote of Wallace Everette Pratt (1885-1981), a pioneer American petroleum geologist. He said *"Oil must be sought first of all in our minds."* His quote is one of the most quoted in oil and gas exploration worldwide. Let me modify his quote for our purpose: *"Attraction is firstly found in our mind."* It is our first motto during tourist attraction exploration.

3.5. ACTIVITY AS THE SECOND RELATION

Once the attraction is determined, the next step is to define the activity on the site. In this book, the activity is categorized according to the interest. The activity examples, which you might add later, are as follows.

- Geoscientific-related activities; geomorphology observation, stratigraphic section study, fossil or mineral observation, gold panning, or fossil hunting.

- Scenic-related activities; sightseeing, taking photographs or video recording, painting, scenic drive / ride, and scenic flight.

- Curative-related activities; therapeutic-related activities such as stone massage, spa, and mud bathing.

- Physical outdoor-related activities on a particular landform; principally, these can be categorized as to where the activity will be conducted (Table 3.3): land-based (trekking, rallying, snowboarding), aero-based (paragliding, wingsuit flying), season-based (ice climbing, ice skating), water surface-based (swimming, rafting), and subsurface based (caving).

- Art-related stone and mineral activities; suiseki and gem hunting.

- Activity in giant crystal cave, drilling accident related, hydrothermal vent, and powerful geological processes are similar to sightseeing and geologic-related activities.

- Earthquake attraction activity; feeling a ground-shaking sensation in a determined area.

- Moon and Mars attractions activity comparable to sightseeing, outdoor activities, and geological-related activities. But, gravity force there won't be the same as on Earth. Mars has one-third while the Moon has one-sixth of Earth gravity. In consequence, your body weight will be lighter than on Earth. Think about what you can do; your hiking will probably be much easier and your jump will be higher, like the movie titled "John Carter" (2012).

3.5.1. Safety as Primary Need

When tourists visit and do something at a destination, what they get is primarily an experience. Later on, they bring the experience to their home. Positive experience generates satisfaction. It potentially promotes the destination economy. However negative experience, such as injury or fatality, hardly promote the destination. Consequently, negative experience will be difficult to support tourism business. Hence, positive experience is also supported by the safety factor.

Safety should be our priority before we do all activity. Safety also should be put above profit of any business. The need for safety means there is a risk that can lead to injury, illness, or fatality; and damage or loss of a system, equipment, or property.

Geologists and tourism-related professionals should identify, analyze, and mitigate the risk to ensure tourist activities able to be performed with lower to no risks. However, it doesn't mean an area, route, or spot should be free of any kind of hazard. It means natural hazards in natural destinations must be identified and their characteristics analyzed. Moreover, the exposure to tourists should be measured and be controlled.

The most important thing is that everyone knows what they should do when the hazard occurs in a destination or when an activity requires safety procedures. Mitigation systems should be established, such as signs to avoid injury, illness, or fatality; evacuation route with signs leading to a safe area; early warning systems; a particular structure for temporary evacuation area; and also availability of personal protective equipment.

In the scope of tourism geology, the major concern is geological features as hazards that can develop to be a disaster. Thus, safety factors are a must when geologists recommend an activity crossing or near the hazard zone. It is meaningless if a destination has the most demanded attraction but does not consider safety.

In this context, geological features as hazards can be categorized into three groups. The first two are temporary while the third is mostly permanent. The three groups are as follows.

- Geological process occurs in a destination, such as landslide, tsunami, volcanic eruption, earthquake.

- Geological process occurs in another area but has high probability of impact to the destination, such as the spreading of volcanic eruption material, or a trans-ocean tsunami.

- Geological site that has dangerous features for any activities, such as toxic substances contained in clay-water mixes or geothermal waters, active volcano crater with lava flow or toxic gas, quicksand, rocky shoals in highly choppy nearshore, and also particular landforms with a safety requirement for particular physical outdoor activity. For instance, the minimum requirement of cliff height for BASE jump activity is about 32 to 33.5 m. BASE is a term that stands for fixed objects of four categories from which one can jump; they are building, antenna, span (e.g., bridge), and Earth (i.e., cliff).

An abandoned mine tunnel should be firstly considered as a restricted zone before it will be used as a destination. Its risk should be studied and determined before visitation. The reason is that it is an unstable environment and may contain various hazard potentials, such as remaining explosives and explosive gas concentrates (Burghardt, 2002, p. 29).

3.5.2. Safety in the Context of Difficulty Rating

Safety in the context of difficulty rating differs from safety in context of geological features as hazards. In difficulty rating, accidents are caused by tourists' incapability to deal with certain activity difficulty levels. For example, if a beginner paddler does an activity in a river that has an advanced difficulty level, the beginner will be prone to have an accident. On the other hand, almost no one will survive when people are faced with toxic gas from a volcanic eruption. That is a safety in the context of geological features as hazards.

In an outdoor activity, outdoor enthusiasts have developed difficulty levels. Certain difficulty levels on an adventurous activity will need a particular level of experience, skill, equipment, and physical ability. Thus, this difficulty level means safety or enjoyment, depending on their skill or experience.

If an activity is conducted within a route that has various difficulty ratings, then the geologist should identify which route segment has higher and lower ratings. It is important to define which segments are allowable for the tourist who does not have a particular skill for safety reason.

3.5.3. Geologist's Tasks in the Context of Safety

The geologist's task in the context of safety is to identify safe, restricted, and/or hazard-prone areas and recommend any kind of activity that can be performed in an area, lane, or spot along with safety consideration. The task is part of the Health, Safety, Security, and Environmental (HSSE) management system. In addition, implementation of safety considerations in a destination, such as control and mitigation programs and evacuation structure, might be used as destination branding; for example, safest nearshore for kids, safest beach in tsunami-prone area.

Geologists should understand potential hazards in an attraction area. It can be studied from hazard-prone area maps, such as prone area maps of earthquakes (e.g. locked fault zone), landslides, tsunamis, or volcanic eruptions. Each geological agency produces those maps. However, those maps are usually available in larger scale. If those maps are not available, then it should be constructed using a simple and low-tech method. In detail scale or in each attraction zone, the geologist should be able to identify each-hazard prone area. Local newspapers might be used as references for proven areas where natural processes work as hazards, such as injury or fatality due to being caught by rip current near shore.

Particularly in a safety context, geologists should assess the potential risk of each activity. The risk is as follow.

- High risk when fatality is potentially high.

- Moderate risk when physical injury is likely high.

- Low risk when physical injury is potentially low.

- No risk when no physical injury will potentially occur. It is typical for activity that does not require any movement, such as sightseeing. However, a risk might arises during reaching the location.

When a risk—whatever the scale—is identified in an area, an action is needed to eliminate or lower the risk. It might include engineering to avoid fatality or injury during tourist visitation, such as a tsunami evacuation structure.

3.6. IMPACT AS THE THIRD RELATION

An activity that requires physical contact will inevitably cause physical changes to the site, which might reduce the attraction quality. Examples of physical change are rock erosion, soil erosion, soil compaction, and sand and water quality degradation. Those environmental impacts are also part of physical carrying capacity. The user, such as an environmentalist or park manager, might find it hard to accept the impact as a consequence. Although it affects a smaller area, it is still main concern.

For instance, a mountain biking route might cause erosion and soil compaction. Eventually, it will break the route, so it is unsuitable to be used for mountain biking. Then, a new lane is made just to break again at a later time. Although at first there is only one deteriorating route, later on, it will affect many more routes, and undesirable environmental changes happen. Another example is soil pollution caused by snowmobiles (National Park Services, 2002, p. 31) or cliff surface changes because of glue, chip, or fixed anchor use for rock climbing (National Park Services, 2001, pp. 4-2).

Visiting vents by diving in the shallow sea also has an impact. For instance, some Italian caves with geothermal springs, and the top of the Dom Joao de Castro Seamount in the Acores regularly visited by diving tourists. Apparently, diving activity may damage the cave ecosystems through the release of exhaust air where the air forms gas pockets under the roof of the cave, killing the bacterial mats, on which much of the cave ecosystem depends, by cutting off their access to the seawater (Dando and Juniper, 2001, p. 8).

In case of Pandawa Nearshore, Bali, the sunblock that used to protect the skin during bathing, surfing, swimming, or similar water activities has an impact to water quality. The seaweed that was nurtured by local people failed to grow because of the reduced water quality, which is suspected to be because of the tourists' sunblock.

3.6.1. Geologist's Tasks in Context of Impact

In the context of impact, geologists identify or predict the impact and also monitoring. The outcome might be described in impact level for an activity. The consequence might cause closing down the lane, maintenance of the lane, or opening of a new lane.

There are three impact levels because of an activity, as follows.

- High impact, when the feature is extremely hard to restore to earlier condition or to be restored.

- Moderate impact, when the feature is possible to restore, with high effort and a large cost.

- Low impact, when the feature is easily to restore, with low effort.

- No impact, when nothing significantly changes on environment.

- The Kiernan Sensitivity Scale (1997) is interesting to be used for insight, although it was built in a geoconservation context (see Table 8.2 in Chapter 8).

Significant environmental change also occurs because of natural processes. In tourism geology scope, a major concern is the impact caused by tourist activity. Therefore, the effects caused by natural processes or other non-tourist activities are excluded from tourism geology's scope.

If geologist observes a potential attraction but it has a negative environmental impact, should he or she recommend it or not? For instance, a flat-lying mud volcano in a national park is an interesting site for mud bathing, where tourists lie down into the mud pool. However, such action might reduce the attractive appearance of the mud pool and might be against conservation policy. The same situation might be encountered in another case, such as a giant crystal cave tour, where the tourist is eager to collect the crystal, or hill climbing motocrossing where soil and stones erode.

In my opinion, geologists do not decide whether or not such activity allowable. The party who will decide it is the next-user, such as the park manager or land owner. They will decide whether or not the impacts are acceptable.

In a greater context, the scope of tourism geology excludes (geo)conservation. Nonetheless, geologists should realize all of the consequence, measure the impact level, and if possible determine the monitoring method needed. This means during analyzing the attraction and its activity, every possibility of environmental impact should be mentioned.

3.7. SUMMARY

Let me summarize this chapter. When a geologist observes a geological feature in the context of tourism geology, he or she will assess the attraction value, predict activities with safety requirements including difficulty rating, and estimate the future environmental impacts on the geological feature because of the activity. It is the entire deliverable package of proper geological knowledge to tourism-related professionals. I put a summary in the reminder sheet in Figure 3.24.

In addition, there are three goals of application tourism geology in an existing destination. The first goal is increasing tourist visitation and/or visitor experience based on geological feature. The second goal is reducing the risk of an activity. The third goal is identification and monitoring of the physical impact to the site. Thus, tourism geology application should make the tourism-related professional's task easier.

In this chapter, I propose the scope of tourism geology to be developed by the next-user and geologist. This outline is a logical frame of whatever should be delivered by the geologist to the tourism-related professional and whatever the tourism-related professional should ask the geologist, so that the geologist and tourism-related professional communicate in the same context and the same content.

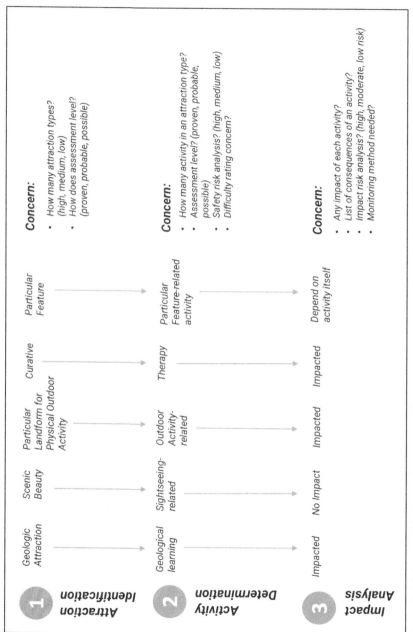

Figure 3.24. A reminder sheet of tourism geology, to advise what is needed to be concerned.

Reference Cited

Agustawijaya, D.S. (2010) *Semburan Sulit Dihentikan*. Blog of Sidoarjo Mud Mitigation Agency, Published Online at 26 Mei 2010, Available via http://www.bpls.go.id/teknis/37-kajian-semburan-sulit-dihentikan. Accessed July 2016

Ashley, J.W., Robinson, M.S., Hawke, B.R., Boyd, A.K., Wagner, R.V., Speyerer, E.J., Hiesinger, H., van der Bogert, C.H., (2011) *Lunar Caves in Mare Deposits Imaged by the LROC Narrow Angle Cameras*, First International Planetary Cave Research Workshop: Implications for Astrobiology, Climate, Detection and Exploration, 25 – 28 October 2011, Carlsbad, New Mexico.

Badino, G. (2009) The Cueva de los Cristales Micrometeorology. p. 1408, 1410, pp. 1407-1412. In: White W.B. (ed), *Proceedings of 15th International Congress of Speleology, Kerrville, Texas-USA. 19-26 July 2009*, 2130 pp.

Badino, G., Ferreira, A., Forti, P., Giovine, G., Giulivo, I., Infante, G., Lo Mastro, F., Sanna, L. & Tedeschi, R. (2009) *The Naica Caves Survey.* p. 1767-1768, pp. 1764-1769. In: White, W.B. (ed) *Proceedings of 15th International Congress of Speleology, Kerrville, Texas-USA. 3, 19-26 July 2009*, 2130 pp.

Beamon, S., Falkenbach, A., Fainburg, G. & Linde, K. (2001) *Speleotherapy for Asthma (Review)*. *Cochrane Database of Systematic Reviews*, Issue 2, John Wiley & Sons, Ltd., p. 2, pp. 1-9

Beaulieu, S.E. (2015) *InterRidge Global Database of Active Submarine Hydrothermal Vent Fields: prepared for InterRidge*, Version 3.3. World Wide Web electronic publication. vents-data.interridge.org/. Version 3.4. Accessed January 2017.

Beaulieu, S.E., Baker, E.T., German, C.R. & Maffei, A. (2013) *An Authoritative Global Database for Active Submarine Hydrothermal Vent Fields. Geochem. Geophys. Geosys*, Volume 14, Number 11, American Geophysical Union, p. 4897, 4899. pp. 4892-4905

Bernabei, T., Forti, P. & Villasuso, R. (2007) *Sails: A New Gypsum Speleothem from Naica, Chihuahua, Mexico. International Journal of Speleology*, 36, Issue 1, January 2007, p. 23, pp. 23-30

Boston, P., Frederick, G., Welch, S., Werker, J., Meyer, T.R., Sprungman, B., Hildreth-Werker, V., Murphy, D. & Thompson, S.L. (2002) *Human Utilization of Subsurface Extraterrestrial Environments: Final Report*. NASA Institute for Advanced Concept, Complex System Research, Inc. p.7, 79 pp.

BPLS (2016a) *Kajian Data Citra Satelit Periode Juli 2015 – Januari 2016*. Blog of Sidoarjo Mitigation Mud Agency, Published Online at 25 August 2016, Available via http://www.bpls.go.id/berita-bpls/484-kajian-datacitra-satelit. Accessed July 2016

BPLS (2016b) *Kondisi Aliran dan Suhu dari Pusat Semburan Lumpur*. Blog of Sidoarjo Mitigation Mud Agency, Published Online at 2 Agustus 2016,

Available via http://www.bpls.go.id/berita-bpls/482-kondisi-aliran-dansuhu-dari-pusat-semburan-lumpur. Accessed July 2016

Brocx, M. & Semeniuk, V. (2007) *Geoheritage and Geoconservation – History, Definition, Scope, and Scale. Journal of the Royal Society of Western Australia*, 90. p.55, pp. 53-87

Burghardt, J. (2002) *Why Investigate Abandoned and Inactive Mine Working? Abandoned and Inactive Mine Safety Training – Underground Mine Hazard.* National Park Service, Geologic Resources Division, August 2003, 29 pp. Available via oregongrotto.com/mines.pdf or go to tinyurl.com/rnsr7o6. Accessed September 2004

Carretero, M.I. (2002) *Clay Minerals and Their Beneficial Effects Upon Human Health: A Review. Applied Clay Science*, Vol 21, Elsevier, p. 159, pp. 155-163

Caufield, C. (1989) *Multiple Exposures: Chronicles of the Radiation Age.* The University of Chicago Press. p. 195, 304 pp.

Chevalier, G., Sinatra, S.T., Oschman, J.L., Sokal, K. & Sokal, P. (2012) *Earthing: Health Implications of Reconnecting the Human Body to the Earth's Surface Electrons.* Journal of Environmental and Public Health, Vol. 2012, Article ID: 291541, p. 1 – 6, 8 pp.

Chevalier, G., Melvin, G., & Barsotti, T., (2015), *One-Hour Contact with the One-Hour Contact with the Earth's Surface (Grounding) Improves Inflammation and Blood Flow—A Randomized, Double-Blind, Pilot Study.* Health, Vol. 7, No. 8, p.1054. pp. 1022 – 1059.

Clarke, J. W. (1988) *Petroleum Geology of the Amu-Dar'ya Gas-Oil Province of Soviet Central Asia.* US Geological Survey, Open-File Report 88- 272, p.31, 59 pp.

Cushing, G.E. & Okubo, C.H. (2015) *The Mars Cave Database*, 2nd International Planetary Cave Database, 20 – 23 October 2015, Flagstaff, Arizona.

Dando, P. & Juniper, S.K. (eds) (2001) *Management of Hydrothermal Vent Sites. Report from the InterRidge Workshop: Management and Conservation of Hydrothermal Vent Ecosystems,* Institute of Ocean Sciences, Sydney (Victoria), B.C., Canada, 28-30 September 2000, p. 8, 29 pp.

Davies RJ, Mathias SA, Swarbrick RE, Tingay MJ (2011) *Probabilistic Longevity Estimate for the LUSI Mud Volcano, East Java. Journal of the Geological Society,* London, Vol. 168, p. 517, pp. 517-523.

Edge, S. (2012) A Summer Tanseki on the Eel River. samedge. wordpress.com/ 2012/08/20/a-summer-tanseki-on-the-eel-river/ or go to tinyurl.com/tfwmd7o. Accessed on December 2019.

Ellis, N.V. (ed), Bowen, D.Q., Campbell, S., Knill, J.L., McKirdy, A.P., Prosser,C.D., Vincent, M.A. & Wilson, R.C.L. (1996) *An Introduction to the Geological Conservation Review.* GCR Series No. 1. Joint Nature Conservation Committee, Peterborough, p. 45, 131 pp.

Fritsch, E. & Rondeau, B., (2009) *Gemology: The Developing Science of Gems*, p.148, pp.147-152. In: Fritsch, E. & Rondeau, B. (Eds), Elements Magazine, June 2009, Volume 5, Number 3, 200 pp.

Gabriela, D. & Alexandru, R. (2015) *Therapeutic Effects of Carbonated Mineral Water in Cardiovascular Rehabilitation. Balneo Research Journal*, Vol. 6, No. 1, February 2015, p. 36, pp. 36-39

Gabrielyants, G.A., Bliskavka, A.G., Morozov, G.I., Khusnutdinov, Z.B., Khadzhinurov, N. & Kolodiy, V.V. (1962) *Zeagli-Darvaza Gas Field. Petroleum Geology: A Digest of Russian Literature on Petroleum Geology*, Vol 6, No 11, p. 671, pp. 671-674

Garcia-Ruiz, J.M., Villasuso, R., Ayora, C., Canals, A. & Otalora, F. (2007) *Formation of Natural Gypsum Megacrystals in Naica, Mexico. Geology*, April 2007, v. 35. No.4, Geological Society of America, p. 329, 330, pp. 327-330

Gazquez, F., Calaforra, J.M., Forti, P. & Badino, G. (2016*) The Caves of Naica: a Decade of Research. Boletín Geológico y Minero*, the Instituto Geologico y Minero de Espana, 127 (1), p. 159, pp. 147-163

German, C.R., Baker, E.T. & Klinkhammer, G. (1995) *Regional Setting of Hydrothermal Activity*. p.3, In: Parson, L.M., Walker, C.L. & Dixon, D.R. (eds) *Hydrothermal Vents and Processes*. Geological Society Special Publication, No. 87. The Geological Society London, 411 pp.

Global Volcanism Program, 2018. *Report on Merapi (Indonesia)*. In: Sennert, S.K. (ed.), *Weekly Volcanic Activity Report, 30 May - 5 June 2018*. Smithsonian Institution and US Geological Survey.

Gomes, C., Carretero, M.I., Poso, M., Maraver, F., Cantista, P., Armijo, F., Legido, J.L., Teixeira, F., Rautureau, M. & Delgado, R. (2013) *Peloids and Pelotherapy: Historical Evolution, Classification and Glossary. Applied Clay Science*, May 2013, Elsevier, p. 32, 33, pp. 28–38.

Gomes, Cd.S.F. (2013) *Naturotherapies Based on Minerals. Geomaterial*, Vol. 3, No.1, Scientific Research Publishing, p. 4,6,8, pp.1-14

Gomes, Cd.S.F., Gomes, J. & Silva, J. (2016) *Advances in Pelotherapy. Poster presented at 32nd International Conference on Environmental Geochemistry and Health, 4th – 8th July 2016 Brussels, Belgium.*

Greeley, R. (2013) *Introduction to Planetary Geomorphology*. Cambridge University Press, p. 11, 77, 78, 238 pp.

Groat, L. A. & Laurs, B. M., (2009) *Gem Formation, Production, and Exploration: Why Gem Deposits Are Rare and What is Being Done to Find Them*, p.153, pp. 153-158. In: Fritsch, E. & Rondeau, B. (Eds), Elements Magazine, June 2009, Volume 5, Number 3, 200 pp.

Hose, T.A. (2016) Thee Centuries (1670 – 1970) of Appreciating Physical Landscapes. p.5, p 1-23. In: Hose, T.A. (ed) *Appreciating Physical Landscapes:*

Three Hundred Years of Geotourism. Geological Society, London, Special Publication 417, 248 pp.

International Congress of Geotourism (2011) *Arouca Declaration 12 November 2011, International Congress of Geotourism.* Arouca Geopark (Portugal) 9 - 13 November 2011, Accessible via europeangeoparks. org/?p=223 or go to tinyurl.com/vv5pcgm. Accessed August 2015.

Istadi, B.P., Pramono, G.H., Sumintadireja, P. & Alam, S. (2009) *Modeling Study of Growth and Potential Geohazard for LUSI Mud Volcano, East Java, Indonesia. Marine and Petroleum Geology,* 26, p.1732, 1724-1739 pp

Katalin, N., Norbert, K., Tibor, K. & Janos, S. (2008) *Radon Therapy and Speleotherapy in Hungary. La Presse thermale et climatique,* Vol. 145. Societe francaise d'hydrologie et de climatologie medicales, p. 222, pp. 219-225

Kiernan, K. (1997) Landform Classification for Geoconservation. pp. 21-34 In: Eberhard, R. (ed) *Pattern and Process: Towards a Regional Approach for National Estate Assessment of Geodiversity.* Environment Australia, 1997, Technical Series 2. Krassmann, I.T. (2007) *The Giant Crystal Project.* http:// giantcrystals.strahlen.org. Accessed May 2016

Krisnayanti, B.D. & Agustawijaya, D.S. (2014) *Characteristic of LUSI Mud Volcano and Its Impacts on the Porong River. Research Article, Journal of Degraded and Mining Lands Management,* p. 207. pp. 207-210.

Malin, M. C. & Edgett, K. S. (2003), *"Evidence for persistent flow and aqueous sedimentation on early Mars," Science, 302,* 1931- 1934, Image is downloaded from msss.com/mars_images/moc/2005/09/20/eberswalde/ or go to tinyurl.com/u9yvypd.

Malin, M. C., Lougen J. A., Shean D. E. & Edgett, K. S. (2008), *Have a Happy Mars,* Malin Space Science Systems Captioned Image Release,

MSSS-14, Image downloaded from msss.com/msss_images/2008/01/31/index. html or go to tinyurl.com/5zgxcv.

MARUM. (—) Hydrothermal Vent photos. MARUM – Center for Marine Environmental Sciences, University of Bremen (CC-BY 4.0). marum. de/Binaries/Binary17395/ MARUM-HTQ-ger-04-920x690.jpg or go to tinyurl.com/wa33ts5. Accessed on December 2019

Mazzini. A., Svensen, H., Akhmanov, G.G., Aloisi, G., Planke, S., Malthe-Sorenssen, A. & Istadi, B. (2007) *Triggering and Dynamic Evolution ofthe LUSI Mud Volcano, Indonesia. Earth and Planetary Science Letter 261,* Elsevier, p. 375, pp. 375-388

Melendez, G., Fermeli, G., Escorihuela, J., Basso, A. & Moreira, J. (2011) *What Do We Mean When We Say Geotourism? Proceeding of International Congress Arouca 2011, Geotouirsm in Action, 9 – 13 November 2011, Arouca Geopark Portugal,* p.100, pp. 98-100

Moreira, J.C. & Melendez, G. (2012) It's Not Only Geotourism! Types of Tourism in Geoparks, An Analysis Based in 37 Geoparks. p.205, 206, pp.205- 206, In: Sa, A.A., Rocha, D., Paz, A. & Correia, V. (eds) *Proceedings of the 11th European Geoparks Conference, 19 – 21 September 2012, Arouca Geopark Portugal*, 319 pp.

Morner, N. A. (2017) *Converting Tsunami Wave Heights to Earthquake Magnitudes. Open Journal of Earthquake Research*, 6, p. 90, pp. 89-97. Scientific Research Publishing Inc. doi.org/10.4236/ojer.2017.62005 or go to tinyurl.com/v2bpe6l.

NASA (2015) *NASA's Journey to Mars*. 15 September 2015. nasa.gov/content/ nasas-journey-to-mars or go to tinyurl.com/nm8pj8w. Accessed June 2016

National Park Service (2001) *Backcountry / Wilderness Management Plan and Environmental Assessment*. Rocky Mountain National Park, July 2001, p. 4-2, 203 pp

National Park Service (2002*) Environmental Assessment for the Management of Snowmobiles in Rocky Mountain National Park*. U. S. Department of the Interior, June 2002, p. 31, 93 pp

Newhall, C.G. & Self, S. (1982) *The Volcanic Explosivity Index (VEI): An Estimate of Explosive Magnitude for Historical Volcanism, Journal of Geophysical Research*, American Geophysical Union, Vol. 87, No. C2, p.144. 143-149 pp.

NOAA (2011), *Riftia tube worm colony Galapagos 2011.jpg*, Image is downloaded from upload.wikimedia.org/wikipedia/commons/f/f6/Riftia_tube_worm_ colony_Galapagos_2011.jpg or go to tinyurl.com/v4vslk7.

Papadopoulos, G.A. & Imamura, F. (2001) *A Proposal for a New Tsunami Intensity Scale. International Tsunami Symposium 2001. Proceedings of International Union of Geodesy and Geophysics, 7-10 August 2001*, Session 5, Number 5-1. p. 573-575, pp. 569-577.

Plumlee, G.S., Casadevall, T.J., Wibowo, H.T., Rosenbauer, R.J., Johnson, C.A., Breit. G.N., Lowers, H.A., Wolf, R.E., Hageman, P.L., Goldstein, H., Anthony, M.W., Berry, C.J., Fey, D.L., Meeker, G.P. & Morman, S.A. (2008) *Preliminary Analytical Results for a Mud Sample Collected from the LUSI Mud Volcano, Sidoarjo, East Java, Indonesia*. Open File Report 2008-1019, US Geological Survey, US Department of the Interior, p.5,6,8. 26 pp.

Prosser, C.D. & King, A.H. (1999) *The Conservation of Historically Important Geological and Geomorphological Sites in England. The Geological Curator*, Vol. 7, Number 1, p.28, pp. 27-33.

Pugh, D. & Woodworth, P. (2014) *Sea-Level Science: Understanding Tides, Surges, Tsunamis and Mean Sea-Level Changes*. Cambridge, p 195. 395 pp.

Robinson, M. (2013) *A Great Place To Rove!*, image is downloaded from lroc. sese.asu.edu/news/index.php?/ archives/828-A-Great-Place-to-Rove!. html#extended or go to tinyurl.com/t722ngv.

Rudolph, M.L., Karlstrom, L. & Manga, M. (2011) *A Prediction of the Longevity of the LUSI Mud Eruption, Indonesia. Earth and Planetary Science Letters* 308, p. 128. pp. 124-130.

Sanna, L., Forti, P. & Lauritzen, S.E. (2011) *Preliminary U/Th dating and The Evolution of Gypsum Crystals in Naica Caves (Mexico). Acta Carsologica*, 40(1), p 24, pp. 17-28.

Schnyder, J.S.D., Eberli, G.P., Kirby, J.T., Shi, F., Tehranirad, B., Mulder, T., Ducassou, E., Hebbeln, D. & Wintersteller, P. (2016) *Tsunamis caused by Submarine Slope Failures Along Western Great Bahama Bank*, Scientific Reports, www.nature.com, DOI: 10.1038/srep35925, p. 4, pp. 1-9.

Siebert, L., Simkin, T. & Kimberly, P. (2010) *Volcanoes of the World. Third edition.* Smithsonian Institution, University of California Press, p.24, 37, 40, 42, 551 pp.

Simkin, T., Unger, J.D., Tilling, R.I., Vogt, P.R. & Spall, H. (compls) (1994) *This Dynamic Planet: World Map of Volcanoes, Earthquakes, Impact Craters, and Plate Tectonics.* USGS, p. 9, 9 pp.

Solo-Gabriele, H., Harwood, V.J., Kay, D., Fujioka, R.S., Sadowsky, M.J., Whitman, R.I., Wither, A., Canica, M., de Fonseca, R.C., Duarte, A., Edge, T.A., Gargate, M.J., Gunde-Cimerman, N., Hagen, F., Mclellan, S., da Silva, A.N., Babic, M.N., Prada, S., Rodrigues, R., Romao, D., Sabino, R., Samson, R.A., Segal, E., Staley, C., Taylor, H.D., Verissimo, C., Viegas, C., Barroso, H. & Brandao, J. (2016) *Beach Sand and the Potential for Infectious Disease Transmission: Observations and Recommendations. Journal of the Marine Biological Association of the United Kingdom*, 96 (1). p. 102, pp. 101-120

Stein, S. & Wysession, M. (2003) *An Introduction to Seismology, Earthquakes, and Earth Structure.* Blackwell Publishing, p. 11, 21, 498 pp

Tourtellot, J. (2011) *UNESCO's Geoparks "Clarify" Geotourism. National Geographic blogs posted on 16th November 2011.* Available via voices.nationalgeographic. com/2011/11/16/unescos-geoparks-embracegeotourism/ or go to tinyurl. com/yx23fxl4. Accessed August 2015 UNESCO (2016)

UNESCO Global Geoparks. Brochure. United Nations Educational, Scientific and Cultural Organization, p.2, 10. pp.17, Available via unesdoc.unesco.org/ images/0024/002436/243650e.pdf or go to tinyurl.com/uxp5p4l. Accessed July 2016

USGS (2016a) *Earthquake Facts and Statistic.* earthquake.usgs.gov/earthquakes/ browse/stats.php or go to tinyurl.com/shhy97v. Accessed January 2017

USGS (2016b) *Magnitude / Intensity Comparison.* earthquake.usgs.gov/ learn/topics/ mag_vs_int.php or go to tinyurl.com/yfbr9ul. Accessed September 2016

Van Driessche A (2010) *Cristales Cueva de Naica.jpg*, Photo is downloaded from upload.wikimedia.org/wikipedia/commons/2/29/Cristales_ cueva_de_ Naica.JPG or go to tinyurl.com/mfqn5b6.

Vanderkluysen, L., Burton, M.R., Clarke, A.B., Hartnett, H.E. & Smekens, J.F. (2014) *Composition and Flux of Explosive Gas Release at LUSI mud volcano (East Java, Indonesia). Research Article, Geochemistry, Geophysics, Geosystems,* American Geophysical Union Publications, 15. p. 2943-2944, pp. 2932 – 2946

Venzke, E. (ed) (2013) *Global Volcanism Program. Volcanoes of the World,* v. 4.4.3, Smithsonian Institution, Downloaded November 2013, dx.doi. org/10.5479/ si.GVP.VOTW4-2013 or go to tinyurl.com/vsdos2g. Accessed October 2013

Young, S.L. (2007) *Evidence for the Consumption of the Inedible: Who, What, When, Where and Why?* p.21,23, pp.17-30. In: MacClancy, J., Henry, J. & Macbeth, H. (eds), *Consuming the Inedible: Neglected Dimension of Food Choice,* Berghahn Books, 231 pp.

Zdrojewicz, Z. & Strzelczyk, J. (2006) *Radon Treatment Controversy. Dose-Response 4 (2), Formerly Nonlinearity in Biology, Toxicology, and Medicine. International Hormesis Society,* SAGE Publishing. p. 106, 112, 113, pp. 106–118.

CHAPTER 4

Research and Cooperation Importance

Highlights

- To develop tourism geology, it is necessary to conduct research and cooperate with tourism-related professionals and/or practitioners.
    - The objective is to study geological variables and tourist activity relation in the real world, as well as learning to recognize the actual problem.

- The research purpose is to construct particular geological concepts related to attraction, activity, and impact.
    - Geological concept means an idea of how geological variables interaction causes the existence of non-living natural tourist attractions, tourist activities and impact in a particular geological environment.
    - Research can be conducted anywhere—in a protected area, an urban environment, on the deep ocean floor, or on extra-terrestrial objects.
    - The spirit of this work is to explore the use of geological knowledge for tourism.

Content

4.1 INTRODUCTION 217
4.2 KNOWLEDGE MATRIX 219
4.3 RESEARCH SUBJECT EXAMPLE.. 220
    4.3.1 The Need to Learn from Practitioner.. 222
    4.3.2 The Need for Cooperation with the Next-User 223
4.4 COMPARING TOURISM GEOLOGY RESEARCH WITH GEOTOURISM RESEARCH..... 226
    4.4.1 Case of Promoting Loess Deposit for Geotourism, North Serbia 226
    4.4.2 Case of Planning Tourism in Sibayak Volcano Tourism, Indonesia 227
    4.4.3 Case of Geotouristic Attraction of the Danakil Depression, Ethiopia........ 228
    4.4.4 How Does Tourism Geology Research Ideas on Those Studies?.............. 230
        4.4.4.1 Review oN Geotourism Research on Loess Deposit of North Serbia and Planning Tourism on Sibayak Volcano, Indonesia...................... 230
        4.4.4.2 Review on Geotouristic Attraction Research of Danakil Depression, Ethiopia 231
4.5 SUMMARY.. 232

Abstract

Research is the heart of science and applied science. Whenever research outcomes are accumulated within various case studies around the globe, a theory might be generated and be used to explain, to predict, and to control. The expectation of tourism geology research accumulation is to construct particular geological concepts related to attraction, activity, and impact.

In addition, it is important for the geologist to cooperate with the next-user and practitioner. The objective is to study geological variables and tourist activity relation in the real world, as well as learning to recognize the actual problem. Furthermore, the next-user and practitioner might decide what kind of geological support is needed. The main goal of cooperation is to produce tourism geological knowledge that is truly useful for the next-user and practitioner.

It is important to emphasize that geotourism research differs from research in tourism geology, because different perspectives deliver different outcomes. Geologists in tourism geology think in three groups of knowledge: attraction, activity, and impact. In addition, a geologist should generate creative ideas to increase the value of the destination.

Keywords: geological concept, tourism geology research, geotourism research, geological variables

4.1. INTRODUCTION

Science and applied science are about systematic knowledge. Systematic means clear cause-consequence relation among the observed facts. The outcome is the scientific truth based on belief, assumption, tool limitation, technology, or particular formula used. Scientific truth is presented in terms of probability and with a list of consequences.

The outcome is communicated in a scientific journal, public meeting, or other communication media. The communication purpose is to obtain the best knowledge when it is applied in real life. Whether or not the scientific truth is accepted, the decision is in the user's hand.

The purpose of science and applied science explains the natural and social phenomena derived from research. Thus research is the heart of science and applied science. In fact, through research, we produce new knowledge and new understanding.

As applied geology, tourism geology needs research accumulation to produce knowledge of tourist interaction with the geological environment. The knowledge accumulation itself should be able to predict an upcoming similar problem in another area. The expectation of research accumulation is to construct particular geological concepts relates to attraction, activity, and impact. When the outcomes are accumulated in a large number, generalization of a geological concept becomes possible, to grasp the best knowledge.

In context of tourism geology, the meaning of a geological concept is an idea of how geological variables interaction causes the existence of non-living natural tourist attractions, tourist activities and impact in a particular geological environment. The relation itself might interact with hydrological and/or meteorological variables, and can act as supporting or constraining factors. The impact is a consequence of every physical contact of tourist activities on the geological feature.

When research outcome accumulated, tourism geology will be able to construct geological concepts. It is because a particular attraction and activity are naturally supported in a certain geological environment as a destination. A constructed geological concept can be used as a predictive tool to explore the destination that supported a particular attraction and activity.

For instance, let me remind about the relation of downhill mountain bike speed records with the geological environment. The environment to reach the fastest speed is a relatively smooth surface (at least same grain size) and a long and straight course (minimum 1,200 meters), on a steep slope (probably a maximum 45°). Previous attempts were conducted on a cinder cone of Cerro Negro Volcano, Atacama Desert, and a ski slope in the French Alps. By understanding such variables, we are able to explore a geological environment that supports the effort of reaching the maximum speed of downhill mountain biking.

Different challenge relate to hydrological and meteorological attractions where geological feature support those attractions. The research challenge might be to understand geological contribution. Mostly, geological variables are relatively constant compared to hydrological or meteorological features, which vary through time (e.g., seasons). In those attractions, geological variable interaction might be high, medium, or low (recall Table 3.3).

For instance, river rafting has a high interaction of geological variables since it contributes to difficulty ratings and safety factors. In a rafting route, geological features of the river contribute to different rafting difficulties. Generally, a steep slope correlates with a harder rating, where a gentler slope is linked to an easier one. Questions as examples need to be addressed in research: What geological factors contribute to the difference in slope? How does the steepness of the slope contribute to a harder rating? How does it define safety factor? Perhaps it might be a different case for different hydrological and/or meteorological attractions, where geological concepts might work or not. For sure, it will require a lot of discussions.

This chapter explains research character in tourism geology, to answer what kind of research subject might be conducted. In addition, what is written in this chapter is a general idea to invoke your interest to do research, so that it can provide detail requirements of each attraction.

4.2. KNOWLEDGE MATRIX

Attraction, activity, and impact are three groups of knowledge in tourism geology. Safety variable should be considered in any tourist activity of any tourist interest. Difficulty rating is estimated to appear mainly in particular landform attractions. A possible knowledge matrix is given in Table 4.1. It shows a prediction systematic knowledge.

Table 4.1. Systematic knowledge matrix in tourism geology.

Attraction		Activity		
Attraction Type	Attraction Criteria	Safety Variable	Difficulty Rating	Impact
Geologic (geologic history)	√	√	---	√
Scenic Beauty	√, A	√	---	---
Particular Landform	√, A	√	√	√
Curative	√	√	---	√
Art-related Stone and Mineral	√	√	?	√
Particular features:				
• Relate to drilling	√	√	---	---
• Giant Crystal Cave	√	√	---	√
• Powerful Geologic Process	√	√	---	---
• Moon and Mars	√, A	√	√	√
• Hydrothermal Vent	√	√	---	?

Explanatory notes for the matrix:

- (√) means potential to generate systematic knowledge, in relation to geological features and tourists.

- (?) means arguable whether it can generate systematic knowledge or not.

- (A) means geosites usually have aesthetic variables.

- (---) means less likely geological variable interaction will be occurred.

Tourism geology research is similar to research of other applied geology. Thus, research in tourism geology needs hypothetical construction, method, fieldwork or desk study, studio work, laboratory analysis, and synthesis. Observation methods are basically geological methods, such as geomorphologic observation, rock description, observing route surface type, or sedimentological rock profiling. The differences are the focus of interest that defines method, outcomes, and so on. Finally, the outcome should be understandable and useful for the next-user.

4.3. RESEARCH SUBJECT EXAMPLE

To stimulate research, examples of a subject are given, as follows.

- Geological control for scenic beauty interest in a volcanic area.

- Determining safe waters for swimming in the western coast of South America from a geological point of view.

- Relation of sediment gravity flow and safe waters for swimming in a lake environment.

- Geological influence in difficulty rating assessment of river rafting in the western Sumatra rivers.

- Any relation of rock type exposure with rising thermal air for aero-sport activity?

- How do geological features influence the proximity wingsuit flying?

- The role of fault and its minor structure in difficulty rating of rock climbing.

- Understanding salt lake deposit character of Salar de Uyuni for a racing car track.

- How does air thermal lift vary in a desert environment?

- Controlling soil erosion on a mountain bike route.

- New cliff-diving spot for competition in Victoria Falls, Zimbabwe.

- Possibility of therapeutic effect of Lake Assal minerals, Djibouti.

- The curative effect of Anak Krakatoa volcanic sand.

- Kaolin effect on off-road track.

- Where is the best river for suiseki hunting in New Zealand?

- Geological control of difficulty rating and safety in Paris-Dakar Rally route.

- Determining the best area for earthquake attraction in San Andreas Fault area.

- The assessment of potential tsunami attractions in the coast of Japan.

- Determining the best observation site for the next eruption of the Merapi volcano, Indonesia.

- Assessment of scenic beauty area in the volcanic region of Mars: geomorphological 3D modeling.

- How to assess a possible curative site on Mars?

- Measuring attractiveness of the active deep-sea hydrothermal vents.

- Tour of the Mesozoic Period: a geological consideration in travel time to the past in terms of attraction, safety, and impact.

Those research subjects provided are derived from my imagination to invoke your idea or memories. The point is that geologists should be creative in defining research subject, hypothesis construction, or method design. Because geological knowledge and its methods in tourism subjects are most likely poorly documented. On the other hand, the next-user might define problems that need to be solved by geologists.

Research can be conducted anywhere, in a protected area or in an urban environment, in the deep ocean floor, or on an extra-terrestrial object, as long as geological feature can be investigated and as long as humans can go to an attractive place and get back to their home safely. If you are interested, then most likely you should have to be a person who was "street smart" rather than "book smart."

4.3.1. The Need to Learn from Practitioners

One might argue that geological support for tourism is unnecessary. The reason is because tourism-related activities have developed without the support of geologists. This is true. For instance, the paddler has constructed difficulty ratings for river rafting without geologic support from the geoscience community. They divide rafting difficulties into six categories based on the river type and the paddler's ability to pass through the river. The paddler made the classification over the years with no involvement of geological investigation.

In fact, it is the geologist who needs to learn from the paddler regarding how to assess relations of the activity to geological variables. Practitioners understand the river features needed. But would probably be hard-pressed to explain and to predict where another river exists that has similar or more challenging features just be seeing a map (Fig. 4.1). That is the opportunity.

Geologists able to extract the existing geological variable interaction in the "proven" river, formulate it and use it for prediction in other areas. The purpose is to bring the knowledge from the context of justification to discovery. In other word, geologists are able to extract a geological concept that controls the attraction and its activity.

Remember, the spirit of this work is exploring the usage of geological knowledge for tourism. As one of the possible consequences, a new destination will be discovered by design, not by chance. Besides, are you sure that every river in this planet has been rafted? Every cliff has been climbed? Or every route to the reach the mountain peak has been traversed?

Figure 4.1. The upstream part of Rogue River in Oregon, in the United States, often used for rafting. The river in the upstream area is characterized by a V-shaped valley, rock exposure, and steeper slope of the riverbed. Circles indicate the two rafts. Image courtesy of Bureau of Land Management Oregon and Washington, 2017. CC BY 2.0.

4.3.2. The Need for Cooperation with the Next-User

It is essential to cooperate with the next-user, e.g., the park manager. The objective is to study geological variables and tourist activity in relation in real world, as well as learning to recognize the actual problem. In such cooperation, the geologist will evaluate geological data and information, while the next-user will decide what kind of geological support they need. It is important to emphasize that cooperation is needed for a reality check of tourism geology's application in the real world.

Geologists document the project outcome in a project report. In a geological report, the language is (tourism) geological language, where the target reader is the next-user (non-geologist). Should the next-user learn geology? Or should they be educated to be a geologist themselves? It would be useful if they learned geology, at the level of being able to read (include understand the meaning) a geological report rather than writing it. Skill is more than knowing. Skill means the ability to take a decision and act based on the knowledge.

Within a geological report, the geologist describes objective, method, and technique to record primary data; describes all the facts observed; mentions laboratory analysis outcome (if needed); and produces maps. Eventually all knowledge is interpreted, concluded, and recommended related to the attraction, activity, and impact. All of the geologist's work should be documented in a scientific context or based on facts that can be verified. Those are the real writing skills.

The next-user reads the report, reconfirms the objective, reviews the literature study, carefully reads the method and technique section, and analyzes the acquired data. Eventually, they evaluate the relation of geological data, interpretation, and recommendation for tourism. The expectation is that the next-user be able to make a decision based on the report. The next-user should be able to extract the knowledge that can increase managing the destination, not "nice to have" or "nice to know." Those are what I mean by reading skill. In addition, tourism geology is geology for tourism-related professional in context of reading skill.

There is a main difference between writing skill and reading skill. In writing skill, the geologist should understand what message needs to be stated in the report. Thus, it is how the geologist serves the next-user through delivering proper geological knowledge in the form of a scientific report. In reading skill, the next-user should be able to grasp the value of the geologist's report. Usually, mastering reading skill is easier than mastering writing skill.

By reading the report, the next-user understands the geological knowledge related to their need and its consequences. Then they are able to make decisions easily.

- Questions related to attraction:
  - Are new attractions identified?
  - How many new tourist interests refer to a geological feature fulfilled in a destination?
  - Does the tourist stay longer because of those new attractions?
- Questions related to activity:
  - How many new tourist activities are related to a geological feature identified?
  - Is the evacuation route established?
  - Are there enough signs to avoid injury / fatality?
  - Will the tourist be back for another visit because of a new attraction or new activity?
- Questions related to impact:
  - Has the impact level of an activity already been measured?
  - Is there a prediction tool to understand future impact established?
  - Is there a strategy to reduce impact of an activity?

The next-user might review whether geological support is useful. Questions might arise during the review process as follows:

- Is the next-user's problem solved?
- Does the outcome make the next-user's task easier?
- Is the outcome useful to be an input during the strategic decision-making process?

4.4. COMPARING TOURISM GEOLOGY RESEARCH WITH GEOTOURISM RESEARCH

In this part, I compare research characteristics of geotourism from published papers with tourism geology research. There are three cases used: the case of geotourism promotion of the loess deposit, North Serbia; Volcano Tourism in Sibayak Volcano, Indonesia; and Geotouristic attraction of the Danakil Depression, Ethiopia.

4.4.1. Case of Promoting Loess Deposit for Geotourism, North Serbia

Vasiljević et al. (2011, p. 392) stated that the loess deposit in Vojvodina, North Serbia, is one of the most important continental records of climatic and environmental changes during the Quaternary. Loess is a paleosol fine-grained clastic deposit formed by accumulation of wind-blown dust. In brief, they conduct a study to present the potential of these sites to be interpreted and promoted as geotourism resources to a wider audience than earth scientists.

Vasiljević et al. (2011, pp. 396-397) showed the significance of the thickness of loess-palaeosol sequences, which have aesthetic and great geomorphological diversity. It is like pseudokarst landforms, e.g., loess caves, wells, cliffs, depressions, pyramids, gullies, and natural bridges. Those unique forms were due to dimentological characteristics and dry climate in the region.

Research by Vasiljević et al. (2011, p. 402) found that one of the most suitable initial solutions for the scientific community to liaise with the environmental and landscape interpretive communities is to produce informational and interpretative media for the public. It is such a construction site-interpretative panel, marking tracks, training courses, and other educational activities, that lead to promotion of geoconservation and geotourism.

4.4.2. Case of Planning Tourism in Sibayak Volcano Tourism, Indonesia

Sibayak Volcano, North Sumatra, is one of the most visited active volcanoes in Indonesia. The last eruption known was in 1881 (Venzke, 2013). Newsome (2010, p. 131) discusses the Sibayak Volcano from the perspective of site access, visitor attitudes, and how it was presented as a geotourism destination.

Observation by Newsome (2010, p. 133) shows the environment of the Sibayak volcano has undergone degradation, which reduces the sense of wonder for those visitors seeking natural experiences. The facts he observed were poor condition of access trails: trail bifurcation, many trail sections are muddy, slippery, and eroded, no clear signage at the summit area. Moreover, the crater floor has been modified by graffiti (Fig. 4.2) and littering, there are no pamphlets to orientate and guide visitor, and interpretation panels to enrich the volcanic experience are absent. Newsome (2010, pp.134-135) pointed out the need for tourism planning in geotourism to plan and manage visitor activity, guide tourism management, foster sustainable tourism, and preserve the natural attributes of Sibayak.

Figure 4.2. Sibayak crater full of graffiti. Image courtesy of Arian Zwegers, 2011. CC BY 2.0.

4.4.3. Case of Geotouristic Attraction of the Danakil Depression, Ethiopia

Danakil Depression is in Ethiopia, western Africa. It has a dimension of about 100 kilometers long and tens of kilometers wide. Geologically, the depression is the northern part of the greater depression, called the Afar Depression or Afar Triangle, which is part of the East African Rift. The Afar Depression had been caused by moving apart of the three tectonic plates (or triple junction). The plates are Nubian Plate in the west, Somalian Plate in the southeast, and Arabian Plate in the northeast, which cause most of the area below sea level.

Cieśluk et al. (2014, p. 33) discuss extraordinary geological attractions of the Danakil Depression. As part of tectonic plate divergence area, the area is connected with volcanic activity and frequent earthquakes. Tens of volcanoes are in the Danakil Depression. The Erta Ale—which means "smoking mountain" in the local Afar language—is active and the most visited volcano in the depression. It has a moving hot lava lake in its crater (Fig. 4.3).

Figure 4.3. Lava lake of Erta Ale, Ethiopia. (Image courtesy of Petr Meissner, 2011. CC BY 2.0.)

As plate features diverge, many fractures open where the magma chamber is situated, at a relatively shallow depth. These cause geysers, geothermal hot springs, and extraordinary mineralization in the surface; and sulfuric fumes lift from the ground that are dangerous to humans.

Millions of years ago, the region was flooded by the Red Sea. But since the Pleistocene era (1.8 million years ago), tectonic activity cut off the region from the sea. Because of evaporation, the region dried up and left a vast dry land area about 1,200 km sq and a thick salt deposit. The deposit is the white gold of the Afar Tribe, who mine the salt deposit. There are many places showing unique salt structures and extraordinary features such as salt-mineral walls on the western edge of the Dallol Volcano.

Water flows to lakes where most of the lakes are hypersaline, a couple times saltier than sea water, such as Lake Assal, Lake Abbe, and Lake Afrera. Some flows to Lake Dallol, which is acid water. In the subsurface, the hot water supersaturated with salt rises from below and creates colorful crystals and evaporation formation in the lake, making it the most unique lake.

Cieśluk et al. (2014, p. 41) mentioned that the Danakil Depression is not a popular tourist destination. Those who are interested to go might find challenges. To mention a few: it is the hottest place on earth during dry season, where the temperature might reach 50°C; it is a very remote area with no access to a mobile network; and visiting the region should be accompanied by a military escort. Moreover, the hot desert climate, barren soil, no rain for most of the year, hard-to-find water, make the Danakil environment one of the most challenging destinations. In fact, many people call it "Hell on earth." Finally, Cieśluk et al. (2014, p. 42) state that the region should become a national park and be added to the World Heritage List of UNESCO.

4.4.4. How Does Tourism Geology Research Ideas on Those Studies?

I have no objection to their research outcome, recommendation, or opinion. In the context of geotourism, their researches are great and are interesting to be implemented. Their researches are dedicated to geoscientific tourist interest, sustainable geotourism destinations, and promoting geoconservation.

If their research area is seen in the context of tourism geology, what are the results? Different perspectives deliver different outcomes. Recall that geologists in tourism geology think in three groups of knowledge: attraction, activity, and impact. In addition, a geologist should generate creative ideas to increase the value of the destination.

4.4.4.1. Review on Geotourism Research on Loess Deposit of North Serbia and Planning Tourism on Sibayak Volcano, Indonesia

If tourism geology research was conducted in Sibayak Volcano and the Vojvodina region, the outcome might be to explore the other natural non-living attractions and the activities. For example, identification of new spots for taking photographs or scenic observation, new hiking and mountain biking routes, sites for aero-sport take-off and rock climbing, a curative potential area of pyroclastic sand, and a possible area for observing art-related stone and mineral. Such recommended activities must pay attention to safety factors. In addition, those identifications also should be accompanied by impact predictions. Even though the prediction results only have consequence in a small area, the results still need to be delivered.

The outcome is not only dedicated to geologic interest but also to outdoor scenic beauty and curative enthusiasts. In addition, what kind the tourism theme in each area will be the authority of the land owner, investor, business planner, or other tourism-related professionals.

Tourism geology's scope excludes designing geological informational or other geological interpretative media for tourists, promoting geoconservation, being a geological tour guide, or even construction tourism planning and management. The main reason is that these variable-type interactions are non-geological variables.

4.4.4.2. Review of Geotouristic Attraction Research of Danakil Depression, Ethiopia

Despite the Danakil Area seeming to be inhospitable to be visited, there are many spectacular tourist attractions. For instance, volcanic eruptions, earthquakes, and particular landforms for physical outdoor activity.

Based on the Global Volcanism Program (2013), there are about 11 active volcanoes in the Danakil Depression where the eruptions were observed. VEI was recorded in a range of 0 to 4, but most of it was VEI 2. This means the eruption is an attraction, which I proposed to be at a maximum of VEI 4. Erta Ale holds the record of most active eruption among volcanoes, with 7 eruption times since 1873. The Erta Ale also holds the longest eruption record, from July 1967 to mid-2017 with VEI 0 (Global Volcanism Program, 2017).

As for the character of seismic activity within the Danakil Depression, based on the USGS Earthquake Database (USGS, 2017), it was estimated about 250 to 300 earthquakes from 2000 to 2017 alone. The strongest quake was 5.7 magnitude; the weakest was 4 magnitude; and the average was 4.5 magnitude. I propose earthquake magnitude as an attraction when the magnitude is between 4 and 5.5 magnitude. The year 2005 was exceptional for earthquake frequency, with hundreds of quakes occurring. Using available data for 2000 to 2017 in the region—but excluding 2005 earthquake data—there were an average of four earthquakes each year in the region (USGS, 2017).

All of those geological features coupled with geographical features make the Danakil Depression a very challenging destination and an unforgettable adventure for those who visit. With its vast area, an adrenaline-infused outdoor activity will be interesting, such as an off-road endurance race event. Perhaps call it the Danakil Rally: an electric vehicle race in the Hell on Earth, crossing the toughest environments on the planet. The rally will use geological attractions as checkpoints such as saline lakes and active and dormant volcanoes.

Within the depression, it seems there is only one geological feature necessary to consider related to the safety/health factor: the natural fractures emit sulfur. As a consequence, it should be delineated and marked as a hazardous area. On the other hand, a possible impact of outdoor physical activity (Danakil Rally) is soil erosion. In context of impact, it might be considered low risk.

Thus, geological observation in the context of geotourism and tourism geology focus on the same geological feature on site. But different perspectives deliver different outcomes. Despite geotourism and tourism geology studying the same subject-matter, both have different focuses of interest since they are designed for different purposes.

4.5. SUMMARY

To develop tourism geology, research is needed to accumulate knowledge derived from various case studies around the globe. While research subjects remain within three knowledge groups—attraction, activity, and its impact—it requires passion and imagination to explore research subjects. On the other hand, the next-user might define the problem to be solved by the geologist.

There are two tasks when geologist learn from practitioners and cooperate with the next-user. The first task is that the geologist learns their unique point of view on the attraction and activity. The second task is to convert their view to be a geological concept, so that the knowledge of tourism geology can be used as prediction and controlling tools.

Let me remind that the main task of scientists refers to Suriasumantri's mind (1984, p. 366): to explain, to predict, and to control. Explaining the cause-consequence relation of the variables is the nature of every science and applied science. The explanation satisfies the know-why knowledge. In case of applied science, however, the user demand is higher since they need the knowledge to predict and control.

Thus, it is expected the outcome of tourism geology research will be not only to explain—such as why is a geological feature capable of being a tourist attraction? Or why can a particular tourist activity be conducted in a particular geologic landform? When tourism geology research outcomes are able to predict and to control, the knowledge generated will have a higher value.

Reference Cited

Cieśluk, K., Karasiewicz, M.T. & Preisner, Z. (2014) Geotouristic Attractions of the Danakil Depression, Geotourism, No. 36, p.33,41,42, pp. 33-42

Global Volcanism Program (2017) Report on Erta Ale (Ethiopia). In Venzke, E (ed.), Bulletin of the Global Volcanism Network, Vol. 42, No.7 (July 2017). Smithsonian Institution.

Newsome, D. (2010) The Need for a Planning Framework to Preserve the Wilderness Values of Sibayak Volcano, North Sumatra, Indonesia. p. 131,133,134-135, pp.131-141. In: Erfurt-Cooper, P. & Cooper, M. (eds) Volcano and Geothermal Tourism. Sustainable Geo-Resources for Leisure and Recreation, Earthscan Publisher, 378 pp

Suriasumantri, J.S. (1984) Filsafat Ilmu: Sebuah pengantar populer. Pustaka Sinar Harapan, fourteenth print, p. 366, 384 pp

USGS (2017) Earthquake Catalog, earthquake.usgs.gov/earthquakes or go to tinyurl.com/hb8mfxz. Accessed October 2017.

Vasiljević, D.A., Marković, S.B., Hose, T.A., Smalley, I., O'Hara-Dhand, K., Basarin, B., Lukić, T. & Vujičić, M.D. (2011) Loess Towards (Geo) Tourism – Proposed Application on Loess in Vojvodina Region (North Serbia). Acta geographica Slovenica, 51-2, p. 392, 396-397, 402, pp. 390-406

Meissner, P., (2011) Erta Ale (6900576021).jpg, Image is downloaded from commons.wikimedia.org/wiki/File:Erta_Ale_(6900576021).jpg or go to tinyurl.com/w4rhw9l

Zwegers, A., (2011) Gunung Sibayak (6931901723).jpg, Image is downloaded from commons.wikimedia.org/wiki/File:Gunung_Sibayak_(6931901723). jpg or go to tinyurl.com/yx77zbcm

Bureau of Land Management Oregon and Washington., (2011) Rogue River Rafting (34837510982).jpg, Image is downloaded from commons. wikimedia.org/wiki/File:Rogue_River_Rafting_(34837510982).jpg or go to tinyurl.com/wtckll7

Global Volcanism Program (2013). Volcanoes of the World, v. 4.6.2, Venzke E (ed). Smithsonian Institution, Downloaded October 2017, dx.doi.org/10.5479/ si.GVP.VOTW4-2013 or go to tinyurl.com/t8bxs3v. Accessed October 2017

CHAPTER 5

Make It More Clear

Highlights

- Geotourism and tourism geology are similar but designed for different purposes.

- To demonstrate the differences, an imaginary case is provided.
  - It is about two settlements separated by long hill where the two governments have the same economic problems.
  - Four different geologists (a geotourism practitioner, a geologist with a tourism geology mind, a petroleum geologist, and an engineering geologist) who grew up in that neighborhood intend to do something for the community. They asses the landscape and propose their unique idea to local governments based on the nature of their own discipline.

- There will be possible challenges ahead during introducing tourism geology:
  - Defining the scope of tourism geology and geotourism, and about conservation and environmental issues in tourism geology.
  - It will challenge our understanding of the nature of each discipline.

- This book is a proposal of tourism geology as an applied geology to tourism.
  - Tourism geology is dedicated to the tourism-related professional.
  - The idea needs to be explored for its usefulness and limitations from other perspectives.

Content

5.1   BACKGROUND 239
5.2   A LANDSCAPE ON DIFFERENT VIEWS 239
    5.2.1 The Landscape Character 239
    5.2.2 Engineering Geology Point-of-View 242
    5.2.3 Petroleum Geology Analog Study 243
    5.2.4 Geotourism Action Plan 244
    5.2.5 Focus of Interest of Tourism Geology 245
    5.2.6 Assessing the Idea 246
    5.2.7 Nature of Each Discipline 248
5.3   THE POSSIBLE CHALLENGE AHEAD 251
5.4   CLOSING THOUGHTS 253

Abstract

To more clearly differentiate tourism geology from geotourism, an imaginary case is provided as an example. The case is about two settlements separated by a long hill. At the same time, the two governments have same problems: increasing unemployment because of crop failures, a smaller fish catch, and impact of the monetary crisis a year before. They need innovative ideas that will lead to economic recovery within a short time.

This imaginary case also includes four men who grew up in the vicinity. They are concerned about the social problems and intend to do something. They are geologists who have different specialties: an engineering geologist, petroleum geologist, geotourism practitioner, and a geologist with tourism geology mindset. After they study the landscape, they come up with four different proposals. This case demonstrates four different applied geological disciplines, each of which has its own focus of interest when viewing the landscape.

In addition, there will be challenges ahead during introducing tourism geology, such as defining the scope of tourism geology and geotourism, about conservation and environmental issues in tourism geology. It will challenge our understanding of the nature of each discipline, such as the use of its knowledge accumulation along with its limitations.

This book is a proposal of tourism geology as an applied geology to tourism and dedicated to the tourism-related professional. It provides the know-why and the know-how knowledge for geologists who interest to contribute their skills to tourism. The idea, however, needs to be explored, including its uses and limitations, from other perspectives.

Keywords: geotourism, tourism geology, engineering geologist, petroleum geologist, tourism-related professional, focus of interest

5.1. BACKGROUND

I realize, there will be many barriers to accept my version of tourism geology. One is the understanding of geotourism as the only relationship between geology and tourism. Moreover, the idea of geotourism was already introduced in 1995.

In addition, since my version uses the same term as earlier workers, such as Komoo (1997, p. 2970) and Chen et al. (2015, p. 2), confusion might arise using the term "tourism geology." To avoid it, I will show the differences between tourism geology and geotourism by using an imaginary example.

5.2. A LANDSCAPE FROM DIFFERENT VIEWS

Every discipline in applied geology has the same subject matter, which is the geosphere. But they have different focuses of concern or different ways to study the geosphere. I use an imaginary landscape to describe the difference. In addition, I present four imaginary geologists who has different specialties: Mike is an engineering geologist, John is a petroleum geologist, Ritchie is a geotourism practitioner, and Dwayne is a geologist with a tourism geology mindset.

5.2.1. The Landscape Character

The imaginary landscape is an onshore to offshore area where two settlements in a suburban area are situated, called the Fisherman Village and the Farmer Town (Fig. 5.1). The Fisherman Village is near the shoreline, with a population of 500. They trade with the Farmer Town, which has about 3,000 people, in the inland area. A narrow and poorly maintained road connects those two settlements, extending about 150 km and taking about three to four hours to drive.

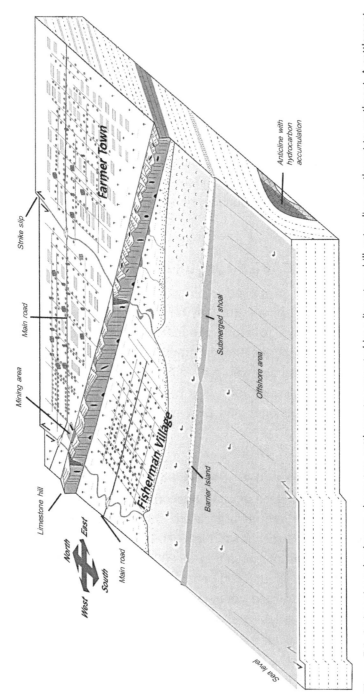

Figure 5.1. An imaginary landscape shows two settlements separated by a limestone hill, extending northwest to southeast. A settlement with a smaller population, called Fisherman Village, is in the south, in a coastal area. A bigger settlement with a denser population, called the Farmer Town, lies in the north. Landscape is sketched by the author.

The most prominent landform is a limestone hill range on the northeastern part, oriented northwest to southeast, separating the two settlements. The hill ranges isolate the Fisherman Village. The Farmer Town is a bigger settlement, since it has better access to the bigger cities.

The limestone hill rises up to 175 m, extending northwest to southeast. The limestone hill forms a cliff and overhang on the southern part, and a gentler slope on the northern part. Hot springs associated with faults surround the cliffs. The hill has a gentler slope on the northern side, about 30° of bedding attitude and about 350 m width. Limestone is a rock derived from ancient coral reefs growing in a shallow marine environment dense in Calcium Carbonate ($CaCO_3$), and thus soluble by rainwater, which is naturally more acidic. The limestone hill typifies the karst landscape, meaning the landscape consist of hills, valleys, and caves. Those features are more intense in the southeastern part. Thousands of bats live in a few caves.

In some spots, a few people use the peaks of the hill for sightseeing. In other spots, local people excavate the limestone in the northwestern part, to be used for home and building construction and decoration. Because of increasing demands for construction and decoration, excavation will be expanded wider.

Offshore, barrier islands and submerged shoals protect the shoreline from the waves of the open ocean. The beach is a small piece of heaven on earth. White sand grains spread within the beach, and coral reef grows in the shallow water. However, only few people visit the beach, since it is necessary to cross the swamp area and river, while no road and bridges are built. The people of the Fisherman Village are nature-minded who love their landscape. Many local paintings show their love of the breath-taking landscape.

Two long fractures (strike slip) cross the limestone hill in the north and extend to the offshore zone in the south. Those fractures became the path for rivers crossing the hills and created small waterfalls. Those fractures also cross the submerged shoal, so that gaps form among the shoals. It allows the fishermen to sail to the offshore area for bigger fish.

The rivers meander where pebble-size sediments with a unique shape and color are scattered in the riverbanks. Those unique stones are derived from the mountains far to the north, where tectonic activity uplifted various rock types. Finally, the rivers form estuaries on their way to the sea.

Despite nature's great beauty, the social environment in those two settlements shows opposite condition. The local governments experience the main problems of increasing unemployment because of crop failures, a smaller fish catch, and the impact of a monetary crisis a year earlier. They are afraid the problems will lead to higher crime rates. Hence, they need an innovative idea that will lead to economic recovery in a short time.

Mike, John, Ritchie, and Dwayne—who grown up together in the two settlements—are concerned about the social problems and intend to do something for the people. They observed the landscape and came up with different plans. Moreover, they will propose them to the governments as the next-users. In other words, they will determine how to assess the landscape according to their focus of interest.

5.2.2. Engineering Geology Point-of-View

Mike, the engineering geologist who works for a private consultant, observes the area and interviews the people, asking what their aspirations are. As a engineering geologist, he is interested in building useful thing for the people.

His interviews come out with people's needs and wants. The people of Fisherman Village need a shorter time to reach Farmer Town, to keep the fish fresher to sell in the town market. The people of Farmer Town also wish to have better access to reach the Fisherman Village and the swimming nearshore, because of its beauty nearshore.

Finally, Mike plans to build a tunnel crossing the hill to shorten travel time between the two settlements to less than an hour. Mike is also interested to build a road and a bridge so that people can reach the beautiful beach easily. Finally, Mike constructs a site investigation proposal to understand rock and soil mechanic characters within the area where bridges, road, and tunnel would be built. The result of his investigation will become an input to construction projects be conducted by a civil engineer.

5.2.3. Petroleum Geology Analog Study

John is a petroleum geologist who works for a national oil company, which is still in exploration phase. The boundary of company working area is from the coastline which extends several kilometers to offshore. Meanwhile, the government of Fisherman Village has a smaller share of the company's share, which means the government will have a cash flow once the petroleum is found and produced.

What appears in John's mind when he observes the landscape is in terms petroleum systems. He understands that the exploration target in his company is a typical karst reservoir in the form of folding rock layer in the subsurface (anticline). It is an offshore area where petroleum might be accumulated within the upper part of the folding rocks. Eventually, he is interested in using the karst landscape as an analogue study of exploration targets. In other words, he intends to investigate the geology of the karst landscape for a subsurface analogue. He uses an assumption that rocks investigated in the karst landscape have characteristics similar to rocks in the subsurface in his company's area.

His proposal is about field geology study to understand carbonate porosity in the karst area. He needs to ask permission of the government to conduct research for several weeks in the area. The outcome will be submitted to his management as part of encouraging opportunities for an exploration well campaign in his concession area.

When the well successfully discovers and produces petroleum, then job opportunities will open up for the people. Eventually, shared profit will come to the local government.

5.2.4. Geotourism Action Plan

Viewing the landscape in a geotourism dimension is Ritchie's character as a geotourism practitioner. He realizes the area has geotourism attraction potential ranging from macroscale (e.g., landscape) to microscale (e.g., fossils). The benefit of converting the area to a geotourism context means economic growth potential.

But his discomfort with local mining of limestone is unavoidable. Natural processes to form such features need thousands to millions of years. The first thing he needs to do is to promote a geoconservation campaign to protect the area from man-made destructive activities— that is, rock excavation. It won't be an easy mission, since many people depend on mining as their main job.

Eventually, Ritchie comes up with a geotourism master plan to convert the area into a world-class geotourism destination. It includes some important things as follows.

- Selecting potential geotouristic sites, such as karst features, hot springs, local mining, and even some homes built that use the stone from local mining.

- Setting up a visitor center to inform about the things needed during tourist visitation, including information on accommodations, transportation, tour agent, and tour guides.

- Constructing geotourism products. For instance, a geological guide book and brochure, geological souvenirs, and a geological interpretative panel to explain geologic processes in the past. Those will be put on the sites.

- Designing geological tours programs. It includes a virtual tour and training local people to be geological tour guides.

- Looking carefully at available accommodations and redesigning them to have a geological atmosphere.

- Raising awareness and training the people to develop sustainable geotourism and geoconservation, so that the people might receive the benefits of multiple geotourism effects.

5.2.5. Focus of Interest of Tourism Geology

It is also a unique opinion when assessing the landscape from Dwayne's perspective. As a geologist with tourism geology mindset, he has his own focus of interest. His view of the landscape is in the context of non-living natural tourist attractions, activities, and impact.

Dwayne explores what kind of tourist interest might be fulfilled by the landscape and landform, more than just geologic interest such as curative, sightseeing, adventure enthusiasts, and art-related stone and minerals. Several ideas appear as follows.

- Many peaks have the potential for sightseeing spots.

- Karst for cave tourism or health tourism (e.g., speleotherapy).

- Hot springs might be used for a spa (health tourist interest).

- Cliff on the southern side might be utilized for rock climbing-related activities.

- The northern side might be needed for take-off of paragliding, a downhill mountain bike route, or hill-climbing motocross.

- The nearshore area might be utilized for swimming and snorkeling.

- The riverbank is rich in uniquely shaped and colored pebble-size sediment for suiseki or a gemstone hunting tour.

Dwayne's action is to construct a research proposal on the interesting spots to gather more information. He should answer several questions as follow.

- Is it safe to swim in the nearshore?
- Are there any other activities that should be recommended in the beach?
- How hard is it to reach the peak, since only a few people just go there for sightseeing?
- What is the difficulty rating in the cliff for rock climbing and in the northern slope for a downhill mountain bike championship?
- Can speleotherapy be done in the cave?
- Are there any other effects of hot springs?
- Where is the best location for gemstone hunting?
- What are the impacts of each activity?

If his proposal is accepted and executed, the outcome will be presented to the people. He will tell them that their beautiful place has various tourist attractions and could be able to fulfill many types of tourist interests. The conclusion of his research might be a consequence to several tourism-related events and various tourism types such as rock climbing championships, fascinating sun and beach tourism, and speleotherapy. However, to make it come true, tourism-related professionals should follow up the research outcome, since Dwayne's scope of work is limited to geological variables only.

5.2.6. Assessing the Idea

Those four geologists have different proposals that show different points-of-view when assessing the landscape. It is a similar situation to using different-colored sunglasses while seeing a landscape. If seeing using a red lens, then the landscape will have a reddish color, and so on when seeing through yellow, brown, or blue lenses. Every geologist might consider his idea is the best. However, the people's representatives might have a different point-of-view. Their need, as the next-users, is to solve the problems of unemployment and economic recovery.

In this imaginary case, every proposal has a social impact. Debate occurred when the people's representatives discussed every proposal, as follows.

- Although Mike's idea of a tunnel would decrease travel time, it is still debated whether a tunnel will increase employment. Moreover, it would destroy the karst system, which is contradictory to the spirit of the people who are nature-minded. Project funding is another problem.

- The positive impact of John's research proposal will benefit in the long term. If petroleum is found, most likely the company will need more than one year to produce petroleum, while drilling delineation wells and preparing a surface facility.

- Geotourism's Ritchie is considering a specific tourism market, since the people are not geologic minded. Moreover, forbidding local mining will create a new problem of unemployment. In addition, it is hard to get a stone supply for home construction and decoration elsewhere if mining is prohibited.

- Accepting Dwayne's research idea of tourism geology is also considered still far from beneficial. His idea needs to be followed up by other tourism-related professionals for tourism master planning and also to seek a funding source for the project.

In this work, it is unnecessary to mention which proposal is chosen by the people's representative. This imaginary case demonstrates that the four geologists have their own view based on the focus of interest during assessing the same landscape. In addition, the people's representative as the next-user might also have their own mind during the decision-making process.

5.2.7. Nature of Each Discipline

It is interesting to examine the proposals of Mike (engineering geologist), John (petroleum geologist), Ritchie (geotourism practitioner), and Dwayne (geologist with tourism geology mind). The natures of Mike's, John's, and Dwayne's proposals stay in an applied geology scope, where only geologic variables play the main role. The scopes of their disciplines are already formed, and they follow them. On the other hand, Ritchie's proposal of geotourism is beyond the scope of geology, where many non-geological variables interact.

If local government agrees to all of their proposals, then Mike needs civil engineers to conduct construction projects, John needs petroleum engineers to drill an exploration well and to produce petroleum, and Dwayne needs tourism-related professionals to follow up on his research outcome. But Ritchie is able to do the entire project, since his scope of discipline is broader although limited to geoscientific tourist interest.

Focusing on the case of geotourism and tourism geology, it needs to be emphasized what can actually happen when Ritchie and Dwayne assess the landscape. What is observed by Ritchie as a geotourism practitioner is the same feature that Dwayne observes as tourism geology minded because of the same subject matter. However, their outcomes are different because of the different focus of interest (recall Table 2.4 on the difference between geotourism and tourism geology).

- Purpose and Tourist Interest Type

  - Ritchie's purpose is to prepare the area to be sustainable for geotourism and to support geoconservation, raising awareness and training the people to conduct sustainable geotourism. The end of his purpose is to make the people have a benefit of a multiplier geotourism effect.

  - Dwayne's purpose is to explore the geology of the area that

potentially fulfills any tourist interest types, including curative /
health, sightseeing, adventure, and art-related rock and mineral
interests. See Fig 5.2 for graphical illustration about those two
differences in context of tourist interest type and user type.

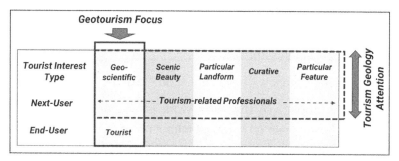

Figure 5.2. Illustration of tourism geology and geotourism differences. In
context of tourist interest type and user type, geotourism focus on geoscientific
tourist interest only but its scope is able to reach tourist. Tourism geology
study pays attention to various types of tourist interest whose the results are
dedicated to tourism-related professionals.

- Variables

  - The variable type in Ritchie's mind are mostly social variables,
    since he should raise awareness of the people of sustainable
    geotourism and geoconservation.

  - On the contrary, because of tourism geology's scope, Dwayne
    is unable to conduct what Ritchie is able to do, since Dwayne's
    mind is focused only on the geological variable interaction.
    Dwayne's idea is to scrutinize geological variable interaction
    on attraction, such as difficulty rating for rock climbing, slope
    change for downhill mountain biking, cave complexity for caving,
    minerals in the hot springs for curative interest, and rip current
    on the shore for swimming nearshore.

- Product Type

  - Ritchie is able to generate tourism products related to geology
    dedicated to geotourists. For instance, a geological interpretative
    panel, guide books and pamphlets, designing a geological tour, a

training program for local people to be geological tour guides, and a geoconservation campaign. All of those details are included in his geotourism master plan.

- What Dwayne is able to do is generate geologic reports of tourist attraction potentials, activities, and impacts of the area dedicated for tourism-related professionals.

- Tourism Market Impact
  - Ritchie's work will have impact on the geotourism market segment.
  - The impact of Dwayne's work is all sorts of tourism market segments related to tourist attraction—e.g., sun and beach tourism, health tourism, and adventure tourism.

Dwayne possibly might be able to do Ritchie's entire plan. However, it means Dwayne would have to change his status to be a tourism-related professional. A similar situation occurs when Mike conducts a tunnel construction project, which will change his position to a civil engineer. When John drills an exploration well or produces petroleum means that John's status changes to be a petroleum engineer (more specifically, a drilling engineer). It is a great achievement when a person is able to master several disciplines (e.g., engineering geology and civil engineering, petroleum geology and petroleum engineering, or geotourism and tourism geology).

However, this discussion is not about a person's skill to master more than one discipline. In this book, the discussion is about defining the discipline's scope. Geotourism and tourism geology look like similar disciplines but have different purposes. Their similarities can be analogous to a spoon versus a fork, or a bowl versus a plate. They are similar but designed for different purposes. Geotourism is a tourism type among many others, whereas tourism geology is (proposed to be) an applied geology among many other disciplines that study tourism as a subject. Tourism geology is similar to an application among any other applications in your cell phone.

5.3. THE POSSIBLE CHALLENGE AHEAD

We should realize that diversity exists not only in nature (e.g., geodiversity) but also in our perceptions when we put a value on the same feature. Moreover, tourism geology emerges by design, not by chance.

I point out several possible challenges might be encountered during developing tourism geology.

1) Defining scope of tourism geology and geotourism.

Since the geotourism idea is widely accepted, many people perceive every tourist attraction and its activities related to geological features as categorized into geotourism. It is interesting to remember the research outcome of Moreira and Melendez (2012, p. 206). They exposed that actually there are many tourism types other than geotourism in Geopark itself, where they did research based on questionnaires to 37 Geoparks around the globe. For instance, cultural tourism, culinary tourism, rural tourism, and adventure tourism. However, most geologists have an interest in the geological history of the attraction. In addition, it is possible that some tourism geology scope is in the scope of geotourism as well. Thus, those who adopt tourism geology should scrutinize its scope with geotourism's scope.

Let me remind of the characteristics of tourism geology:

- It has a wider spectrum than geotourism because of its effort to fulfill various tourist interests.

- It is fulfill the character of applied geology.

- It is intended to support tourism-related professionals.

- Although it is not meant to conserve a geological feature, tourism geology addresses the natural consequences of any tourist activities that have physical contact to the feature.

2) Conservation mission.

Conservation problems in a tourist destination might be categorized as tourism problems and capable of being scrutinized by geological knowledge. But if the same problem is found in another area, which is not a tourist destination, then it means the problem is not a typical problem in tourism. Hence, the conservation problems should be solved by conservation science or geoconservation, where the issue belong to those disciplines.

For instance, The Twelve Apostles in Victoria, Australia, is a collection of limestone stacks situated off the shore of Port Campbell National Park. It is also a tourism icon of Australia. The stacks were formed by erosion where waves eroded the lower part of the rock and eventually it collapsed. Until 2005, there were seven of twelve.

Despite it being a natural tourist attraction, it is hard to make it a concern in tourism geology. The reason is that wave erosion as a natural process also occurs in other areas that are not a destination.

On the other hand, if conservation problems are only found in tourist destinations, then the issue is already studied in tourism geology as part of the impact. This means the possibility of what will become an environmental impact should be mentioned in analyses of attraction and activity. Tourism-related professionals, as the next-users, will decide which part of the area will be developed or whether or not the impact is acceptable.

This discussion does not mean to denigrate the spirit of conservation in a tourist destination. Yet discussion in this book is about defining tourism geology as applied geology. Although I realize that excluding a conservation mission in tourism geology might cause unpopularity.

3) Environmental issues.

Negative environmental impact because of tourism is also a tourism problem related to geological variables. For instance, soil pollution because of waste disposal or decreasing ground water resources. But, such issues are basically environmental issues, studied by environmental geology, and not a tourist attraction issue. According to Doyle (2005, p. 26), the scope of environmental geology is the geology of resource management, of the built environment, of waste management, and of natural hazards.

5.4. CLOSING THOUGHTS

This book is a proposal of tourism geology as an applied geology to tourism. It provides the know-why and the know-how knowledge for geologists who intend to contribute their skills to tourism. Tourism geology's idea is dedicated to tourism-related professionals who need support from a geologist in a context of attraction, activity, and impact. The idea described is an outline. The idea, however, needs to be explored concerning its use and limitations from other perspectives. It is needed to be equipped here and there for the best outcome.

I predict two contributions during developing tourism geology. First, developing particular geological knowledge to study tourism. Second, developing tourism as its consequence if the outcome of tourism geology studies benefit tourism-related business. If so, tourism geology studies for the next-users are useful for the decision-making process, where they have a stronger scientific basis. The spirit I offer is the opportunity for geology and tourism to develop more, to become wider and deeper. We should consider such an opportunity, since the human mind naturally has the curiosity to enlighten the dark area, to explore the new knowledge.

Reference Cited

Chen, A., Lu, Y. & Ng, Y.C.Y. (eds) (2015) *The Principles of Geotourism.* Springer & Science Press Beijing. p.2, 264 pp.

Doyle, P. (2005) *Environmental Geology.* p. 26. In: Selley, C.R., Cocks, M. Robin. & Plimer, R.I. (eds) Encyclopedia of Geology. Vol. II. Elsevier, 807 pp

Komoo, I. (1997) *Conservation Geology: A Case for the ecotourism industry of Malaysia.* 2970, pp. 2969-2974. In: Marinos, P.G., Koukis, G.C., Tsiambaos, G.C. & Stournas, G.C. (eds) Engineering Geology and the Environment. Balkema Publication, Rotterdam, Vol. 3. 3357 pp.

Moreira, J.C. & Melendez, G. (2012) *It's Not Only Geotourism! Types of Tourism in Geoparks, An Analysis Based in 37 Geoparks.* p. 205, 206, pp 205- 206. In: Sa, A.A., Rocha, D., Paz, A. & Correia, V. (eds) Proceedings of the 11th European Geoparks Conference, 19 – 21 September 2012, Arouca Geopark Portugal, 319 pp.

PART II

Research Demonstration

This section explains five chapters, for example of tourism geology research, carried out in Kalimantan, Jawa and Lombok Islands

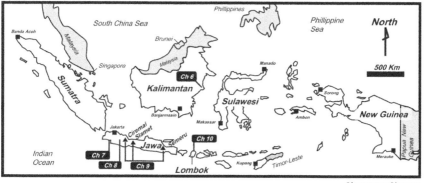

Ch means Chapter

Identifying Tourist Attraction Potential in Samarinda and Surroundings, Eastern Kalimantan

Highlights

- Samarinda, the capital city of the Eastern Kalimantan, has tourist attraction potential for geoscientific and non-geoscientific tourist interests.

- They are the great Mahakam Delta, hydrocarbon seepages, mud volcanoes, abandoned wells, world-class geoscientific outcrops, a (new) cave, and a peak to view the cityscape.

- Tourist activities range from learning geoscientific history to sightseeing, which can be conducted safely and with a low impact.

- Those attractions have potential for further development into tourist destinations where just a few peoples know of these attractions.

Content

6.1 INTRODUCTION 261
6.2 GENERAL GEOLOGY OF SAMARINDA 261
6.3 NATURAL TOURIST ATTRACTIONS IN SAMARINDA 262
    6.3.1 Modern Mahakam Delta 262
    6.3.2 Hydrocarbon Seepages 263
    6.3.3 Mud Volcanoes 264
    6.3.4 Abandoned Wells 265
    6.3.5 Outcrops 265
    6.3.6 Caves 266
    6.3.7 The Peak to View the Cityscape 266
6.4 SUMMARY 267
FIGURES AND TABLES 269

Abstract

There are potential natural tourist attractions in Samarinda and its surrounding, ranging from the great sedimentological features of modern Mahakam Delta, hydrocarbon seepages, and mud volcanoes, to the world-class outcrops. The tourist interest is geoscientific and non-geoscientific interests, such as geoscientific and scenic beauty interests. Tourist activities range from learning geoscientific history to sightseeing, which can be conducted safely and with a low impact. Those attractions have the potential for further development into tourist destinations where just a few people know those attractions.

Keywords: tourist attraction, geoscientific interest, scenic beauty interest, Mahakam Delta, outcrop, mud volcano, hydrocarbon seepages, abandoned well, peak to view the cityscape.

6.1. INTRODUCTION

Samarinda is the capital city of Eastern Kalimantan Province, Indonesia. In a business context, Samarinda is known as a mining city where there are many oil and gas working area as well as coal-mining area within it.

The research purpose is to understand potential tourist attractions from a geoscientific point of view in the preliminary phase. I conducted this research in 2001, where the outcome was dedicated to the government of Samarinda. Information of tourist attraction potentials described below were mostly obtained from Dr. Andang Bachtiar and his colleagues during geological mapping several years earlier.

6.2. GENERAL GEOLOGY OF SAMARINDA

Samarinda is located in the Kutai Basin, where the Mahakam River passes through the city (Fig 6.1). Today, the river is also the main route of the local people to the upstream area. Coal delivery also uses the route to transport coal to be distributed to the other islands.

The geoscientific history of Samarinda is strongly related to the Mahakam River and its delta sedimentation. The rocks exposed in Samarinda represent fluvial-deltaic sedimentation of the ancient Mahakam Delta since the Early Miocene era (Bachtiar et al., 2013; Figs. 6.2 and 6.3, Table 6.1). Today, modern sedimentation of Mahakam Delta occurs to the east of Samarinda.

Paleo-deltaic sedimentation means many coal deposits, which are now being explored by mining companies. The paleosedimentation also means there are thick sandstone beds producing oil and gas (e.g., the Handil and Tunu Fields). The rocks folded with north northeast–south southwest orientation of the Samarinda Anticlinorium, constructing the city to be a hilly area (Fig. 6.1).

6.3. NATURAL TOURIST ATTRACTIONS IN SAMARINDA

Seven natural and man made attractions in Samarinda and surrounding areas have been identified (Table 6.2, Fig. 6.4). They range from the great modern sedimentological feature of Mahakam Delta, and hydrocarbon seepages, to the world-class outcrops. Some of those features are the sites of geoscientific field trips, known by the participants of local and international geologists.

6.3.1. Modern Mahakam Delta

The Mahakam River has a width of approximately 800 m to 1 km in downstream area. The river has a length approximately 980 km from Long Apari, far to the west in the upstream, to the Makassar Strait to the east.

The acreage of modern Mahakam Delta is 1,800 km sq. It is a world-class example of Fluvial and Tide-dominated Delta type (Galloway, 1975, p. 92). The ancient and modern sedimentation style is a natural reference for petroleum geologists all over the world. For instance, Dr. Andang Bachtiar, an expert on the Kutai Basin who has over 20 years of experience, organized geoscientific field trip at least once to twice a year before pandemic era. With his motto, "Let's look at the rock, back to basics," he takes participants to observe the ancient and modern fluvial-deltaic sedimentation directly in nature.

Tourist interest types of the Mahakam Delta are geoscientific and scenic beauty interest. Traveling in the Mahakam River itself was a fascinating way to adore the Samarinda cityscape from the river and the natural scenery of the delta. Geoscientific activities were performed in the head of passes of Mahakam River, the Upper and Lower Delta Plain distributary channels, and during low tide in the Delta Front mouth bar (Figs. 6.4 and 6.5). Geoscientific activities range from traditional coring of modern sediments using PVC pipe, grabbing river bed sediments and observing river depth using an echo-sounder.

There is no geoscientific impact for scenic-beauty-related activities. Impacts might occur from geoscientific-related activities. For instance, when PVC pipes were stacked during sediment coring and the pipes were left in the delta's surface.

6.3.2. Hydrocarbon Seepages

Hydrocarbon in the reservoir situated deep in the subsurface sometimes leaks to the surface through natural cracks as seepages. The hydrocarbon seepages indicate the presence of a reservoir containing oil and gas in the subsurface.

Several locations of seepages are observed. For instance, the Semberah Anticline axis in Gunung Palaran and Bambu Kuning Areas. Seepages in the Gunung Palaran area were composed of small holes, 20 cm wide and 25 cm long. They were located in the middle of the jungle where small volumes of flammable gas were ejected.

The seepages in Bambu Kuning area were more interesting. Gas was ejected from over ten holes and cracks in an area of 4 m wide and 50 m long. During observation, gas was flamed with fire causing the temperature increase to 35° to 40°C (Fig. 6.6, left). Seepages were located in the 10° to 28° slope of the woods area. The surface was vulnerable to soil movement feature, where many cracks were observed. Oil seepages were also observed in a small pool (Fig. 6.6, right). To get there requires one hour of driving by Multi-Purpose Vehicle (MPV) through poorly maintained roads where soil erosion often occurs in the roadside.

Tourist interest types are of geoscientific interest, in order to see the seepages. The oil and gas seepages are interesting features since they are not a common feature in most of the tourist's daily life. In fact, only experienced geologists know the location of seepages in Samarinda.

The seepages in the Gunung Palaran Area are not considered a geoscientific hazard. However, soil movement in Bambu Kuning Area was a hazard where many cracks were observed. Moreover, when stronger wind blows to the area, the fire could be distributed to a wider area. So, 5 to 10 meters around the seepages should be categorized as a restricted area. The activity has no impact, except for oil collecting in seepages for a souvenir. This should be not be permitted because of the small volume of oil flow from the subsurface. It would take weeks just to fill the small pool.

6.3.3. Mud Volcanoes

Mud volcano means a mud cone in the surface that slowly ejected by volcanic gas or petroliferous gas. It was formed by a fault-related fold cross-cutting sedimentary rock in the subsurface. In Samarinda, the fold is the Separi Anticline. Fault becomes the route for natural gas to flow to the surface. Gas also takes mud from the surrounding rock. The feature is similar to hydrocarbon seepages, but the ejection comprises mud and gas.

An active mud volcano phenomenon was observed in the Air Putih area. It forms a cone with 10° slope and has a diameter of 47.5 m (Fig. 6.7). A small volume of flammable gas was ejected every five to ten seconds from a small "crater" along with cool dark gray mud and low water saturation. Mudflow also brought the Early to Middle Miocene microfossils from the subsurface. The mud volcano could easily change its ejection point in the surface. Its movement was unpredictable.

During observation, the location was prepared for a housing complex. The existence of mud volcanoes in the location for a housing complex soon becomes a hazard rather than an attraction because mud volcanoes easily move unpredictably. It affects the integrity of building foundations. Fortunately, several years later, the housing complex was abandoned after recommendations were sent to the government.

Those with geoscientific interest might observe the mud flow ejected. Oil and gas seepages, and mud volcanoes, are interesting features. Mud volcanoes are not a geoscientific hazard for tourists since they eject only small volumes of flammable gas. The volcano has no significant impact upon any activity. In fact, the mud, which contains 20 million years' worth of micro fossils, might be further made into souvenirs.

6.3.4. Abandoned Wells

There was exploration drilling to get oil in Samarinda. Some of them were plugged and abandoned because of failure of finding a significant accumulation of oil and/or gas in the reservoir subsurface during drilling. But the abandoned wells act as exploration witnesses.

Many abandoned wells can be seen in the city. Many of them were exploration wells during the Dutch colonization era and were located in the bushes area or plantation area. Some of them still have the pipe, but most have lost it. Most of the wells are poorly plugged, thus ejecting gas from the subsurface.

Tourist interest type is geoscientific interest for observing the "exploration witness." It can be further developed similar to mining heritage. The geoscientific hazard in abandoned wells is that ejected gas might be flammable. The observation activity has no impact.

6.3.5. Outcrops

An outcrop is an important geoscientific feature to be studied. The ancient Mahakam Delta was represented by outcrops in the Middle to Late Miocene age, which represented environments of fluvial, delta plain, and delta front. Many of them show spectacular ancient sedimentation features, world-class features often revisited by international researchers.

To mention a few, outcrops visited for geoscientific field trips are the outcrops in the Pesona Mahakam House Complex and the Palaran

Stadium Gate. The dimensions of the outcrop in the Pesona Mahakam House Complex were 25 meters high and 75 meters long. The sedimentological feature was sandstone channel deposit showing lateral accretion and clay plugged (Fig. 6.8). The outcrop was distributary channel deposit in lower delta plain paleo-environment. The dimensions of the outcrop in the Palaran Stadium Gate were 35 meters high and 450 meters long. It shows a variation of delta plain to delta front paleo-environments. One of the interesting features on the roadside was migrated tidal channel deposit overlaid by distributary channel of the lower delta plain deposit (Fig. 6.9).

Tourist interest type is geoscientific interest to observe sedimentation style of the ancient Mahakam Delta. Geoscientific hazard in the outcrop is a possibility of slope failure. A possible impact is rock collecting.

6.3.6. Caves

A natural cave is mostly formed in carbonate rock. It was formed when the rocks uplifted to the surface and dissolved by meteoric water. A cave in the Batubesaung Area was unexpectedly discovered during rock mining for the building foundation material. Field work showed five rooms with dimension of up to 18 meters long, 8 meters wide, 5 meters high, and a gentle slope. The inner cave has stalactites and stalagmites, floored by mud where many biotas live, such as bats and spiders. There also should be many undiscovered caves in the surroundings.

Tourist interest type is geoscientific and scenic beauty interest. There is almost no geoscientific hazard considered in the cave. A possible impact during the activity is caused by stalactite and stalagmite collecting.

6.3.7. Peak to View the Cityscape

Samarinda is a hilly area. Gunung Segara in the southern part, and Gunung Batuputih in the northern part, are peaks to admire the cityscape of Samarinda and Mahakam River. Gunung Batuputih—also called Puncak Suryanata—has an elevation 150 m above sea level. This hill is composed of bedded limestone excavated by local people. It will need a little bit of scrambling to get a sight in the southern direction to adore the cityscape and the river crossing the city. There was a wider area for getting sight in the north direction. The cliff, about 50 to 75 m in height, was also used by local people for rock climbing.

Gunung Segara has an elevation 105 m above sea level. The peak was wider and had better access than Gunung Batuputih. There were two sites to see the cityscape. The first site was near the local RCTI TV station office, with sight range from N 300° E to N 28° E. The second site was near the backyards of the local people's homes, with sight range N 75° E to N 200° E.

Tourist interest type is scenic beauty and geoscientific interests to admire the cityscape. Possible geoscientific hazards in those peaks are landslides. The sightseeing activity has no impact to the site.

6.4. SUMMARY

There were many undeveloped attractions identified within Samarinda City. Although the attractions are basically geoscientific features, the tourist interest described is intended both for geoscientific and non-geoscientific interests. Hence, many tourist interest types might be fulfilled. The activities range from learning geoscientific information to sightseeing, which can be conducted safely and with low impact.

Reference Cited

Bachtiar, A., Purnama, Y.S., Suandhi, P.A., Krisyunianto, A., Rozalli, M., Nugroho, D.H.H. & Suleiman, A. (2013) The Tertiary Paleogeography of the Kutai Basin and Its Unexplored Hydrocarbon Plays. Indonesian Petroleum Association Convention and Exhibition 37th, Jakarta, May 2013.

Galloway, W.E. (1975) Process Framework for Describing the Morphologic and Stratigraphic Evolution of Deltaic Deposition Systems. p.92, pp.87- 98, In: Broussard, M.L. (ed) Deltas, Models for Exploration. Houston Geoscientific Society.

Supriatna. S., Sukardi & Rustandi, E. (1995) Geological Map of the Samarinda Sheet, Kalimantan, Scale 1:250,000. Geological Research and Development Centre, Bandung, Indonesia

Figures and Tables

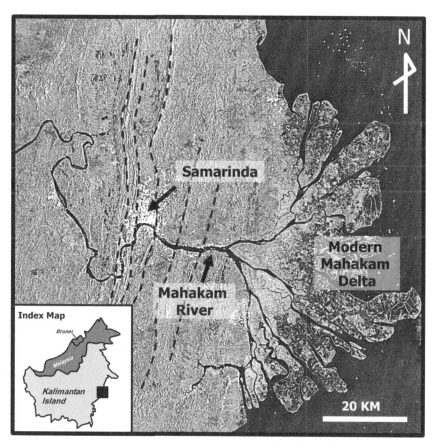

Figure 6.1. Satellite image of Samarinda and the Modern Mahakam Delta in Eastern Kalimantan. NNE–SSW lineaments crossing Samarinda and surrounds are the fold axis of the Samarinda Anticlinorium constructed hilly area. The black dashed line shows few-fold axis. Inset map is index map. Satellite image is courtesy of GDA Consulting.

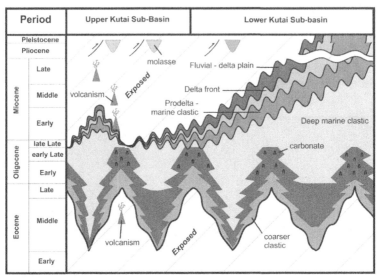

Figure 6.2. Stratigraphy of the Kutai Basin (after Bachtiar et al., 2013) shows fluvial deltaic deposition since the Early Miocene.

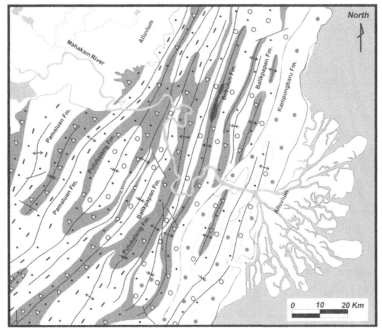

Figure 6.3. Geological Map of the Samarinda and surrounding area (after Supriatna et al., 1995) in Lower Kutai Basin. The stratigraphy on the map refers to lithostratigraphy, where sedimentary rocks formed during the Miocene (see Table 6.1 for lithostratigraphy).

Table 6.1. Simplified lithostratigraphy of the Samarinda Area (Supriatna et al., 1995.)

Age	Formation	Lithology Description
Pliocene	Kampungbaru	sandstone intercalation with shale, silt, and lignite
Middle to Late Miocene	Pulubalang	alternating greywacke and sandstone intercalation with limestone, claystone, and coal
	Balikpapan	sandstone and clay intercalation with silt, shale, limestone and coal
Early Miocene	Pamaluan	sandstone intercalation with claystone, shale, limestone, and siltstone
	Bebuluh	reef limestone intercalations with shale

Table 6.2. Potential tourist attraction in Samarinda and surroundings. Position of those sites in Fig. 6.4.

No	Attraction Type	Tourist Interest Type	Tourist Activity	Location
1	Modern Mahakam Delta	Geologic, Scenic beauty	Geologic, Sightseeing	Mahakam Delta, composed of: (1A) Sanga Sanga, (1B) Muara Bayur, (1C) Datu Island and (1D) Muara Bujit
2	Hydrocarbon seepages	Geologic	Geologic	(2A) Palaran, (2B) Bambu Kuning Areas
3	Mud volcano	Geologic	Geologic	(3) Batuputih Area
4	Abandoned wells	Geologic	Geologic,	(4A) Sambutan, (4B) Samarinda-Bontang, (4C) Lantung Areas
5	Outcrops	Geologic	Geologic,	(5A) Perjuangan, (5B) Palaran, (5C) Pesona Mahakam Area
6	Cave	Geologic, Scenic Beauty	Geologic, Sightseeing	(6) Batubesaung
7	The peak to view the cityscape	Geologic, Scenic beauty	Geologic, Sightseeing	(7A) Gunung Batuputih, (7B) Gunung Segara Area

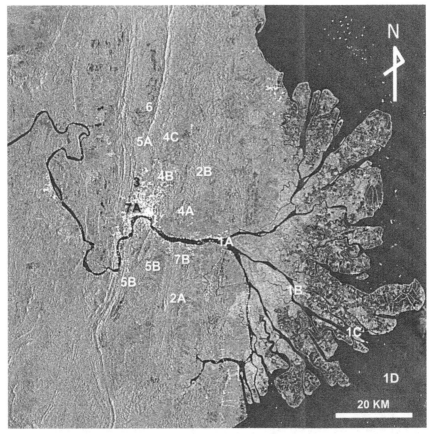

Figure 6.4. Position of potential tourist attractions investigated in Samarinda and surroundings (see also Table 6.2). Several geoscientific stop sites in the modern Mahakam Delta, for example, were organized by Dr. Andang Bachtiar and his team (GDA Consulting). (1A) Sanga Sanga or Sungai Mariam Area represents the head of passes, (1B) Muara Bayur represents the Upper Delta Plain, (1C) Datu Island represents the Lower Delta Plain, and (1D) Muara Bujit represents the Delta Front mouth bar which is not exposed on the satellite image since it was taken during high tide. Satellite image is courtesy of GDA Consulting.

Figure 6.5. A group of explorers—led by Dr. Andang Bachtiar (arrow)—landed in the mouth bar of modern Mahakam Delta during field study in 2015. The study purpose was to investigate sedimentation character of mouth bar as modern reservoir analog for petroleum exploration and production industry. Three people on the sediment (including Dr. Andang) and another small group were making a core sample on the boat side (circle), while the others were observing from the boats (actually unwilling to get wet). Image courtesy of Gesit Mutiarta, 2015.

Figure 6.6. (Left) Flamed gas in Bambu Kuning Area located in the slope (arrow for person scale); (Right) oil seepages in small pool of Bambu Kuning Area. Photos were taken by author, 2002.

Figure 6.7. An active mud volcano in Batuputih Area, which ejects small amounts of flammable gas. Photo was taken by author, 2002.

Figure 6.8. Outcrop of sandstone channel shows lateral accretion (white arrows) overlaying the clay plugs in the Pesona Mahakam House Complex. White vertical line indicates scale 1.6 m. Photo was taken by author, 2011.

Figure 6.9. Outcrop of migrated tidal channel overlaid by distributary channel of the lower delta plain in the Palaran Stadium Gate. Photo was taken by author, 2012.

Geological Control on Identification of Aesthetic and Safety Factors for Swimming in Southwestern Nearshore of Banten, Western Jawa

Highlights

- A study was conducted in the Lebak coast, southwestern Jawa coast, to understand the best nearshore for swimming.
  - Two points should be considered: aesthetic and safety factors.
  - Aesthetic factors relate to clear seawater and white sand beach.
  - Safety factor relates to rip current.

- Suspended sediments nearshore were localized in the western part while the clear water is situated in the eastern part.
  - The suspended sediment composed of finer-grain clastic makes the water brownish in color and greatly reduces visibility.
  - Such nearshore is easily observed by satellite image or direct observation.

- The aesthetic area in eastern part, Manuk Island, Ciantir and Legon Pari Bays, is chosen to be further analyzed for safe waters for swimming.

- Field investigation suggests there is particular geological characteristic to determine the safe nearshore for swimming.
  - It is a bay with a cape width of up to 450 m, where the cape comprises hard rock that juts into the sea.
  - Such a bay acts as a natural barrier to reduce stronger waves.
  - Consequently, the weaker waves, and the weaker rip current, prevent swimmers from being dragged by rip current.

Contents

7.1   INTRODUCTION 281
    7.1.1 Sae Waters for Swimming 281
    7.1.2 Problem Statement 287
    7.1.3 Method.. 287
7.2   GENERAL GEOLOGY 287
7.3   GENERAL OCEANOGRAPHY 288
    7.3.1 General Beach and Nearshore Character....................................... 289
    7.3.2 Aesthetic Nearshore... 289
7.4   MANUK ISLAND BAY.. 290
7.5   CIANTIR BAY 291
7.6   LEGON PARI BAY.. 292
7.7   DISCUSSION 293
7.8   CONCLUSION 294
FIGURES AND TABLES.. 296

Abstract

The shore and nearshore of southwestern Jawa, such as Lebak coast, are proven tourist attractions. The attraction is the natural environment where clear seawater is integrated with a white sand beach. Swimming in the nearshore is one of the most popular tourist activities.

However, swimming in the southwestern Jawa nearshore is hard to be a recommended activity. Many visitors have gotten into accidents because of being trapped on rocks in the surf zone and pushed by strong wave to the rocks, caught by shore breaks close to the shore, and caught by rip currents and eventually dragged into to the open ocean.

A study was conducted in the Lebak coast to understand the best nearshore for swimming. Two points should be considered for the best nearshore: aesthetic and safety factors. The aesthetic factor relates to clear seawater and white sand beach. The safety factor relates to rip current in the nearshore.

Satellite observation outcome indicate suspended sediment nearshore was localized in the western part while the clear water is situated in the eastern part. The suspended sediment composed of finer-grain clastic makes the water brownish in color and greatly reduces visibility. The sediment is usually derived from river sedimentation in the upstream area.

The aesthetic area is chosen to be further analyzed for safe waters for swimming. The area was Manuk Island, Ciantir, and Legon Pari Bays, which face the Indian Ocean. The Manuk Island and the Legon Pari Bays are considered safe for swimming by local people, while no one recommend swimming in the Ciantir Bay.

Field investigation suggests there is particular geological character in the Manuk Island and the Legon Pari Bays that determines the safe nearshore for swimming. It is a bay with a cape width of up to 450 m, where the cape comprises hard rock that juts into the sea. Such a bay acts as a natural barrier to reduce stronger waves coming to the nearshore. Consequently, the weaker waves and the weaker rip current. Eventually it prevents swimmers from being dragged by the rip current.

Keywords: rip current, safe waters for swimming, smaller bay, hard rock, natural wave protection

7.1. INTRODUCTION

The southwestern coast of Jawa, which faces the Indian Ocean, has a potential tourist attraction. If tourist activity in the destination is swimming or just playing in the water, then it is necessary to identify the aesthetic and safety factors. In those two factors, geological knowledge might make a significant contribution. This research objective is to understand the aesthetic and safety factors of swimming nearshore in the southwestern coast of Jawa, Lebak Area from a geological point-of-view.

The study area is located in Darmasari and Sawarna Villages, Bayah Area, Lebak Regency, Banten Province. The area of study is about 66 km to the south from Rangkasbitung, or 5 km to the east from Bayah city (Fig. 7.1).

7.1.1. Safe Waters for Swimming

Beach is a transition area of land and standing body of water (e.g. ocean or lake), which is composed of loose sediment accumulation such as mud or sand as result of marine or lake sedimentation. A beach is a dynamic interaction outcome of tectonic, wave, current, tide, sedimentation, marine organism, and also human influences.

Wave characteristics when approaching the beach have four different forms: wave, breakers, surf, and swash, respectively (Fig. 7.2). The zone that extends from the tide area or the swash zone to the breaker zone is called the nearshore zone. It is the area where most tourists swim or play in the water.

Generally, the southern Jawa coast is unsuitable for swimming nearshore. It is because swimmers might get trapped on rocks in the surf zone and pushed by strong wave to the rocks, caught by shore break close to the shore, and caught by rip currents and eventually dragged to the open ocean.

Of those three causes, rip current is the main casualty. In the United States alone, based on data reported from 2005 to 2014, the United States Lifesaving Association identified rip currents as the primary cause (about 80%) of surf rescues (United States Lifesaving Association, 2015, p. 5).

Rip current is a natural feature. It is formed when a wave approaches shoreline, water is piling up in the surf zone, and eventually flows back seaward by forming a rip current or a rip neck (Fig. 7.3). Generally, the bigger the wave produced, the bigger the breaker and eventually the faster the surf-zone currents (MacMahan et al., 2011, p. iii), including the rip current.

Hence, the bigger wave has a consequence of the faster rip current. Usually, swimmers who get captured by the rip current will panic because of being dragged offshore, which has a consequence of exhaustion and drowning.

The study of rip current character in several open coasts suggests the current forms circular current or rip current vortex (Fig. 7.3; McMahan et al., 2010, p. 11). It implies that the swimmer who gets caught by the rip current most likely will drift to the shallower depth (swash zone). In practice, usually the rip current zone is marked by flag by the beach guard to alert swimmers. Other surf-zone currents, that are undertow and longshore currents, are not the cause of drowning (MacMahan et al, 2011, p. iv).

I conclude generally there are four basic cross-section types from shore to nearshore and to wave zones based on elevation above sea level and seabed slope steepness. They are flat–drop-off; ramp; ramp–drop-off; and drop-off types (Fig. 7.4). Distance from shore to offshore in this cross section type is generally less than two kilometers, while sight distance from beach to the horizon is about 4.8 Km. In reality, however, the cross-section towards the offshore may face another island in few kilometers. The nearshore bottom may consist of three substrate kinds: gravelly or rocky (bedrock exposure), sandy, and muddy bottoms. Those types of cross-section and nearshore bottom might exist within the same shoreline. In addititon, the wave energy in all types of cross-sections can be low or high, depending on the wind speed.

An overview of the four types of cross-section types is as follows.

- Flat–drop-off type.

  In the flat zone, water depth might be less than one meter during low tide and the wave energy is low. The flat area might reach hundreds of meters from shoreline to the drop-off zone. The breakers hardly reach the flat zone, but situated in the boundary of flat zone and drop-off zone. In the drop-off zone, the slope is steep and the water column is deeper abruptly. In those zone, usually the bedrock located and reef grows. Rarely boats dock in the flat-drop off area.

- Ramp–drop-off type.

  The slope of this type is probably up to 11° in the ramp zone. However, in the drop-off zone, the slope is steeper and the water column is deeper abruptly. Usually, this slope type face to the open sea. A narrower area might exposed during low tide and many boats dock in the ramp zone. The breaker is usually located in the boundary of ramp zone and drop-off zone, but might reach the ramp zone when the wind speed is slower. Many surfing activities performed in this area.

- Drop-off type.

  This type is characterized by a sea cliff as the boundary between the land and the sea. A narrow beach with gravel to boulders might exist among of the cliff bottom and the sea. Another situation is no beach but directly a deeper water column allowed cliff jumping activities to be performed. Seabed profile is generally steep, where the wave directly erodes the cliff wall. Hence, rock fall is a common process.

- Ramp type.

  Slopes of this type are probably up to 11° but usually gentler slope, the water depth is gradually deeper and many boats dock in this area. During low tide, the nearshore exposed might reach a wide area (more than one kilometer length). Usually on the slopes of this type there are other islands in the vicinity. Tidal forces usually stronger indicates by tidal channel. Based on sediment grain size at the nearshore bottom, there are two main ramp types: muddy and sandy substrate. If nearshore area is dominated by muddy substrate derived from river sedimentation, then water is not clear because contain muddy sediment, wave energy is usually very low, and most of the time no breaker develops. In the contrary, if substrate mostly contain sandy substrate then water has better visibility, wave energy is usually higher, and small breaker develops.

I compiled seven characters for safe waters for swimming. Requirement number 1 and 2 are related to the rip current, while the others (no. 3 to 8) are not related. Generally, safe waters for swimming in nearshore zones are nearshores that have the character of flat–drop-off; ramp (with sandy substrate); and ramp–drop-off types.

Ramp with muddy substrate and drop offf types are considered unsafe waters for swimming. The water of ramp with muddy substrate usually contain muddy sediment so that poor visibility to the bottom. Moreover, standing on a muddy bottom is uncomfortable compare to the sandy bottom. When wave energy is high in the drop off types, the wave directly hit the rock. Swimmer who get caught by wave in the nearshore zone may suffer injury or fatality.

Although some aspects are needed to be further discussed, general description for safe water characters for swimming in nearshore is concluded as follow.

1. The flat–drop-off type has a wide area of shallow nearshore that might reach hundreds of meters. The breaker zone is situated in

the boundary of flat zone and drop-off zone, which is far from the shoreline. It has a consequence that the waves on the nearshore are smaller and there is a low possibility for rip current to develop. As a result, the safe swimming area is a wide zone.

2. In ramp (with sandy substrate) and ramp–drop-off types, the shallow nearshore is a narrow zone and the breaker zone is closer to the shoreline compare to flat-drop-off type. As a consequence, the wave is stronger in the nearshore zone. In this type, usually rip currents develop where the velocity varies and easily change because of tides, waves, weather, and the bottom shape. Usually, rip currents are seen crossing perpendicular to the breaker zone or to the shoreline. For those who have sharp observation, rip current is usually seen as a long white foam that juts into the sea.

Rip current occurrence is also influenced by monsoon during particular months, and shoreline architecture. If monsoon direction is relatively parallel to the shoreline, then the cape or other natural structure (e.g., headland composed of hard rock, barrier bar) might act as natural barrier to prevent rip current development (will be further discussed in this chapter). However, if monsoon direction is perpendicular or forms an obtuse angle to the shoreline, then during the time where wind blows from the hinterland to the shore, the rip current will be less developed compared to during wind blows from the ocean directly to the shore. Remember, the bigger the wave produced, the bigger the breaker and eventually the faster the surf-zone currents including rip current. Hence, the nearshore will be relative safe for particular months.

In such nearshore zones, choose to get activity in the free rip current zone and also far enough from the breaker zone. In this zone, the safe area is generally narrow. Ask the beach guard or local people who know more about the sea state. This chapter will discuss nearshore type of ramp–drop-off.

Some clues for Google Earth observation on the nearshore zone: darker area indicates deeper, lighter area suggests shallower, the breaker zone shows by long foamy white line and parallel with the shore, rip currents are seen crossing the breaker zone. So that when rip current develops, the swimming safe areas are bounded by the rip current zones and the breaker zone.

3. Whatever the cross-section types, for safety reason swimming should be conducted during calm wave. It is because the bigger the wave produced, the bigger the breaker and eventually the faster the surf-zone currents (MacMahan et al., 2011, p. iii), including the rip current. How big the wave produced is strongly related to the wind condition (Table 7.1). In addition, rocky beach, sea cliffs, or rock that sticking out nearshore can be dangerous during high wave. A situation like this occurs when a swimmer hits those rock because pushed by a high wave.

4. Water temperature in range of 26°C (78.8°F) to 30°C (86°F) is considered comfortable temperature for most swimmers throughout prolonged periods of moderate physical exertion (World Health Organization, 2006, p. 20).

5. For health reasons, the nearshore should be free from pollutants and pathogens.

6. The nearshore is relatively free from fauna that can cause injury or fatality such as sea urchins, jellyfish, and sharks.

7. High visibility, crystal clear, or very low sediment suspension in the water is a must, so that someone is able to see the bottom of the nearshore zone. It is needed to observe fauna such as sharks, sea urchins or even injured or sinking swimmers. In addition, high visibility is psychologically comfortable.

Last but not least, before going into the water, ask the locals about the character of the water, as they live there and observe the sea character every day.

7.1.2. Problem Statement

There was an important observation from local fishermen who every single day observe the sea state. They concluded that the Legon Pari and the Manuk Island nearshores were safe for swimming, while swimming in the Ciantir nearshore was not recommended. Unfortunately, they hard to explain the why. In this case, their opinion is used as local wisdom. Thus, the problem to be solved is why a particular nearshore is relatively safer for swimming.

7.1.3. Method

Using the assumption "the bigger the wave produced, the bigger the breaker and the faster the surf-zone currents," then the observation method was designed. The observation was focused on beach geometry, its composition, and the sea state. Observation was composed of beach measurement, seabed profile, visibility, identifying beach rock at the headlands, and visual observation of breaker height. Geographic positioning was recorded by GPS receiver. Bathymetry and visibility measurements were performed using measurement tape.

7.2. GENERAL GEOLOGY

Geology of the Lebak Area is a part of the Banten Block. According to Martodjojo (1989), Banten stratigraphy consists of three sedimentation cycles (Fig. 7.5). The first cycle was terrestrial to shallow marine during the Eocene to Early Miocene. The second cycle was gravitational sedimentation during the Middle Miocene. The third cycle was shallow marine to transitional area during the Late Miocene to Pliocene. Pleistocene to Holocene Volcanic deposits covered most of the Lebak Area.

Uplifting up to about 1,000 meters above sea level occurred in the Lebak Area during the Pliocene to Pleistocene eras. It created most of the Lebak landscape to be a mountain area, called the Bayah

Mountain (Van Bemmelen, 1949). The southern part of the Lebak Area is a coastal area formed by uplifting. As a result, most of the beach is composed of rocky beach with sea cliff and erosional features in many spots. The coastal area faces to the south, to the Indian Ocean.

7.3. GENERAL OCEANOGRAPHY

Oceanography of the Lebak area is influenced by monsoons. From October to April is the rainy season, the season when wind blows from the west (west monsoon). From April to October (dry season) is when the wind blows from the east (east monsoon). According to local fishermen, wind blows are weaker during the west monsoon and stormy during the east monsoon.

The Tanjung Layar headland in the coastal area was composed of Early Miocene breccia volcanic rock of Cimapag Formation. The headland acts as a natural protection from the wind and the wave. The headland divides Ciantir Bay in the west and Legon Pari Bay in the east (Figs. 7.6 and 7.7).

Fishermen from Sawarna Village choose those two bays to dock the boats. During the east monsoon, they dock in the eastern part of Ciantir Bay, while during west monsoon they will approach to the Legon Pari Bay. Local fishermen from Darmasari Village choose Manuk Island Bay to dock their boats. It is because Manuk Island is composed of hard Miocene limestone that also serves as a natural protection from waves (Figs. 7.6 and 7.7).

The west and the east monsoons also influence the preferred time for activity in the nearshores. The west monsoon is the best time for swimming, since the weather is usually calm because of weaker wind.

7.3.1. General Beach and Nearshore Character

Geologically, the Lebak coast is tectonically active due to being situated in the convergent margin. Beach type of the Lebak coast is generally characterized as follows.

(1) Pocket beaches or beaches bounded by hard rock.

(2) Outcrops of hard rocks with bedding altitude of 30° to 60°.

(3) Erosion forms of the headland such as sea stacks or rocks forming columns are easily found in eastern part of Lebak coast.

(4) Cross-section type from shore to nearshore area is ramp–drop-off and drop-off types.

(5) High-wave energy where the breakers reach 2 to 3 meters.

(6) Beach slope varies from 1° to 11°.

(7) Beach width varies from 14 to 70 m.

(8) Beach sediments mostly composed of medium to coarse-grained sand dominated by white color calcite. Pebbles beach sediment is found to particularly surround the steep river mouth.

(9) Sediment suspension in nearshore area is situated surrounding estuary.

(10) Free from chemical pollutants.

7.3.2. Aesthetic Nearshore

Before determining safety factors of the safe swimming area, the first thing to do was identify the aesthetic area. It is because the nearshore area for tourist destinations is strongly correlated with aesthetics. An aesthetic nearshore means that the nearshore is free from sediment suspension that makes the water "dirty" or have a brown color and low clarity. The sediment suspension usually derives from estuary or delta. It is where the finer-grained-size sediment is carried out from upstream to be deposited downstream and in the sea. Free sediment suspension is also important for safety factor, since the beach guard can inspect an injured swimmer or even a shark below the water surface.

Based on satellite image (Fig. 7.8), a sediment suspension area was identified in the western part, while free suspension sediment area was in the eastern part. Thus, the eastern part was chosen for further investigation: that is, the nearshore area of Manuk Island, Ciantir and Legon Pari.

7.4. MANUK ISLAND BAY

Topography surrounding the area was characterized by hills. Land cover comprised forests and coconut farms. Outcrop observed was composed of limestone, where some of it formed reef of Citarate Formation, Early Miocene age (Sujatmiko and Santosa, 1992).

Beach and seabed profiling was conducted in three locations: A, B, and C profiles (Fig. 7.9, Fig. 7.10, and Table 7.2). Beach slope range was 3° to 11°. Beach profiles show the western part (Profile B & C) was steeper than in the eastern part (Profile A), suggesting higher wave energy in the western part (Fig. 7.10). Surf zone width was approximately 40 m wide. Bathymetry measurement outcome indicates the eastern part was shallower and had higher clarity than the western part. Wave height and breakers were observed less than 1 meter height. I interpreted the longshore current flow to the northwest.

Beach sediment was comprised of medium-grained sand, light brown, angular sub-rounded, good sorting, calcite dominated, quartz and coal chips. Those sediments were obtained from sedimentation of Cipamubulan river, which cropped out the coal and quartz sandstone beds. Cipamubulan River was an intermittent stream.

The bay is facing to the south where distance of the headland tips was about 300 m. The Manuk Island was the southwestern tip.

The island was composed of hard rock of limestone, acting as a natural protection from waves. Coupling it with 300 m of headland tip distance, leads to interpretation why the area is relatively safe for swimming or other activity in the surf zone. Field observation outcome shows a safe zone for swimming was in the eastern part, since it has higher clarity, shallower water depth, and a gentler beach profile. Local fishermen who dock their boats in the eastern part support this interpretation.

Most of the local visitors during weekends also play in the eastern part. In relation with monsoon coupling with the bay's open direction to the ocean, perhaps the best time to play in the bay is during west monsoon.

7.5. CIANTIR BAY

The topographic in the western part of Ciantir Bay was characterized by hills, while in the middle and in the eastern parts are relatively flat areas. Land cover was coconut farms. Outcrop observed in the western part was composed of limestone of Citarate Formation of Early Miocene age. Outcrop of the eastern part was comprised of volcanic breccia of Cimapag Formation, also Early Miocene age (Sujatmiko and Santosa, 1992). The limestone has undergone karstification where many caves are found.

Beach profiling was conducted in two locations in the eastern part of the Ciantir Bay, D and E profiles in Figures 7.11 to 7.13. The western part, characterized by a steeper beach slope and higher wave energy, was an unsafe situation for further investigation. D profile indicates 1° to 8° slope, while 1° to 11° slope in E profile (Fig. 7.13). Surf zone width was approximately 60 m wide. The bay was facing to the southwest. The distance from Tanjung Layar headland in the east to Ujung Karang Bokor headland in the west was approximately 3.3 km. Tanjung Layar was composed of volcanic breccia, while Ujung Karang Bokor was made of limestone.

The bathymetry measurement outcome and the darker color of the sea suggest the water depth is abruptly deeper to the southwest. Breakers were observed up to 3 meters in height. I interpreted longshore current flowed to northwest. Local fishermen docked in the eastern part of the bay only during east monsoon since the breaker height is smaller than west monsoon.

Beach sediment was formed of medium-grained sand, light brown, angular to sub rounded, good sorting, calcite dominated, quartz and coal chips. Those sediments were obtained from sedimentation of Cisawarna, Ci Asem Gede, and Ci Asem Leutik streams. Beach sediment also possibly eroded from Tanjung Layar and Ujung Karang Bokor headlands, which bounded the Ciantir Bay.

Steeper beach, seabed profile, and high breakers suggest the nearshore of Ciantir Bay has a higher risk for swimming activity. However, it is the best spot for surfing. International surfers had known the challenging breakers since the early 1990s. Generally, they choose the eastern part as spot to wait for the breaker to be formed. The breakers could form 3 meters high, which is equivalent to the sixth level on the Beaufort scale (Table 7.1), allowing surfing as far as 300 to 350 meters. Surfing activity can be performed during the west or the east monsoons. The difficulty rating of surfing during the east monsoon will probably be higher because of stronger wind.

7.6. LEGON PARI BAY

Topography surrounding the area was flat areas (Fig. 7.14) and was covered by coconut farm. Outcrop was constructed of volcanic breccia of Cimapag Formation of Early Miocene age (Sujatmiko and Santosa, 1992).

Beach profiling was conducted in one location (Profile F), characterized by 2° to 8° slope (Fig. 7.15). Bathymetry measurement outcome indicates shallow water with higher clarity. Breaker height was observed less than one meter. I interpreted longshore current flowed to northwest. Surf zone width was approximately 50 m wide.

Beach sediment was comprised of medium-grained sand, light brown, angular – sub rounded, calcite dominated, quartz and coal chips. Those sediments were derived from intermittent streams near the beach and also reef erosion. The bay was facing to the south. The headland tip distance of Karang Bodas in the west to Karang Palisir in the east was 450 m. Those headlands were composed of hard rock of volcanic breccia. Karang Bodas was more protrusive than Karang Palisir.

Bay morphology, which was bounded by headlands composed of hard rocks and coupled with 450 m of headland distance, provided natural protection from waves. So it was relatively safe for swimming. Field observation of this bay shows higher clarity, shallow depth, and gentle beach and gentle seabed profiles. During the west monsoon (October to April) might be the best schedule for swimming in this bay, as wave height will usually be lower than 1 meter. Local fishermen also dock in this bay during west monsoon since the breaker height is smaller than in the east monsoon.

7.7. DISCUSSION

Based on observation, the reason why a nearshore area might be relatively safe for swimming while others are not is related to geological control. The control is headland distance and its composition. The rock composition of headland coupled with headland distance acted as a natural protection to lower the wave and breaker energies, to be less than one meter. Headland distance was 300 m for Manuk Island Bay, 3.3 km for Ciantir Bay, and 450 m for Legon Pari Bay. All headlands were composed of hard rocks.

A formulation is drawn where in this case the shoreline is relatively parallel to wind direction (east and west monsoons). If a headland distance is shorter, like the 450 m maximum of Legon Pari Bay distance, then breaker height is lower. It is because the nearshore is more protected from the waves. If the breaker height lowers, then the rip current velocity is also slower, so that the nearshore zone is relatively safe for swimming.

Observation through Google Earth images shows possible rip current positions (Figs. 7.16 to 7.18). Rip current in smaller bays, such as in Manuk Island and Legon Pari, developed in the middle part. However, rip current in a larger bay (Ciantir Bay) was more intense in the western part.

7.8. CONCLUSION

Despite general characteristics of the southwestern coast of Jawa as unsafe for swimming in the nearshore zone, particular areas that are relatively safe for swimming might be found. This research is an effort to explain why Manuk Island and Legon Pari Bays in Banten coast were relatively safe for swimming. In the study area, cross-section type of shore to nearshore zone is ramp–drop-off type and the shoreline is relatively parallel to the wind direction (east and west monsoons).

The particular area safer for swimming is concluded to be controlled geologically. It is a small bay bounded by headlands composed of hard rocks where the nearshore slope is steeper. The allowable distance between those headlands is possibly a maximum of 450 m. Those headlands act as a natural protection from waves and breakers, so that the breaker height is smaller, which in this case is less than one meter. As a consequence, rip currents develop at low velocity. Nevertheless, I realized that further research of rip current characteristics with a better method, (i.e., using drifters) is needed in search of the best outcome.

Reference Cited

MacMahan, J., Brown, J., Brown, J., Thornton, E., Reniers, A., Stanton, T., Henrizuez, M., Gallagher, E., Morrison, J., Austin, M.J., Scott, T.M. & Senechal, N. (2010) Mean Lagrangian Flow Behavious on an Open Coast Rip-Channeled Beach: A New Perspective. Marine Geology, Elsevier, Vol. 268, p.11, pp.1-15.

MacMahan, J., Reniers, A., Brown, J., Brander, R., Thornton, E., Stanton, T., Brown, J. & Carey, W. (2011) An Introduction to Rip Currents Based on Field Observations. Journal of Coastal Research, Coastal Education and Research Foundation, Vol. 27, p.iii, iv, pp. iii-vi

Martodjojo, S. (1989) Stratigraphic and Tectonic Behaviour of a Back Arc Basin in West Java, Indonesia. Proceedings Annual Meeting of IAGI, 1989, Jakarta.

Sujatmiko & Santosa, S. (1992) Geological Map of Leuwidamar Quadrangle. Scale 1: 100.000. Geological Research Development Centre, Bandung, Indonesia.

United States Livesaving Association (2015) National Lifesaving Statistic Report 2014. p.5, 6 pp.

van Bemmelen, R.W. (1949) The Geology of Indonesia. Vol I A, General Geology of Indonesia and Adjacent Archipelagoes. The Hague, Martinus Nijhoff, Netherland, 732 pp.

World Health Organization (2006) Guidelines for Safe Recreational Water Environments. Volume 2: Swimming Pools and Similar Environments. p. 20, 118 pp.

Figures and Tables

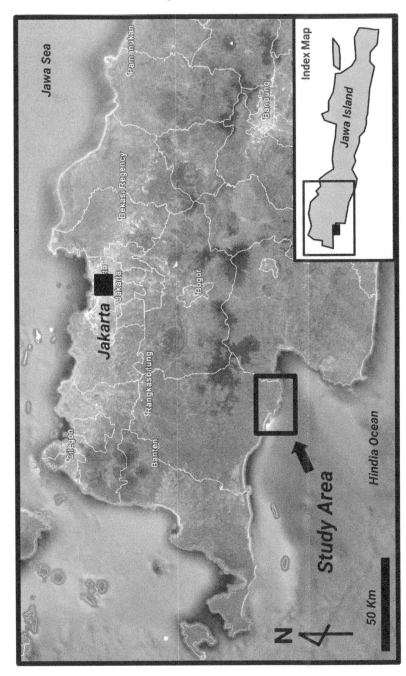

Figure 7.1. Study area on the southern coast of the western part of Jawa Island. Inset is index map. Base map is taken from Google Earth image.

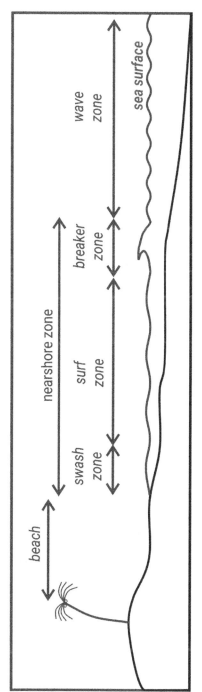

Figure 7.2. Simplified profile of the coastal area shows the principal zones of waves. Characteristics of waves approaching to the beach are divided into four types: wave, breakers, surf, and swash. Figure is not to scale.

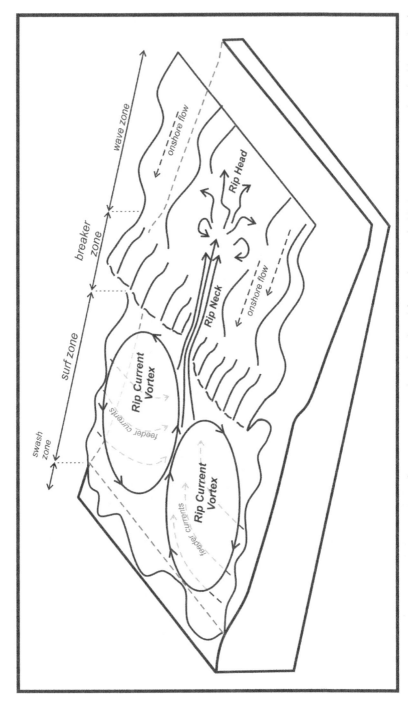

Figure 7.3. Rip current anatomy consists of rip vortex, rip neck, and rip head (McMahan et al., 2010, p. 11. Figure is sketched by author.) Rip current character in several open coasts suggests the current form circular current or rip current vortex.

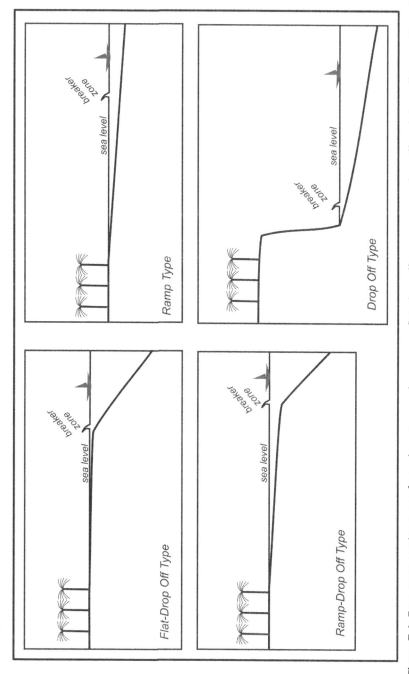

Figure 7.4. Four cross-section types from shore to nearshore zones: flat–drop-off, ramp, ramp – drop-off, and drop-off types. Figure is not to scale.

Table 7.1. The Beaufort Scale.

Scale	Wind Speed (Knot)	Wind Condition	Sea State
0	Less than 1	Calm	Flat, mirror-like sea.
1	1 – 3	Light air	Gently scaly ripples.
2	4 – 6	Light breeze	Small wavelets. May have glassy crests but these will not break.
3	7 – 10	Gentle breeze	Large wavelets. Crests begin to break. Possibly some white horses.
4	11 – 16	Moderate breeze	Wave becoming longer with white horses.
5	17 – 21	Fresh breeze	Moderate waves with white horses and possibly occasional spray.
6	22 – 27	Strong breeze	Large wave forming with extensive white crests and spray.
7	28 – 33	Near gale	Sea heaps up and foam from breaking waves blows in streaks.
8	34 – 40	Gale	Moderately high wave. Edge of crest break into spindrift. Well marked streaks.
9	41 – 47	Severe gale	High wave. Confused breaking crests. Spray affects visibility.
10	48 – 55	Storm	Very high waves with long overhanging crests. Sea surface become white
11	56 – 63	Violent storm	Exceptionally high wave hiding ships from view. Sea covered in white foam.
12	64 plus	Hurricane	Air full of driving spray. Very bad visibility.

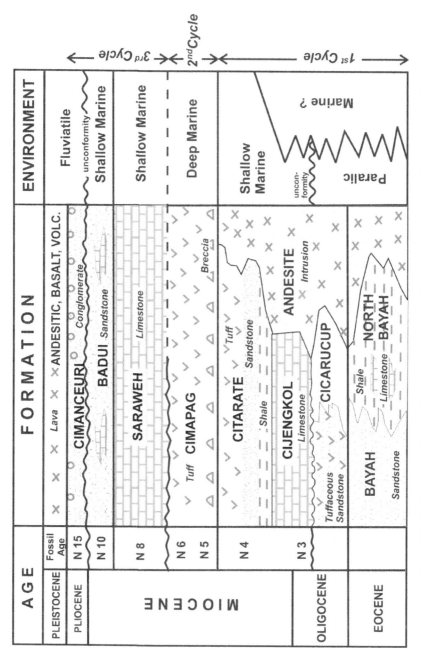

Figure 7.5. Stratigraphy of Banten Block shows three sedimentation cycles (after Martodjojo, 1989).

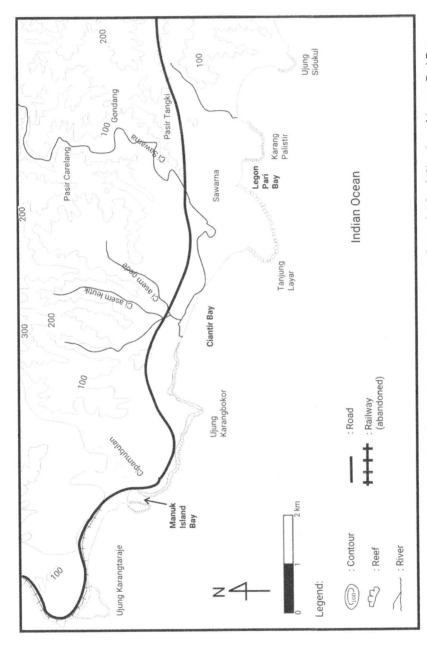

Figure 7.6. Geographic map of study area shows the three locations of Manuk Island, Ciantir, and Legon Pari Bay.

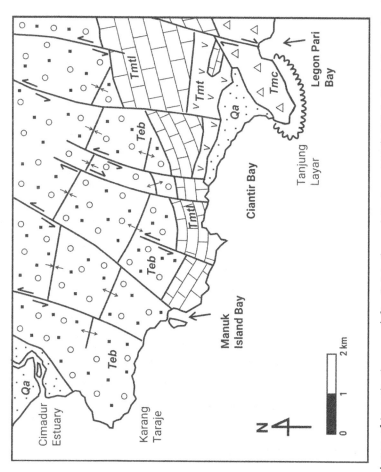

Figure 7.7. Geological map of investigation area (after Sujatmiko and Santosa, 1992). Teb is Bayah Formation (Fm.), Conglomerate Member (Mbr), Eocene Age (55.8 – 33.9 mya); Tmtl is Citarate Fm. Limestone Mbr, Early Miocene Age (23 – 20.4 mya); Tmt is Cimapag Fm. Tuff Mbr, Early Miocene Age; Tmcl is Cimapag Fm. Limestone Mbr, Early Miocene Age; Tmc is Cimapag Fm. Volcanic Breccia, Early Miocene Age.

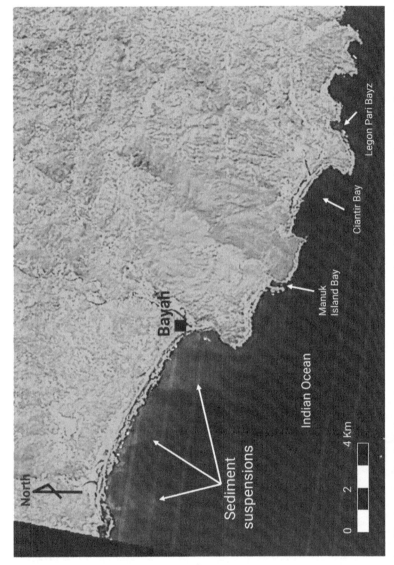

Figure 7.8. Satellite Image of Lebak Area shows sediment suspension—looks like white cloud— in the western part indicates river sedimentation. Free sediment suspension area is positioned in the eastern part, composed of Manuk Island Bay, Ciantir Bay, and Legon Pari Bay. (Satellite image courtesy of Indonesia Geologists Association.)

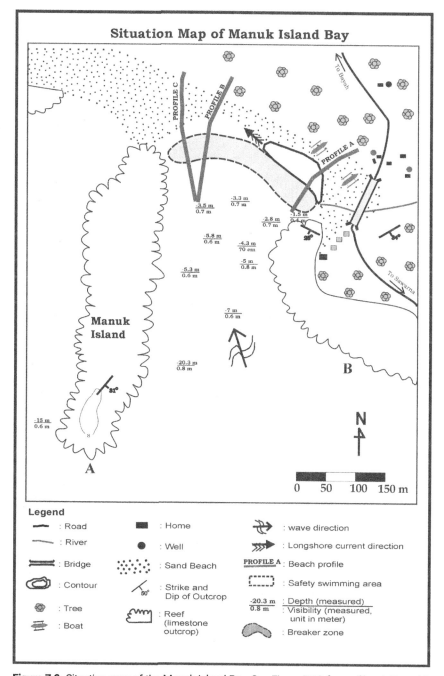

Figure 7.9. Situation map of the Manuk Island Bay. See Figure 7.10 for profiles A, B, and C

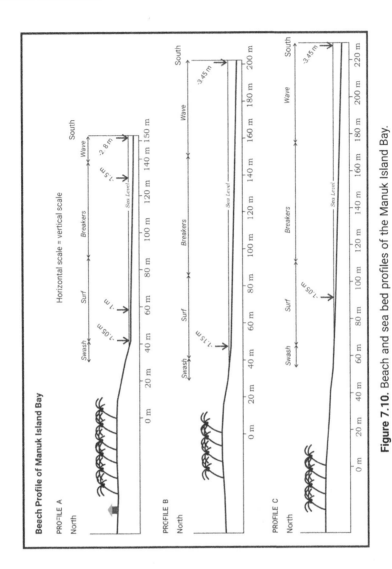

Figure 7.10. Beach and sea bed profiles of the Manuk Island Bay.

Table 7.2. Beach profile measurement of the Manuk Island Bay

Location*	Slope	Beach width**
Profile A	3° - 11°	45.4 m
Profile B	3° - 10°	28.2 m
Profile C (Figure 7.9)	3° – 7°	51.35 m

* = beach profile position is in Figure 7.8.
** = beach width is measured from permanent vegetation to the surf zone.

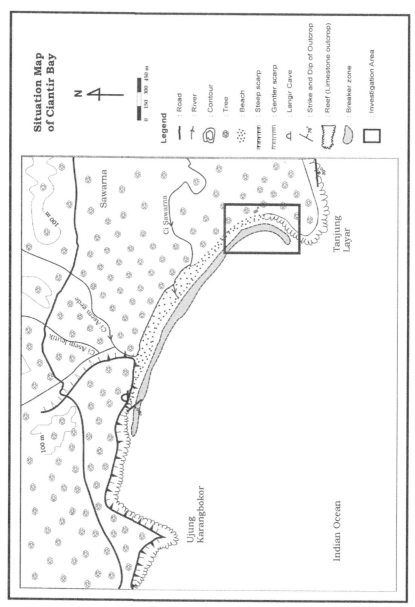

Figure 7.11. Situation map of the Ciantir Bay. See Figure 7.12 for inset.

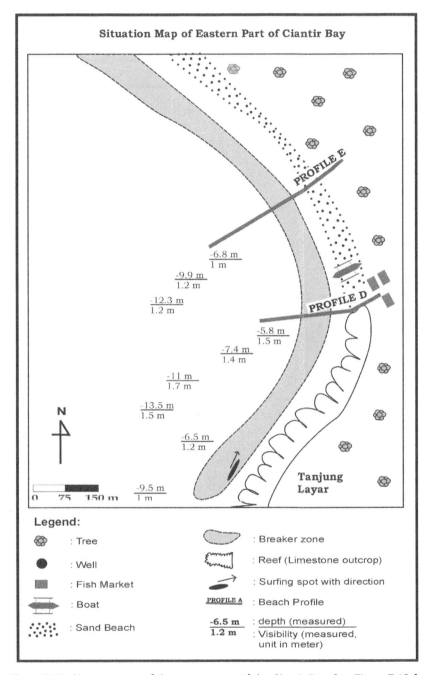

Figure 7.12. Situation map of the eastern part of the Ciantir Bay. See Figure 7.13 for profiles D and E.

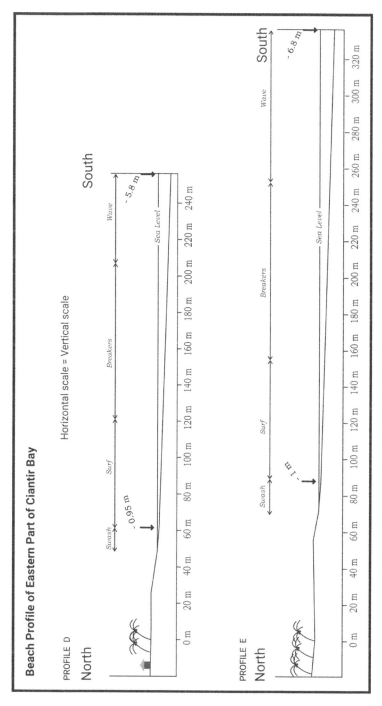

Figure 7.13. Beach and sea bed profile of the eastern part of the Ciantir Bay.

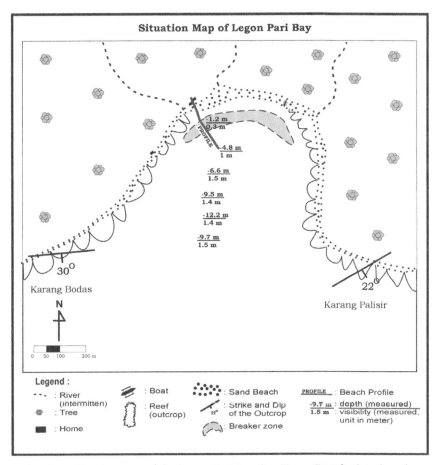

Figure 7.14. Situation map of the Legon Pari Bay. See Figure 7.15 for beach and sea bed profile.

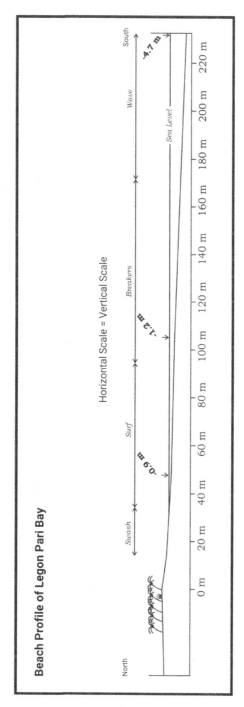

Figure 7.15. Beach and sea bed profile of the Legon Pari Bay

Figure 7.16. Google Earth image of the Manuk Island Bay taken September 14, 2016, during west monsoon. Two possible rip currents were observed in the white circles. Manuk Island separated into two islands during high tide.

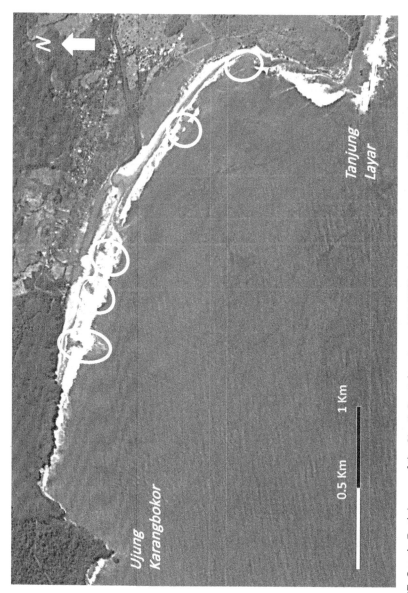

Figure 7.17. Google Earth image of the Ciantir Bay taken August 26, 2016, during west monsoon. Possible rip currents were more intense in the western part.

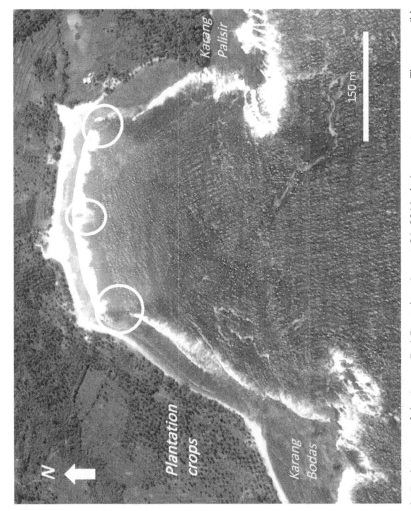

Figure 7.18. Google Earth image of the Legon Pari Bay taken August 26, 2016, during west monsoon. Three possible rip currents were observed in the white circles.

CHAPTER 8

Geological Approach for Tourist Destination Planning in Gunung Batu, Western Jawa

Highlights

- Geological information should be able to be used for tourist destination planning when the attraction is strongly related to a geological feature using the case of Gunung Batu, West Jawa Province.
  - It is needed to design a geological approach and translate geological data and information for destination planning where tourism-related professionals will use it as an input for decision-making process.

- The approach is composed of supporting and prohibitive factors.
  - Supporting factor is geological characteristic that draws visitor attention and develops activities.
  - Prohibitive factor is geological feature that decreases visitor activities and/or decreases all of the supporting factor.

- The outcome is also put in two maps called attraction and activity maps.
  - Attraction map describes attraction position.
  - Activity map depicts any tourist activity able to be done in each attraction zone.
  - Tourism-related professionals might choose what kind of attraction and activity will be presented to visitors, and also consider risk and prohibitive factors.

Content

8.1	BACKGROUND	319
8.2	GEOLOGICAL APPROACH	320
8.3	METHOD	321
8.4	GEOLOGY OF GUNUNG BATU	321
	8.4.1 Geography	321
	8.4.2 Topography and Slope	322
	8.4.3 Geomorphology	322
	8.4.4 Stratigraphy	322
	8.4.5 Structural Geology	323
	8.4.6 Geological History	323
8.5	SUPPORTING FACTORS	324
	8.5.1 Attraction	324
	8.5.2 Activity	324
8.6	PROHIBITIVE FACTORS	325
8.7	CONCLUSION	326
	FIGURES AND TABLES	328

Abstract

Geological information should be able to be used for tourist destination planning when the attraction is strongly related to a geological feature. It is needed to design geological approach and translate geological data and information for tourist destination planning, where tourism-related professionals will use it as an input for the decision-making process. In addition, it should be realized that commonly, tourism-related professionals who are non-geologists will use the information, so that proper geological knowledge for them will be highly useful.

The approach is composed of supporting factor and prohibitive factor. A supporting factor is a geological characteristic that draws visitor attention and develops activities. A prohibitive factor is a geological feature that decreases visitor activities and/or decreases all of supporting factor. The approach was applied during study in Gunung Batu, Bandung Regency, West Jawa Province, which is well known but not prepared yet for a better destination.

The supporting factors in the study area are composed of the attractions—geological and man-made geological attractions; and activities—geological-related and physical outdoor activities. The prohibitive factors are composed of the sensitivity scale of the geological features (e.g., sensitive to rock mining and rock vandalism) and geological features as hazard potential (e.g., earthquake, ground movement, and low risk area of pyroclastic fall from the nearest volcano.)

The outcome is also placed on two maps called attraction and activity maps. The attraction map describes attraction position while the activity map depicts any tourist activity that could be done in each attraction zone. Later, tourism-related professionals might choose what kind of attraction and activity will be presented to the visitor, while at the same time considering the risk and prohibitive factors.

Keywords: translation geological information, supporting, prohibitive, attraction, activity, tourist destination, attraction map, activity map

8.1. BACKGROUND

The scenic beauty of the Bandung landscape has been acknowledged since the Dutch colonial era. For instance, in the early 1900s, they erected a horseshoe-shaped structure at waist height in Ijzerman Park (now Ganesha Park, more precisely the structure is located surround the cube monument). The structure shows the location of the southern mountains with its name and its height. In the same era, they built a government building, called Gedung Sate, where in the blueprint it showed the view to the Southern Volcano Range and its volcano's name.

Today the scenic beauty still becomes an attraction even for local people. One of these landforms is Gunung Batu in Bandung Regency, West Jawa Province, which formed by volcanic and structural geology processes in the past. The term "Gunung" means mount or hill. Although the area has not been prepared for a tourist destination, local people visit it at least every weekend for leisure. From the peak, they can see 360° of scenery without obstacles. If the area is prepared to be a tourist destination, it will have two benefits: multiplier effect and new local income. Thus, preparation of Gunung Batu for a tourist destination is necessary.

In this context, I describe two main factors from a geological point of view related to tourist destination planning: supporting factor and prohibitive factor. Supporting factor relates to a geological feature that could be used to draw visitor attention and develop visitor activities. Prohibitive factor is a geological feature that decreases visitor activities and/or decreases all of the supporting factor. A prohibitive factor is a factor that could decrease the supporting factor. The purpose of prohibitive factor identification is to understand all the things needed to increase safety and to minimize the decline in the attractiveness of a destination.

Before developing a tourist destination, it is necessary to identify those two factors. There are two purposes of prohibitive and supporting factors from a geological point of view. Firstly, to enable tourism-related professionals—who usually are not geologists—to understand geological information for tourist destination planning. Secondly, to be one input to their scientifically based decision-making process.

8.2. GEOLOGICAL APPROACH

To understand the prohibitive and supporting factors, an idea is constructed related to geology for tourist destination development (Tables 8.1 and 8.2). In brief, supporting factor is composed of attraction and activity, while prohibitive factor is composed of sensitivity scale on geoconservation and geological feature as a hazard.

Geological hazard needs to be determined and measured. The identification has a consequence to particular engineering. The measurement outcome is a risk factor in three scales, as follows.

(a) High: potential of fatality.

(b) Medium: high potential of injury.

(c) Low: small potential of injury.

In this chapter, there are a few terms used, as follow.

(1) Geological attraction: attraction of a geological feature that could draw attention of a person to visit it. It divides the attraction into three types: landscape, such as mountain fold belt, volcano, karsts; landform, such as slope, rock, mineral; and geological process, such as geyser or waterfall.

(2) Man-made geological attraction: man-made work related to a geological feature, such as earthquake observation station and fossil prints.

(3) Physical outdoor activity: an outdoor activity conducted on a geological feature such as rock climbing and take-off aero-sport.

(4) Geologic-related activity: an activity to understand geological information in an area.

(5) Sightseeing activity: an activity to appreciate nature by sightseeing.

(6) Geoconservation: An action taken with the intent of conserving and enhancing geological and geomorphological features, processes, sites, and specimens (Burek and Prosser, 2008, p. 2).

8.3. METHOD

This study was performed in four steps, as follows.

(1) Preparation: reconnaissance, analyses on regional topography, and aerial photograph.

(2) Field observation: field work mapping and documentation on geological and non-geological features.

(3) Studio work: constructing maps of topography, slope, geomorphologic, geologic, land cover, geological hazards, and scenic observation.

(4) Synthesis: interpretation of data and information as prohibitive and supporting factors.

The relation of variables, collecting data techniques, data analysis, and its synthesis are given in Table 8.3.

8.4. GEOLOGY OF GUNUNG BATU

The discussion topic of Gunung Batu geology is composed of geography, topography and slope, geomorphology, stratigraphy, and geological structure.

8.4.1. Geography

Geographically, Gunung Batu is one of the Northern Volcano Range that bound the Bandung Highland in the northern part. The northern volcano range is composed of Gunung Burangrang, Tangkubanparahu

Volcano, Gunung Bukittunggul, and Gunung Manglayang. Geologically, Gunung Batu is a part of the Lembang Fault (Fig. 8.1) (Van Bemmelen, 1949; Silitonga, 1973; Harsolumakso, 1996).

8.4.2. Topography and Slope

Gunung Batu is a small hill with an area of ± 280 × 190 m sq (Fig. 8.2). Slope classification on a percentage slope map (Fig. 8.3) uses the classification of Van Zuidam (1985; Table 8.4).

8.4.3. Geomorphology

The geomorphic stage of the area is interpreted as young stage. Geomorphology units are divided into three units (Fig. 8.4), as follows.

(1) Structural Denudation Unit, dominated by slope of 4° to 35°, two-ground movement signs.

(2) Fault Scarp Unit, controlled by slope of 35° to 55° and > 55°, covered partly by colluvial.

(3) Volcanic Slope Unit, dominated by slope of 8° to 55°, interpreted as a part of Tangkubanparahu Volcano.

8.4.4. Stratigraphy

Gunung Batu Stratigraphy has two units. The oldest rock unit is Lava unit while the youngest one is Colluvial unit. Geological-map, cross-section, and stratigraphy column are given in Figure 8.5.

The stratigraphy unit is described as follows.

(1) Lava Unit, composed of andesite, columnar joint structure, cropping out 10 to 35 meters thick, deposited from 508,000 to 507,000 years ago (kya, Early Pleistocene) from Sunda Volcano eruption (1,125 to 210 kya; Sunardi, 1996).

(2) Colluvial Unit, comprised of lava boulder to sand sized on sand matrix, recent age.

8.4.5. Structural Geology

Based on information from Seismotectonic Division, Geological Research and Development Centre Bandung (A. Soehaini, personal communication, 2014), the Lembang Fault is still active. It showed by the 1972 earthquake in Tanjung Sari (Sumedang) in the eastern part of the fault, and by a 2003 earthquake in Ciater, Lembang. Orientation of the Lembang Fault (normal fault) is generally N 280° E. This fault shows a long scarp facing to the north (Fig. 8.1).

There are two geological structures features, as follows.

(1) Tectonic structure, characterized by lineament of fault scarp (N 261° E/80° NW) in northern cliff with 10 to 35 meter height as smallest fault displacement (Fig. 8.6) and joint.

(2) Non-tectonic structure, represented by columnar joint and sheeting joint.

8.4.6. Geological History

In the Pleistocene, there was a bigger volcano called Sunda Volcano in 1,125 to 210 kya (Sunardi, 1996). It was situated to the west of present-day Tangkubanparahu Volcano. The Gunung Batu itself was the lower part of the volcano.

In the Early Pleistocene era, the Sunda volcano erupted, and its lava (Lava Unit) flooded to the location in the present day of the Gunung Batu area. Since about the Middle Pleistocene era, the Lembang Fault has been active where it crossed the Gunung Batu location. The fault produced a fault scarp where the Gunung Batu location formed a cliff.

The Sunda volcano was still active until large exploration in 210 kya (Sunardi, 1996) formed a caldera and a smaller volcano birth, called Tangkubanparahu Volcano. Until now, geological processes in Gunung Batu are weathering and erosion that formed the Colluvial Unit that is deposited unconformably on top of the Lava Unit.

8.5. SUPPORTING FACTORS

Components of supporting factors are composed of two components, that is, attraction and activity.

8.5.1. Attraction

Attraction identification outcome is mapped (Fig. 8.7). Generally, it is composed of man-made and geological attractions. Man-made geological attraction in Gunung Batu is an earthquake monitoring station.

Geological attraction is composed of landscape and landform attractions. Landscape attraction is comprised of the whole Gunung Batu itself as part of the Lembang Fault. Landform attraction is comprised of several zones, that is Slope Zone 1 (4° – 35°); Slope Zone 2 (8° – 35°); Slope Zone 3 (4° – 8°); Fault Scarp (80°); lava outcrop; colluvial and other structural geology features including columnar joint, brecciation, sheeting joint, and tectonic joint.

8.5.2. Activity

The outcome of activity identification is mapped (Fig. 8.8) where the activities are performed on identified attraction. Description of attraction and activity relation is given in Table 8.5 and also described as follows.

Geologic-related activities (proven activities). Such activity consists of observing and learning about Gunung Batu. These activities are conducted in geological and man-made attractions where students, geologists, or the public might be interested. The purpose is to learn the geology of Gunung Batu. Those activities are proven activities where many geology students visit to learn.

Sightseeing activity is comprised of 360° panoramic observation and camping.

- 360° panoramic observation (proven activity). This activity is performed on the crest of Gunung Batu (Slope Zone 1). Mapping of panoramic observation on the regional map of the Western Jawa shows that the observation covers about 20% of West Jawa Province. However, weather might restrict observation.

- There are four paths to the peak of Gunung Batu. Those four paths are divided into two classes, class 1, with a slope of $0° - 2°$ to $8° - 16°$; and class 2, with a steep slope ($16° - 35°$) to very steep ($35° - 55°$). Camping can be conducted on Slope Zones 1 and 3 (proven activity).

Physical outdoor activity is composed of rock climbing and airport take-off potential.

- Rock climbing can be performed on Fault Scarp (mostly in western cliffs; proven activity). Generally, difficulty rating of rock climbing is interpreted as medium.

- Aero sport potential on Slope Zone 2 ($8° - 16°$ and $16° - 35°$) as take-off of paragliding or hang gliding (possible activity). Correspondence with some aero-sport experts informs that the lowest height to take off is 10.7 meters above sea level with a slope $8°$ to $35°$.

8.6. PROHIBITIVE FACTORS

There are two factors under prohibitive factors, which are the sensitivity scale and geological features as hazards. Overall, it is concluded that risk factors in Gunung Batu are low to medium risk.

Sensitivity scale (Table 8.2). Since there was a small-scale rock excavation, it is interpreted the Gunung Batu in small-scale mining (scale 7). There were many graffiti on the outcrop, which decreases the outcrop value.

Geology features as hazard comprise three factors.

(a) Geological hazard on the area. It consists of earthquake and ground movement.

(b) Geological hazard from other area. Gunung Batu is situated near Tangkubanparahu volcano, which is still active. Hadisantono et al. (1999) stated that the product of this volcano's eruption are craters that can reach over 5 km from the eruption center, which are the Upas and Ratu craters. They call this the low pyroclastic fall area. Distance from Gunung Batu to the eruption center is 8.5 km. It is concluded that Gunung Batu falls in the low pyroclastic fall area or low-risk area.

(c) Geological feature as hazard for a particular activity. This is only valid for a specific attraction. Nevertheless, this aspect can be an attraction for other activity. The activity is panoramic observation near the northern or western cliffs. When the visitors are too close to the cliff, they can fall from 10 to 35 meters. Thus, that cliff is a restricted zone for panoramic observation. However, those cliffs act as an attraction zone for rock climbing.

8.7. CONCLUSION

The point of this chapter is how to provide geological knowledge and translate the data and information in the Gunung Batu case study. It is hopefully understandable by tourism-related professionals during the stage of tourist destination planning. The outcome of translation process is in form of supporting and prohibitive factors including attraction and activity maps. The next-user might choose what attraction and activity will be presented to visitors while at the same time considering the risk and prohibitive factors.

Attraction potential as the supporting factor in Gunung Batu is geological and man-made geological attractions. The activities are in range of geologic-related sightseeing to physical outdoor activities. Those factors are implemented into maps of the Attraction Map and Activity Map.

The prohibitive factor is sensitive to rock mining and also geological hazard, e.g., earthquake. Fortunately, the hazard from other area, which is eruption of Tangkubanparahu volcano, is considered to be low risk.

Reference Cited

Burek, C.V. & Prosser, C.D. (2008) The History of Geoconservation: An Introduction. p.2, pp.1-5. In: Burek, C.V. & Prosser, C.D. (eds) The History of Geoconservation. Geological Society Special Publication No. 300, The Geological Society of London, 312 pp.

Hadisantono, R.D., Sumpena, A.D. & Pudjowarsito (1999) Pemetaan Zona Risiko Bahaya Gunungapi Tangkuban Parahu, Jawa Barat. Directorate of Volcanology, Directorate General of Geology and Mineral Resources, Bandung, Indonesia (unpublished)

Harsolumakso, A.H. (1996) Ekskursi Geologi Struktur Sesar Lembang. [Lecture] Laboratorium Geologi Dinamik Jurusan Geologi, Institut Teknologi Bandung (unpublished).

Kiernan, K. (1997) Landform Classification for Geoconservation. pp. 21-34 In: Eberhard, R. (ed) Pattern and Process: Towards a Regional Approach for National Estate Assessment of Geodiversity. Environment Australia, 1997, Technical Series 2.

Silitonga, P.H. (1973) Geological Map of Bandung Quadrangle, Java. Geological Research and Development Centre, Bandung, Indonesia

Sunardi, E. (1996) Magnetic Polarity Stratigraphy of the Plio – Pleistocene Volcanic Rocks around the Bandung Basin. Doctoral Dissertation, University of Padjajaran

van Bemmelen, R.W. (1949) The Geology of Indonesia. Vol I A, General Geology of Indonesia and Adjacent Archipelagoes, The Hague, Martinus Nijhoff, Netherland, 732 pp

van Zuidam, R.A. (1985) Aerial Photo-Interpretation in Terrain Analysis and Geomorphologic Mapping, The Hague

Figures and Tables

Table 8.1. Components of supporting and prohibitive factors and the impact possibility. Table 8.2 is mentioned in this table as detail of sensitivity scale on geoconservation.

Factor	Classification			Outcome	Impact(example)
	Geological Scope				**Non Geological Scope**
Supporting	Attraction	Geological Attraction	Landscape	Description of Attraction & Attraction Map, Description of Activity & Activity Map	Special treatment on attractions & activities, Varian tourism product/package, visitor impact management, physical and planning design.
			Geological Process		
			Landform		
		Man-made geological attraction			
	Activity	Geological related Activity			
		Sightseeing Activity			
		Physical outdoor Activity	Activity type		
			Difficulty rating on each type of activity		
Prohibitive	Sensitivity scale on Geoconservation	10 scale (from most sensitive to most robust). Detail is on Table 8.2.		Sensitivity Scale	
	Geological feature as hazard	Geological hazard on the area		Risk factor (3 scale: high, medium, low)	
		Geological hazard on another area which has impact to the area			
		Restricted zone for specific activity			

Table 8.2. Sensitivity scale on geoconservation (after Kiernan, 1997).

Scale	Sensitivity	Sensitivity scale	Example
1	Values sensitive to inadvertent damage simply by diffuse, free ranging human pedestrian passage, even with care	Most sensitive	Fragile surface that may be crushed underfoot such as calcified plant remains, or gypsum hairs in some karsts cave that can be broken by human breath
2	Values sensitive to effects of more focused human pedestrian access even without deliberate disturbance		Coastal dune disturbance, defacement of speleothems simply by touching their surface
3	Values sensitive to damage by scientific or hobby collecting or sampling, or by deliberate vandalism or theft		Some fossil and mineral sites, karts caves
4	Values sensitive to damage by remote processes		Fracture/vibration due to blasting in adjacent areas (e.g. stalactites in caves)
5	Values sensitive to damage by higher intensity shallow linear impacts, depending upon their precise position		Vehicular tracks, minor road construction
6	Values sensitive to higher intensity but shallow generalized disturbance on site		Clear felling of forests and replanting but without stump removal or major earthwork but possibly some light snig tracks, associated drainage changes
7	Values sensitive to deliberate linear or generalized shallow excavation		Minor building projects, simple road construction, shallow borrow pits
8	Values sensitive to major removal of geo-material, or large scale excavation or construction		Quarries, sites of large dams construction
9	Values sensitive only to very large scale contour change		Mega-quarries
10	Special case	Most robust	Erosion caused by sea level rise resulting from humanly-induce Greenhouse warming.

[*]: based on the intensities and patterns of disturbance entailed in particular land-use practice

Table 8.3. Relation of variable, collecting data technique, data analysis, and synthesis.

Variable	Collecting Data Technique	Data Analysis	Outcome
Topographic	Measurement using GPS receiver, photograph	Interpolation Method, topographic map and slope percentage map	• Slope map
Slope	GPS receiver measurement	Slope Map and Slope classification (Van Zuidam, 1984)	• Identification geological attraction; • Identification physical outdoor activity; • Identification geological feature as hazard.
Result and Process of Geomorphic	Field observation	Geomorphologic Map	• Identification geological attraction; • Identification physical outdoor activity and geologic-related activity; • Identification geological feature as hazard; • Sensitivity scale
Panoramic	Photograph	Scenic view analysis on regional map	• Identification geological attraction; • Identification physical outdoor activity and geologic-related activity;
Outcrop	Field observation	Geologic Map and stratigraphic	• Identification geological attraction; • Identification physical outdoor activity and geologic-related activity;
Geological Structure	Field observation, aerial photo, regional topographic map and Gunung Batu topographic map	Aerial photo, regional topographic and Gunung Batu topographic analysis	• Identification geological attraction; • Identification physical outdoor activity and geologic-related activity; • Identification geological feature as hazard;
Impact of Tangkuban-parahu Volcano eruption to Gunung Batu	Regional topographic map and map of hazard prediction of Tangkuban-parahu volcano	Analysis distribution of Tangkubanparahu eruption product to Gunung Batu	• Identification geological feature as hazard;
Socio-cultural condition in Gunung Batu, Land Cover Pattern, and Land Ownership Distribution	Field observation, photograph, and interview	Land Cover Map, Land Ownership Map, and its use by villager.	• Identification of man-made geological attraction and recreational activity attraction; • Identification of geologic-related activity, physical outdoor activity; • Identification of sensitivity scale

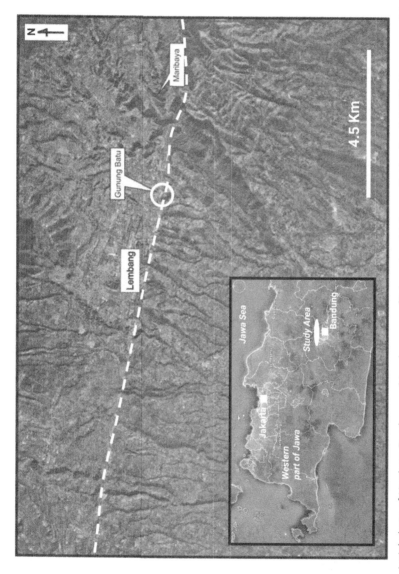

Figure 8.1. Aerial photo of Northern Bandung and Lembang area (Bakosurtanal, taken on September 3, 1993). Lineament of the Lembang Fault oriented N 280° E (white dashed line). Gunung Batu location is circled. Inset map is index map (white boxes are city, white oval is study area). Aerial photo courtesy of Dr. Budi Brahmantyo.

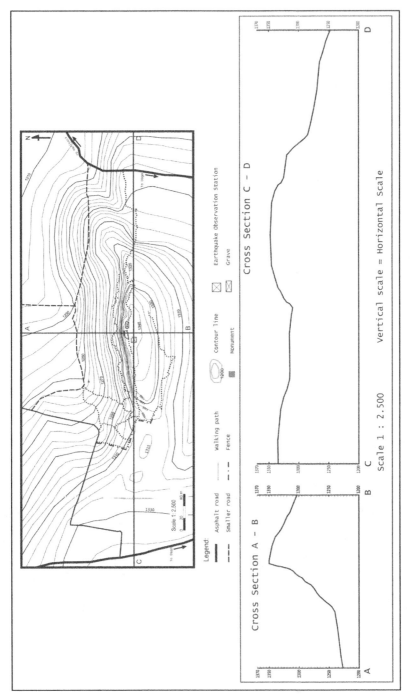

Figure 8.2. Topographic map and its profiles of the Gunung Batu.

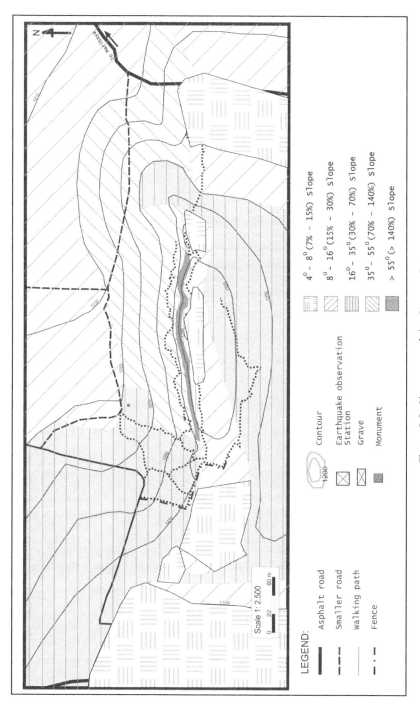

Figure 8.3. Slope map of the Gunung Batu.

Table 8.4. Slope classification and geomorphic process (after Van Zuidam, 1985).

Slope Classification	Common Process
4° – 8° (7% - 15%)	Inclined; High velocity ground movement, sheet erosion, rill erosion (prone to erosion).
8° – 16° (15% - 30%)	Slightly steep; Frequent ground movement and erosion, especially slumpy landslide
16° – 35° (30% - 70%)	Steep; intensive denudation process, frequent ground movement and erosion
35° – 55° (70% - 140%)	Very steep; generally, there are many outcrops, rather intensive denudation process, and starting to generate colluvial sediments
> 55° (> 140%)	Extremely steep; full outcrops, prone to rock fall, very strong denudation process, limited vegetation.

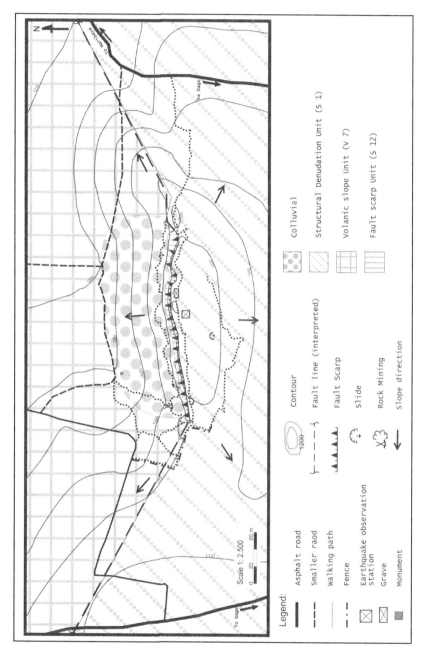

Figure 8.4. Geomorphologic map of Gunung Batu.

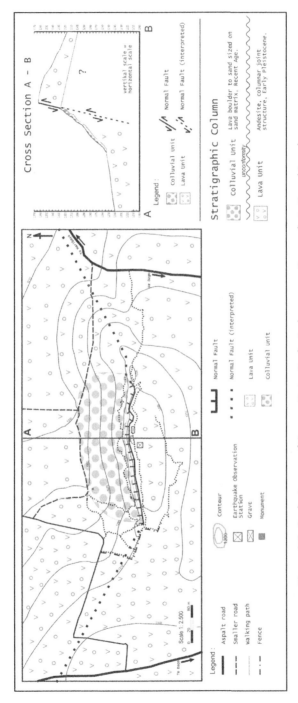

Figure 8.5. Geologic map of Gunung Batu, Geological cross-section, and stratigraphic column.

Figure 8.6. Gunung Batu landform (seen to the east direction) shows that the northern cliff as fault plane or fault scarp (shaded area) has a 10 to 35 meter height. The height is interpreted as minimum displacement of the Lembang Fault in Gunung Batu. The north side is moving downward (arrow). (Photo was taken by the author in 2004.)

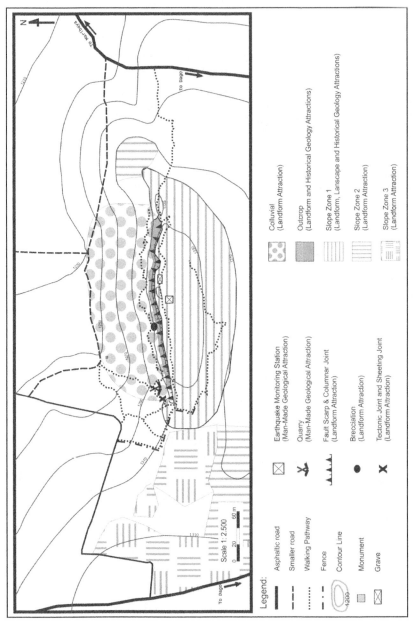

Figure 8.7. Attraction map of Gunung Batu.

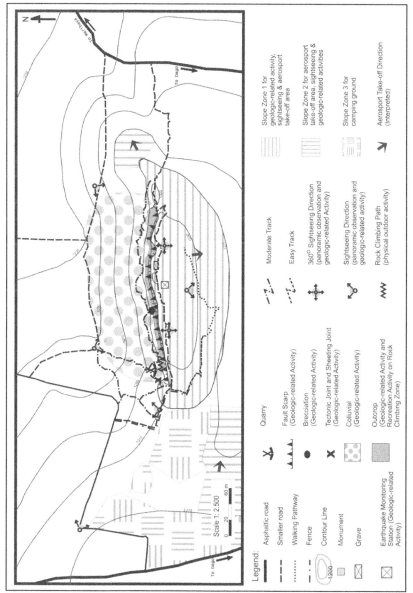

Figure 8.8. Activity map of Gunung Batu suggests activity type in a particular attraction area.

Table 8.5. Summary of attraction and activity in Gunung Batu.

Attraction			Activity
Geological Attraction		Landscape attraction (the whole Gunung Batu and the Lembang Fault from distance)	Geologic-related & Sightseeing activities (panoramic observation) are proven activities
	Landform attraction	Slope Zone 1 (4° – 35°)	Geologic-related activity & Sightseeing activity (panoramic observation & camping) are proven activities. Physical outdoor activity (aero sport take-off area) is possible
		Slope Zone 2 (8° – 35°)	Physical outdoor Activity (aero sport take off; possible activity)
		Slope Zone 3 (4° – 8°)	Sightseeing Activity (camping; proven activity)
		Fault Scarp (80°)	Physical outdoor Activity (rock climbing; proven activity)
		Other geological features: Lava outcrop, Colluvial, Structural Geology Feature (Fault Scarp, Brecciation, Tectonic Joint & Sheeting Joint)	Geologic-related activity (proven activity)
Man-made Geological Attraction (Earthquake Monitoring Station)			Geologic-related activity (proven activity)

Assessment of Geological Variable to Mountaineering Difficulty Rating and its Application to Mountaineering in Cereme, Slamet, and Semeru Volcanoes

This chapter is written in collaboration with Aridy Prasetya, Febrio Baroes, Joko Wiyono, Suwondo and Sapto Wibowo

Highlights

- Mountaineering difficulty rating is strongly related to geological variables.

- Four main variables of mountaineering are constructed.
  - It is comprised of terrain (geological variable), route condition, weather, and physical ability.
  - Terrain and route condition were described during mountaineering in Cereme, Slamet, and Semeru Volcanoes.
  - The outcome of this research is mountaineering route maps and tables with a difficulty rating on each route segments. They can be used for awareness both for mountaineers and park rangers.

- Four conclusions show geological variables control mountaineering difficulty rating.
  - First, rock units consisting of a single rock type consistently increase the difficulty rating on the ascending route.
  - Secondly, when a fault displaced the rock unit, the slope might change, whether steeper or gentler.
  - Thirdly, route surface type was composed of soil in lower altitude, where the route was easy to moderate. Within the higher altitude, the route surface type was composed of loose pyroclastic and/or exposed rocks, where the route had strenuous to extreme difficulty.
  - Fourthly, the non-eruption period means the periods for rock weathering, soil erosion, and vegetation growth.

Content

9.1 INTRODUCTION 345
9.2 MOUNTAINEERING DIFFICULTY VARIABLES... 345
    9.2.1 Terrain 345
    9.2.2 Route Condition 347
    9.2.3 Weather... 348
    9.2.4 Physical Ability... 349
    9.2.5 Rating the Mountaineering Difficulty.................................... 350
    9.2.6 Rating Application 351
    9.2.7 Volcano Mountaineering in Indonesia 352
9.3 CEREME VOLCANO MOUNTAINEERING 352
9.4 SLAMET VOLCANO MOUNTAINEERING 355
9.5 SEMERU VOLCANO MOUNTAINEERING 357
9.6 CONCLUSION 359

FIGURES AND TABLES.. 363

Abstract

Mountaineering difficulty rating is strongly related to geological variables. To get a better understanding of all variable types influencing the activity, four main variables are constructed: terrain (geological variable), route condition, weather, and physical ability. Furthermore, terrain and route condition were described during mountaineering in Cereme, Slamet, and Semeru Volcanoes. The outcome of this research is mountaineering route maps and tables with a difficulty rating on each route segment. It can be used for awareness both for mountaineers and park rangers.

In addition, the other message of this paper is an effort to use geological variable interrelation for mountaineering activity.

Four conclusions show geological variables control mountaineering difficulty rating. First, rock units consisting of a single rock type consistently increase the difficulty rating on the ascending route. It is because the route has the same slope steepness. Secondly, when a fault displaced the rock unit, the slope might change, whether steeper or gentler. Thirdly, route surface type was composed of soil in lower altitude. It has gentle to moderate slope where the route was easy to moderate and sometimes strenuous difficulty. Within the higher altitude, the route surface type was composed of loose pyroclastic and/or exposed rocks with moderate to the steeper slopes. The route has strenuous to extreme difficulty where the geological hazard possibly develops.

Fourthly, the non-eruption period means the periods for rock weathering, soil erosion, and vegetation growth. The longer the period, the stronger those natural processes. It might increase potential hazard (e.g., soil erosion) as well as increase supporting factor, such as vegetation growth surrounding a crater as a bonding agent of soil and stone that prevent erosion.

Keywords: mountaineering difficulty rating, mountaineering route map, terrain, slope, rock type, easy route, moderate route, strenuous route, extreme route, geological hazard.

9.1. INTRODUCTION

Mountaineering is an activity to fulfill someone's desire "to get close" to nature in the mountains. Mountaineering has a focus on the mountain, more technical work, getting to the top, and associated with activity on a rougher terrain (Stan VanderWerf, 2013, personal communication).

Mountaineering difficulty rating is one of the most measured activities. "Difficulty" means the effort to conduct an activity. "Rating" refers to ranking or scale. Integrating those two words in mountaineering means the efforts needed to reach the mountain peak. More effort means increasing the difficulty rating.

One of the mountaineering difficulty's components is geological variable, since the mountain is a geological feature such as a volcano, fold mountain belt, or granitic rocks. This chapter describes an attempt to understand geological variable influence in measuring mountaineering difficulty rating. It was applied during mountaineering in Cereme, Slamet, and Semeru Volcanoes in Jawa Island.

9.2. MOUNTAINEERING DIFFICULTY VARIABLES

There are various difficulty ratings that have been constructed by many parties. The rating is qualitatively measured, such as easy, moderate, and hard, where the variables most considered are elevation and distance.

We construct four main variables that influence mountaineering difficulty rating: terrain, route condition, weather, and physical ability. The only one geological variable is terrain.

9.2.1. Terrain

Terrain is composed of slope and route surface type, where those two are geological features. Maximum slope for mountaineering is approximately 30° or whenever only feet are used to ascend (Fig. 9.1). If the activity conducted is on a steeper slope, then it is called scrambling or climbing, when the hands are used to ascend. Scrambling is conducted in slopes approximately of 30° to 60°, while climbing is conducted in slopes approximately of 60° to 90° and even overhang walls.

Route surface type is the matter that covers the surface of a route. Route surface type is various. It ranges from the bedrock itself, if it is exposed, to loose sediment, or a mixture of loose sediment sand-sized to boulder-sized, snow, ice, water surface, mud, soil, and also vegetation influenced (e.g., root system, falling trees). Those material compositions determine angle of repose as the maximum slope constructed by a material without sliding. The structure of material will collapse if there is a disturbance.

In a mountaineering context, it is pressure disturbance by the mountaineer body, increasing water contained by rain or flood, earthquake, or adding more material to the structure that exceeds the angle of repose, such as volcanic material during eruption or earthquake. The 2018 earthquake in Rinjani Volcano, Lombok Island, caused landslide on the mountaineering route. To give some perspective, most angles of repose are formed in the range of 30° to 35° for dry unconsolidated material.

Angle of repose is strongly related to grain size, grain angularity, and moisture. If the grain size is coarser, more angular grain, or more moisture, then the angle is steeper. When water content in the material is high during heavy rains, the angle of repose might reduce dramatically, and the material will flow. Vegetation also plays an important role where root systems increase the material bond of soil or sediment. It creates a steeper slope but is more stable.

Sediment surrounding the crater of volcanoes is pyroclastic material. It is composed of loose sand to boulder-grain-sized mixtures. It is also found in lower parts of the cliff as a product of mass wasting process. When the mountaineer step on pyroclastic sand near the crater, the slope of the pyroclastic will collapse. As a result, walking will be more difficult where each step up will take half a step down.

Snow is the most common form of frozen precipitation. It usually consists of flakes of star-like crystals, matted ice needles, or a combination. Snow occurs when water vapor in a saturated atmosphere below the freezing point deposits as ice on microscopic particles in the atmosphere. Snow occurrence relates to altitude and latitude. In tropical areas, it occurs at about 4500 m above sea level, while in temperate areas it occurs at about 2750 m above sea level.

Thick and unstable snow accumulation is susceptible to develop into avalanches. Snow that is not well bonded to a hillside is considered unstable snow. Weather, terrain, and snowpack influence avalanche potential. Snow avalanches frequently occur on slopes of 30° to 45°, but they may be released even from a 25° slope. Walking in the snow, especially on steeper slopes, requires crampons. When snow is compacted with time, or melted and refrozen, it can turn to ice. Ice also can directly form from water.

Soil is a mixture of rock-derived material and organic matter capable of supporting vegetation. Mud is a mixture of clay and silt with water and also might contain soil. During heavy rain, water content in the soil is high. The soil is highly saturated and it might turn to mud. If mud is on a steep slope, it might flow downward as mud flow. If the water content is not so high, the mud will become slimy and sticky, which makes it difficult to walk.

9.2.2. Route Condition

Route condition is the state of a route, whether its natural character or human-influenced. It includes variables such as trail width, trail maintenance, route sign, slope beside the route, and natural obstacles.

If mountaineering is performed on established trails, then the trail is usually maintained and has the route signs. If it is organized in a new route, then no trail is available and route-finding skill is highly needed.

Slope beside the route is the slope parallel and situated beside the route whether on one side or two sides (Fig. 9.2). If a wider trail is bounded by a steep slope on two sides, then walking should be done carefully. But walking as usual is possible if a narrow trail is bounded by a gentle slope.

Natural obstacles are composed of fracture crossing the route, vegetation land cover, and river crossings. The example of fracture crossing the route is deep open crack (crevasse), especially in glacier areas. This increases the level of difficulty.

Vegetation land cover type such as tree density and its height affects visibility to the geographic reference point during navigation, usually in the sub-montane to montane zones. Vegetation influence on the steeper route might act as grip support when it is lying on the route side ground, so that the mountaineers can use it as a handle. Vegetation might act as an obstacle when it has the same height or half-height of the mountaineer, such as a tree collapse.

During river crossing in lower altitudes, the river is characterized by a wider stream, U-shaped valley, deeper river depth, sandy to muddy river bed, slower current, and U-shaped valley bounded by a gentler slope. In higher altitudes, the river has a narrower width, shallower depth, gravelly riverbed, faster current, and V-shaped valley bounded by the steeper slope.

9.2.3. Weather

Weather is the state of atmosphere at a place and time concerning heat, cloudiness, dryness, sunshine, wind, rain, temperature, and moisture. Weather plays an important role in mountaineering, where the difficulty will differ during rainy season or dry season, summer or winter. Mountaineering in Indonesia is mostly conducted during dry season. Such a season means better visibility and the route is not slippery. But most importantly, it is safer from the potential of landslides and floods.

During rainy season in tropical areas, rain will induce more water to sediment. During winter in temperate areas, snow will have a high accumulation rate. Oxygen content as a function of altitude is also influenced during mountaineering. Higher altitude means decreasing oxygen content in the atmosphere, with the consequence of increasing difficulty of breathing. For instance, at sea level there is 21% oxygen, while ascending to 3,500 m altitude there is only 13% oxygen available.

Oxygen lack really limits the height at which humans can breathe without supplemental oxygen. The highest altitude was about 5,950 m where a human was able to survive for two years. It nears the limit of permanently tolerable highest altitude (West, 2002). The death zone is at 8,000 m altitude. Another consideration is fog. When it forms, mountaineering difficulty will increase, visibility is shorter, and route-finding skill is highly needed.

9.2.4. Physical Ability

A person who would like to conduct mountaineering should consider their physical ability such as conditions of aerobic, anaerobic, upper and lower body strength, and also flexibility (Schurman and Schurman, 2009, p. 4). These factors are strongly related to mountaineering duration and easiness in facing obstacles along the route. Another consideration is The Energy Mile, a theory defined by Petzoldt in 1976. The theory explains how much energy is needed to do a mile distance of walking, whatever personal fitness they may have. As told by Prof. Maurice Phipps (2013, personal communication), the theory of The Energy Mile proposed that one energy mile is the energy required to walk one mile on the flat. While ascending, adding two energy miles for every 1,000 feet elevation gain is needed.

9.2.5. Rating the Mountaineering Difficulty

Difficulty rating refers to a particular skill and energy required to reach the objective. Higher rating means higher skill and more energy needed. In this context, mountaineering difficulty rating is categorized into four ratings: easy, moderate, strenuous, and extreme (Table 9.1) based on terrain and route condition variables, while weather and physical ability variables are assumed constant. The weather is assumed as dry or summer season. The physical ability is assumed that every mountaineer in good physical condition and able to reach the peak.

However, it needs to be reminded that assessing the rating might be subjective. While someone feels it is hard to accomplish a route segment, then it should have higher rating. Meanwhile, new variables might be introduced to modify the assessment.

Table 9.1 also describes consequences of how the rating affects particular skills required and/or the risk associated with natural hazards or risk during activity. Natural hazards are natural processes such as snow avalanche, landslide, rock fall, flash flood, or volcanic eruption. Higher rating means more skill required, more energy, and higher risk. All skills related to safety during mountaineering are highly needed, although a route is considered as low risk.

Terrain is composed of route slope and route surface type variables, while route condition is comprised of vegetation land cover beside the route and route description variables (Table 9.1). In route condition, variables other than vegetation land cover are put to route description, such as route sign, vegetation land cover within the route, slope beside the route, and river or swamp crossing.

Hence, there are four variables to support a mountaineer during assessing the rating on a route. To determine a rating of a track may use a single variable or a combination with other variables. For instance, a route with a 5° slope can be categorized as easy rating.

However, if a route slope is 5° but the route is narrow, bounded by a steep slope on one side and deep (e.g., more than 100 m), then the rating can be judged to be strenuous or extreme, taking into account higher risk faced.

This difficulty rating is constructed that hopefully can be used in various terrain settings such as volcano, fold-mountain belt, or granitic rocks. Of the four variables influencing mountaineering difficulty rating, only terrain is a geological variable. If the four variables are assumed to have the same influence, then the geological variable is estimated to have a 25% influence in the difficulty rating.

9.2.6. Rating Application

In this chapter, the mountaineering difficulty rating in three of Jawa's volcanoes is discussed based on geological and non-geological variables. The three volcanoes are Cereme, Slamet, and Semeru Volcanoes (Fig. 9.3). Mountaineering on those three volcanoes was conducted in 2012 to 2013.

During the activities, variables were noted, such as coordinate, elevation, ascending time, route slope, route surface type, and others. Slope was calculated and calibrated with topographical map. Vegetation types and geological features along the route were observed and mapped, whether it was an attraction or a geological hazard. These include springs, rivers, lakes, craters, sightseeing sites, and soil slides.

Assessment of difficulty rating was conducted during the activity based on observation on slope, route surface type, track condition, slope-bounded route, and vegetation influence. This observation was for awareness and better preparation prior to the future activity commencing.

Elevation and position data in tables and maps might be different with data reported, probably due to tool limitation when receiving satellite signals. As consequences, elevation and distance observed also might be different among observers. Other variables, such as travel time, also might vary among them. Whatever the differences among observers, the other message of this paper is an effort to use geological variable interrelation for mountaineering activity.

9.2.7. Volcano Mountaineering in Indonesia

In Indonesia, mountaineering is mostly conducted on active volcanoes that which formed during the Pliocene to Pleistocene. Due to high volcanic activities, Volcanological Survey of Indonesia (VSI) keeps monitoring them. Mountaineering in an active volcano should be conducted during the normal phase when no volcanic activity is detected.

According to van Padang (1951), Indonesian volcanoes are divided into three types. Type A means the volcano erupted at least once since the year 1600. Type B means the volcano is in solfatara and fumarole stage, where no eruption has occurred since the year 1600. Type C means a volcano with no eruption recorded since the year 1600.

9.3. CEREME VOLCANO MOUNTAINEERING

Cereme Volcano, also written Ciremay or Ciremai, is a symmetrical stratovolcano and has a national park status. The altitude of its peak is 3,078 m. The volcano is classified as Type A (Purbawinata et al., 2001) while the last eruption known was in 1951 (Global Volcanism Program, 2013a).

Quarternary volcanic rock distribution is composed of older and younger volcanic products as explained in a geologic map of Djuri (1973). The younger volcanic products are composed of lava deposit (Qyl) interfingering with undifferentiated volcanic and pyroclastic sediments (Qyu). The older volcanic products are composed of lava deposit (Qvl) interfingering with undifferentiated volcanics (Qvu; Djuri,

1973). The older volcanic products are distributed in the lower slope, while the younger volcanic products are distributed in the upper slope (Fig. 9.4, Table 9.2).

A normal fault oriented west southwest to east southeast (WSW – ESE) is in the southern part of the lower slope. It displaced the older and the younger volcanic rock units. The fault formed a ridge with a gentler slope (Fig. 9.5). But another topographic characteristic, wherein the older and the younger volcanic rock units are exposed, does not represent a slope difference.

There are four routes to the peak, as follow.

1. The Apuy route, heading east northeast (ENE).

2. The Palutungan route, heading northwest (NW) to the peak. The route was the ascending route, Stop 0 to Stop 11, 1,987 m of total elevation increase (Fig. 9.4).

3. Linggajati route, heading west southwest (WSW). The route was the descending trail, Stop 11 to Stop 21, 2,228 m of total elevation increase (Fig. 9.4).

4. Linggasana route, heading west to the peak.

A geological cross-section, interpreted from a geological map, along the routes is given in Figure 9.6. Route mapping in 3D satellite model is given in Figure 9.7. General information during ascending, descending, and difficulty rating accompanied by its geological variables are given in Tables 9.3 to 9.6.

The stop sites mentioned are a geographic reference along the route. They are characterized by a flat area, providing wind protection because of denser vegetation, relatively safe from landslide, with or without shelter, and might be near or far from a water source. Indonesian park managers and mountaineers called such areas "Post." They marked them by a clear name sign, altitude, direction, and distance to the peak. There is no actual number of stop sites on each mountain. The numbers in the table and map are given for simplicity's sake.

Ascending route segment Stop 0 to Stop 2 was an easy route along the ridge. It has a gentler slope because of being parallel with fault orientation. Less vegetation on a wide route also influences rating in this segment. Ascending route segment of Stop 2 to Stop 10 was harder route rating (moderate to strenuous difficulty), heading to north northwest (NNW) and north northeast (NNE). The route segment, where the Qyu unit is distributed, was characterized by a steeper slope, denser vegetation hindering the route, narrower tracks, with more water erosion paths on the route (Fig. 9.8, left).

A lava outcrop representing a rock unit that forms a cave (called Walet Cave, 6 meters long) was observed in Stop 10 at 2,950 m altitude (Fig. 9.8, right). It was the water source formed of dew and/ or haze condensed and dripping through fractures. The tree line was near to the crater rim, most likely because of longer eruption interval (Fig. 9.9, top).

Their descending route was generally harder than the ascending one, particularly from Stop 11 to Stop 19. It was characterized by steeper slopes, longer erosion water paths, and a narrower track. It also had more roots and trunks whether as an obstacle or providing support for holding hands on the track. Because of steeper slope and longer erosion water path, more soil slides were observed (Fig. 9.9, bottom). There was a potential of flash floods in the erosion water paths during rainy days.

Qyu unit is distributed within the ascending route (Stop 2 to Stop 11) and the descending passage (Stop 11 to Stop 21; Fig. 9.4; see also Fig. 9.6). Topographical interpretation suggests that the slopes should have the same steepness. However, the descending route was steeper. Unfortunately, there was no outcrop observed in the descending route to explain why it was steeper. Possibly, rock composition in the descending route contained larger fragments (e.g., breccia fragment) than the ascending one.

Other attractions observed were Walet Cave, sightseeing sites, and the crater at the crest. When the weather was clear, the peak was the best site to view to surrounding area. Geological hazards observed especially on the descending route included mud slides, soil slides, and potential flash floods during rainy days. During higher volcanic activity, poisonous gases might be present.

9.4. SLAMET VOLCANO MOUNTAINEERING

Slamet Volcano is a stratovolcano, with an altitude at the peak of 3,428 m. The volcano is classified as Type A (Purbawinata et al., 2001). The last two eruptions were 2009 and May 2014 (Global Volcanism Program, 2013b).

Quarternary volcanic rock is built of older to younger undifferentiated volcanic deposits (Qvs), lava deposits (Qvls), and lahar deposit (Qls), respectively, as illustrated in a geologic map of Djuri et al. (1996). Qvs and Qvls built the Slamet volcano, where Qls is distributed in the north as reworked sediment (Fig. 9.10, Table 9.7). Qvls is distributed in the eastern part and along the huge valley—probably formed by fault—in the western part, while Qvs is distributed in the western part. Topographic characteristics show that Qvls has a homogeneous slope while Qvs shows a heterogeneous slope (gentle and steep slopes).

There are several trails to the peak. Mountaineering on Slamet Volcano was performed through the Guci route. Ascending and descending routes were conducted on Guci route in April 2012 (Fig. 9.11), with 2,153 m of total elevation gain, heading southeast (SE) along the huge valley. A geological cross-section interpreted from a geological map along the routes is given in Figure 9.12. A route map in 3D satellite image is presented in Figure 9.13. General information during ascending and difficulty rating, accompanied by geological variables, are given in Tables 9.8 and 9.9.

Ascending route segment of Stop 0 to Stop 1 was an easy route rating, where the gentler slope coincides with Qvs rock distribution. The segment was marked by a clear wide route, soil, and slope was up to 10°.

The route segment of Stop 1 to Stop 7 was a harder route rating (moderate to strenuous). It coincides with Qvls rock distribution of Lava deposit where the rock unit shows a steeper slope.

The route segments of Stop 2 to Stop 6 (moderate and moderate to strenuous rating) were represented by a clear wide route, soil, some segments occasionally with water erosion path, and slope up to 20°.

Route segment of Stop 6 to Stop 7 (strenuous rating) was characterized by no clear route, 576 m of elevation gain on loose pyroclastic zone and slope up to 30°. It was the area where sand- and stone-slide were possible. The tree line was situated in Stop 6, where going upward was the loose pyroclastic zone (Fig. 9.14 top). The zone was indicated by pebble dominated in the lower part and sand dominated in the upper part (Fig. 9.14 bottom).

Attractions observed include sightseeing site to the northwest (NW) between Stop 6 and Stop 7, and the crater at the peak. When the weather was good, the peak was the perfect site to view the surrounding area. Possible geological hazards observed in Stop 6 to Stop 7 were sand and stone slide. During observation, a strong sulfur smell was also observed, which affects one's ability to breathe.

9.5. SEMERU VOLCANO MOUNTAINEERING

Semeru Volcano is a symmetrical stratovolcano, and has a national park status. It has an altitude of 3,676 m at the peak. The volcano is classified as Type A (Purbawinata et al., 2001). The last eruptions were in 2021 (Global Volcanism Program, 2013c).

Quarternary volcanic rock is formed of older volcanic products of Ayekayek (Qvj), Tengger (Qvt), and Kepolo (Qvk). The younger volcanic product resulted from Semeru and/or Kepolo-Semeru eruption (Qvs, Qls, Qlks, and Qlv), as shown in a geologic map of Sujanto et al., 1992. In this work, for simplification, volcanic rocks of Qlks, Qls and, Qvs are grouped into a new group of Qvss. Older volcanic products are mostly distributed in the northern area. The younger ones are distributed in the southern area.

Semeru's volcanic rocks resulted from younger volcanic activities (Fig. 9.15, Table 9.10). Recent volcanic eruption material flowed to the southeast as shown by Qlv rock unit distribution where the southeastern part of the crater was broken. The older volcanic products mostly show heterogeneous slope and lower altitude because of highly rate of erosion. The younger one shows higher altitude because they are relatively newly formed.

There are at least three ways to the peak of the Semeru volcano: Ranu Pane route as the most popular route, heading to the south; Watupecah route, heading to the east, where this route was used for expedition only; and Senduro route heading to the north. The Senduro route is closed because the southern slope is the area where eruption material of laharic will flow, particularly during rainy days. It is also the route where nuée ardente will flow.

The ascending route was conducted in Ranu Pane route (Fig. 9.16) and 1,551 m of total elevation gain. A geological cross-section interpreted from a geological map along the routes is given in Figure 9.17. The route map in 3D satellite image is provided in Figure 9.18. General information during ascending, its difficulty rating, and geological variables are given in Tables 9.11 and 9.12.

Ascending route segments of Stop 0 to Stop 14 were rated easy to moderate. The moderate route segments were mostly situated on the older volcanic products. The ascending segments were characterized by clear route, wide, soil surface type and slope up to 20°. Some route segments of Stop 7 to Stop 14 were water erosion path.

Route segment of Stop 14 to Stop 16 were strenuous to extreme rating where the segments situated in the younger volcanic products. The segment of Stop 14 to Stop 15 (strenuous difficulty) were characterized by clear route, the mixture of soil and loose stone, occasionally loose sand, more water erosion path, and slope from 10° up to 20°.

The segment of Stop 15 to Stop 16 (extreme difficulty) was characterized by no clear route, 676 m of elevation gain, loose pyroclastic, and a steep slope (up to 30°). The slides of sand and stones were possible because of reaching the critical angle of repose (Fig. 9.19, top left). The timber line coincides with loose pyroclastic zone boundary.

Attractions observed were sightseeing site near the peak, especially to the north (to the Tengger Caldera), the environment at the volcano peak (Fig. 9.19, top right), and Ranu Kumbolo, where a beautiful lake and flat area are located (Fig. 9.19, bottom).

Flash flooding on the route was one of the geological hazards observed, because the route also has an erosive water path. Slides of sand and stones occurred between Stop 15 and Stop 16 due to the slope reaching the critical angle of repose. The other hazard potential was poisonous gas at the crater. Fortunately, hazardous gas was relatively safe during morning and afternoon due to land breeze.

Most casualties during Semeru mountaineering were because of disorientation during descending from the peak. They get disoriented and lost in the area called 75 Blank Zone (Fig. 9.20). It is an area in the slope situated to the east of Stop 15 to Stop 13. It is called Blank Zone because there is nothing there, just barren and rocky land since it was a laharic flow area. Moreover, in the zone edge there is about a 75-m gorge (Haryono, 2012, p. 20). When mountaineers get lost in the zone, they might fall into the gorge.

It happens when a mountaineer loses his or her own ascending route (Stop 15 – Stop 16) in loose pyroclastic zone, especially at a point where the climber started to ascend from the timber line (Stop 15). Many bifurcation tracks in the vegetation zone between Stop 15 and Stop 14 during descending makes easy to lose direction.

Before 2012, Cemoro tunggal was a single big pine tree that was reported at 3,200 m altitude. The tree was as important reference for mountaineers who descend from the peak. Unfortunately, the tree collapsed because of laharic eruption in 2010 or 2011 to 2012.

In addition, the park ranger had defined that Kalimati (Stop 13) is the highest point of mountaineering for safety reasons. Reaching the crest is not recommended. In 2017, a large stone slide—half-man sized—hit a mountaineer, causing a fatality in the route segment of Stop 15 – Stop 16.

9.6. CONCLUSION

This paper explains geological variable influence on mountain difficulty rating and implemented during mountaineering in three volcanoes. Four main variables that influence mountaineering are constructed: terrain, route condition, weather, and physical ability. Terrain is the only geological variable.

The outcome of this research is mountaineering route maps with a difficulty rating on each route segment. The maps are accompanied by a table contain important information, such as stop sites, coordinates, elevation, distance, ascending time duration, vegetation zones, route slope, route surface type, rock unit, route condition, slope-bounded route, difficulty ratings, and possibly geological hazards. The information can be used for awareness for mountaineers or park rangers.

Four conclusions show geological variables control the mountaineering difficulty rating. Firstly, it is about the relation of rock type to slope type and difficulty rating. Undifferentiated volcanic rock units have a heterogeneous slope, which might be a gentler or steeper slope. The rock unit is composed of various volcanic grain sizes and different rock types, such as breccia, lava, tuffaceous sand, and lapilli. On the contrary, the lava rock unit, which is composed of a single rock type, shows homogeneous slope or consistent slope.

In relation to mountaineering difficulty rating, when the mountaineering route crosses the lava rock unit (e.g., Slamet Volcano), the difficulty rating consistently increases on the ascending route. On the other hand, when a route passes through an undifferentiated volcanic rock unit (e.g., Ciremai Volcano), the difficulty rating inconsistently increases or decreases on the ascending route. Thus, a rock unit composed of a single rock type has the same slope and difficulty rating consistently increasing on the ascending route. On the other hand, the difficulty rating inconsistently increases or decreases on the ascending route within the rock unit comprised of heterogeneous rocks.

Secondly, when a fault displaced the rock unit, the slope might change, whether steeper or gentler. For instance, a fault-oriented WSW-ESE on the southwestern part of the Ciremai Volcano, the route near Stop Site 0 – 2 become gentler, consequently with a lower difficulty rating.

Thirdly, mountaineering in active volcanoes suggests a lower-altitude route surface type was composed of soil. It has gentle to moderate slope. Usually, the route was easy to moderate. Within the higher altitudes, the route surface type was composed of loose pyroclastic and/or exposed rocks. The loose pyroclastic in higher altitudes with moderate to the steeper slope suggests strenuous to extreme difficulty. It was where the geological hazard, such as slides of pyroclastic sand or stone, possibly develops on the steeper slope and might cause casualty.

Fourthly, among three volcanoes, Ciremai Volcano has the longest non-eruption period since the last eruption in 1951. The non-eruption period means periods of rock weathering, soil erosion, and vegetation growth. The longer the period, the stronger those natural processes where the tree line growth comes closer to the rim crater. Slamet and Semeru Volcanoes have one to three years of non-eruption. As shown in Ciremai Volcano, the tree line was located the crater rim. In Slamet and Semeru Volcanoes, the tree lines were situated about 500 meters below the crater rim.

Along the ascending and descending routes of Ciremai Volcano, there were many observed soil erosions as compared to routes in Slamet and Semeru Volcanoes. Eroded soils develop into mud during rain and might increase the rating. It is a hazard during mountaineering. However, vegetation growth in Ciremai Volcano, which particularly surrounds the crater (tree line), might act as a bonding agent of stones and soil so that it prevents more erosion effect.

If a non-eruption period continues, then the soil erosion process also continues and vegetation grows closer to the crater rim. However, when the eruption occurred, then the eruption material changes the landform and the land cover. Whether the eruption occurred or the non-eruption period continued, the mountaineering difficulty rating will change according to those processes.

Reference Cited

Djuri (1973) Geologic Map of the Ardjawinangun Quadrangle, Java, Scale 1:100,000. Geological Research and Development Centre. Bandung, Indonesia

Djuri, M., Samodra, H., Amin, T. C. & Gafoer, S. (1996) Geologic Map of the Purwokerto and Tegal Quadrangles, Java, Scale 1:100,000. Geological Research and Development Centre, Bandung, Indonesia

Global Volcanism Program (2013a) [Cereme (263170)]. In: Volcanoes of the World, v. 4.7.0. Venzke, E (ed.). Smithsonian Institution

Global Volcanism Program (2013b) [Slamet (263180)]. In: Volcanoes of the World, v. 4.7.0. Venzke, E (ed.). Smithsonian Institution

Global Volcanism Program (2013c) [Semeru (263300)]. In: Volcanoes of the World, v. 4.7.0. Venzke, E (ed.). Smithsonian Institution

Haryono, D. (2012) Semeru Death Zone – Blank 75. Ilalang Bulletin, Second edition, 2012, p.20, 27 pp

Purbawinata, M.A., Mulyadi, E., Wahyudin, D., Bacharudin, R. & Hadisantono, R.D. (eds) (2001) Distribution Map of Active Volcanoes in Indonesia, Scale 1: 5,000,000. Directorate of Volcanology and Geologic Hazard Mitigation, Bandung, Indonesia.

Schurman, C. & Schurman, D. (2009) The Outdoor Athlete. Body Result Incorporated, p.4, 288 pp.

Sujanto, Hadisantono, R., Kusnama, Chaniago, R. & Baharuddin, R. (1992) Geologic Map of the Turen Quadrangle, Java, Scale 1:100,000. Geological Research and Development Centre, Bandung, Indonesia

van Padang, M.N. (1951). Catalogue of the Active Volcanoes of the World including Fields. Part I. Indonesia

West, J.B. (2002) Highest Permanent Human Habitation, High Altitude Medicine & Biology, Dec, 2002, Vol.3, No.4, pp 401-407.

Figures and Tables

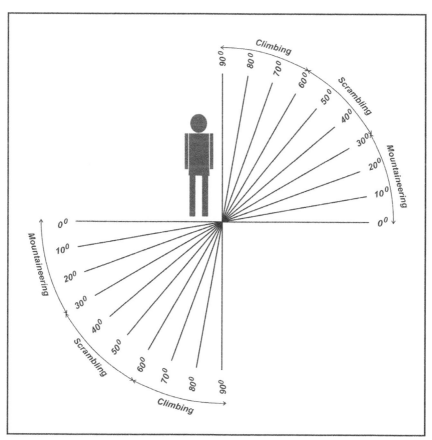

Figure 9.1. Visualization of a slope. Mountaineering is conducted on slopes approximately 0° to 30°, scrambling on slopes approximately 30° to 60°, and climbing on slopes approximately 60° to 90°.

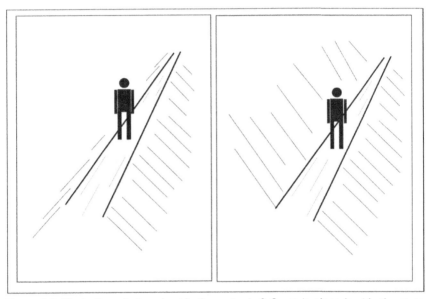

Figure 9.2. Illustration of slope beside the route. Left figure is slope beside the route on two sides (left and right sides). Right figure is slope beside the route on one side (right side). The slope might be gentle or steep.

Table 9.1. Description of terrain and route condition variables of mountaineering difficulty rating with skill required and risk associated with activity. This table might be applied for an established route or a new route.

Difficulty Rating	Terrain		Route Condition	Particular skill required	Risk associated with natural hazard or risk during activity
	Route Slope	Route Surface Type			
EASY	0° - 10°	Mostly rock or consolidated soil. Might encounter mud, snow, or ice.	• Natural footpath with route signs • Slope beside the route is about 0° - 10° • No dense trees / bush. Very easy to navigate	• Almost no particular skill required	• Almost no risk
MODERATE	10° - 25°		• Natural footpath, might be bifurcated, no route signs • Might crossing stream and/or swamp • Slope beside the route is about 10° - 25° • Not too dense trees / bush. Easy to navigate.	• Might need navigation skill	• Low risk: physical injury is potentially low
STRENUOUS	25° – 35°	Mostly unconsolidated sediment. Might encounter snow, or ice.	• No natural footpath. • Might crossing stream, swamp, crevasse and/or deep gorge. • Slope beside the route is about 25° - 35° • Might need scrambling • Dense trees or bushes limit visibility, more difficult to navigate.	• Navigation skill is needed • Scrambling skill and its gear are needed.	• Moderate risk: physical injury is likely high
EXTREME	> 35°		• No natural footpath. • Might crossing stream, swamp, crevasse and/or deep gorge. • Slope beside the route is more than 35° • Might need scrambling and/or climbing. • Dense trees or bushes limit visibility, more difficult to navigate.	• Navigation skill needed • Scrambling and/or climbing skills and its gear needed.	• High risk: fatality is potentially high

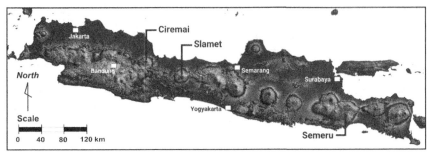

Figure 9.3. Satellite image of volcano distribution in Jawa Island shows the three visited volcanoes: Ciremai, Slamet, and Semeru. Inset map is index map.

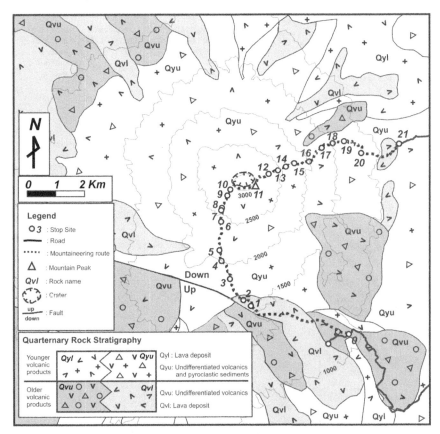

Figure 9.4. Geological map of Cereme Volcano (after Djuri, 1973). Ascending route (Stop 0 to Stop 11) and descending route (Stop 11 to Stop 21) are shown, with their difficulty ratings. Rock unit descriptions are given in Table 9.2. Numbers indicate stop site. See Tables 9.3 to 9.6 for detailed description.

Table 9.2. Simplified volcanic rock unit of Cereme Volcano and its description (after Djuri, 1973).

Rock Unit		Description
Younger Volcanic Products	Qyu	Undifferentiated Young Volcanic Products. Breccia, andesitic and basaltic lava, tuffaceous sand, lapilli, from Tampomas Volcano (to the west) and Cereme Volcano. They form low hills and flats covered by red and grayish yellow soil
Younger Volcanic Products	Qyl	Young Volcanic Products – Lava: Young andesitic lava flows exposed at Cereme Volcano and a young basaltic lava flow exposed at the west edge of the larger geological map.
Older Volcanic Products	Qvu	Undifferentiated Old Volcanic Products: Volcanic breccia, lahar deposits, andesitic and basaltic lava.
Older Volcanic Products	Qvl	Old Volcanic Products – Lava: Old andesitic lava flows with dominant hornblende and strong flow structure.

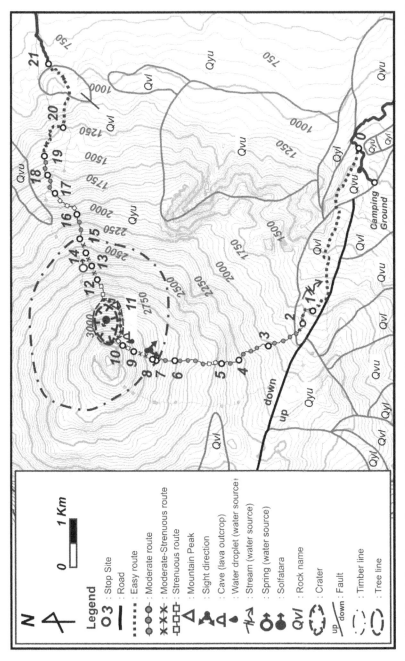

Figure 9.5. Mountaineering route map of Cereme Volcano on topographic map. The map also shows volcanic rock distribution (after Djuri, 1973). Numbers indicate stop site. See Tables 9.3 to Table 9.6 for detailed description.

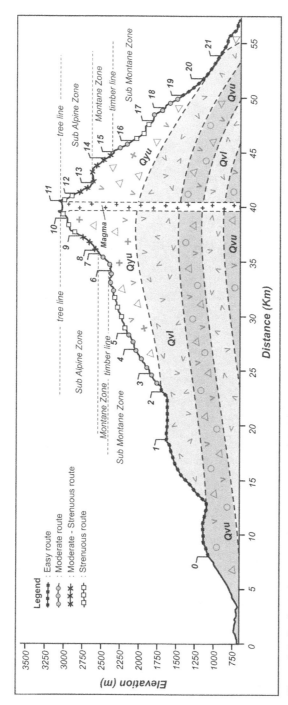

Figure 9.6. Geological section along the ascending and descending route of the Cereme Volcano. Geological subsurface is interpreted based on the geological map of Cereme Volcano. (After Djuri, 1973.) Numbers indicate stop site. See Tables 9.3 to 9.6 for detailed description.

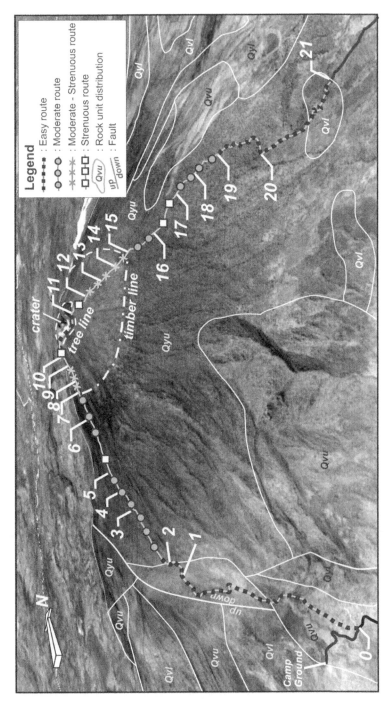

Figure 9.7. 3D topographic model of Cereme Volcano along ascending and descending routes. Rock distribution is based on the geological map of Cereme Volcano. (After Djuri, 1973.) Numbers indicate stop site (see Table 9.3 to 9.6 for a more detailed description). Image is taken from Google Earth.

Table 9.3. General information of ascending route through Palutungan Route, Cereme Volcano.

No	Stop Site	Coordinate	Elevation (m)	Distance (Km)	Elevation Gain (m)	Ascending Time Duration	Vegetation Zone	Remark
0	Palutungan	S6 56.589 E108 26.449	1091	4,00	359	4 hr	Sub Montane	Registration site, the last village
1	Stop 1: Cigowong	S6 56.064 E108 24.589	1450	0,50	250	1 hr 30 mnt		Shelter, camping ground, near Cigowong stream (water source)
2	Stop 2: Kuta	S6 55.961 E108 24.447	1700	1,00	100	1 hr		
3	Stop 3: Paguyangan Badak	S6 55.559 E108 24.189	1800	1,00	250	1 hr		
4	Stop 4: Arban	S6 55.213 E108 24.026	2050	0,50	150	1 hr 30 mnt		
5	Stop 5: Tanjakan Asoy	S6 55.015 E108 23.983	2200	1,20	250	3 hr 45 mnt		Camping ground
6	Stop 6: Pesanggrahan	S6 54.484 E108 24.022	2450	0,50	134	45 mnt	Montane	
7	Stop 7: Edelweiss	S6 54.265 E108 24.019	2584	0,10	66	30 mnt		
8	Stop 8: Sang Hyang Ropoh	S6 54.229 E108 24.023	2650	0,60	198	1 hr 30 mnt	Sub Alpine	
9	Stop 9: Apuy	S6 53.987 E108 24.131	2848	0,30	102	2 hr 15 mnt		Camping ground, cave (lava outcrop) with water droplet (water source)
10	Stop 10: Goa Walet	S6 53.891 E108 24.195	2950	0,30	128	30 mnt	No vegetation (rocky zone)	
11	Pengasinan Peak	S6 53.677 E108 24.711	3078					Near crater

Table 9.4. Difficulty rating and its variables of ascending route through Palutungan Route, Cereme Volcano.

No	Stop Site	Route Slope	Route Surface Type	Volcanic Rock Unit	Route condition	Special Skill Needed	Slope Beside the Route	Difficulty Rating	Possible geological hazard
0	Palutungan	0°-10°	Soil	Undifferentiated volanics of older volcanic product (Qvu), Lava deposit of older volcanic products (Qvl)	Clear route, but dense vegetation. Track width generally 40 cm. Water-eroded and rocky parts are occasionally observed in the lower route segments and more observed in the upper route segments. Disorientation is rare.	Might need to grasp roots to ascend, might need ladder.	Gentle slope	Easy	Possible soil slide?
1	Stop 1: Cigowong	0°-10°	Soil	Undifferentiated volanics of older volcanic product (Qvu), Lava deposit of older volcanic products (Qvl)			Gentle slope	Easy	Possible soil slide?
2	Stop 2: Kuta	10°-15°	Soil	Lava deposit of older volcanic products (Qvl)			Gentle slope	Easy	Possible soil slide?
3	Stop 3: Paguyangan Badak	15°-20°	Soil	Lava deposit of older volcanic products (Qvl), Lava deposit of younger volcanic product (Qyu)			Gentle slope	Easy	Possible soil slide?
4	Stop 4: Arban	15°-20°	Soil				Gentle slope	Moderate	Possible soil slide?
5	Stop 5: Tanjakan Asoy	15°-30°	Soil				Gentle slope	Moderate	Possible soil slide?
6	Stop 6: Pesanggrahan	15°-30°	Soil				Gentle slope	Initially strenuous & then Moderate	Possible soil slide?
7	Stop 7: Edelweiss	15°-30°	Soil				Gentle slope	Moderate	Possible soil slide?
8	Stop 8: Sang Hyang Ropoh	15°-30°	Soil				Gentle slope	Moderate - Strenuous	Possible soil slide?
9	Stop 9: Apuy	15°-30°	Soil				Gentle slope	Strenuous	Possible soil slide?
10	Stop 10: Goa Walet	5°-30°	Compacted rock and soil with less gravel and sand.		Water-eroded path. Disorientation is rare		Steep slope	Initially Strenuous & then Easy	Poisonous gas during high volcanic activity
11	Pengasinan Peak	5°-30°	Compacted rock and soil with less gravel and sand.				Steep slope	Initially Strenuous & then Easy	Poisonous gas during high volcanic activity

Table 9.5. General information of ascending route through Linggajati Route, Cereme Volcano. Although this route was used as the descending route during observation, the stop sites of this table are arranged for the purpose of an ascending route. Hence, the ascending time durations are shown.

No	Stop Site	Coordinate	Elevation (m)	Distance (Km)	Elevation Gain (m)	Ascending Time Duration	Vegetation Zone	Remark
21	Stop 21: Cibunar	S6 53.018 E108 27.413	850	2,00	356	2 hr	Sub Montane	Shelter, camping ground
20	Stop 20: Kondang Amis	S6 53.191 E108 26.677	1206					
19	Stop 19: Kuburan Kuda	S6 52.973 E108 26.346	1450	1,30	244	1 hr		
18	Stop 18: Pangalap	S6 53.009 E108 26.127	1650	0,70	200	2 hr		
17	Stop 17: Tanjakan Seruni	S6 53.095 E108 25.924	1825	0,50	175	1 hr		Camping ground
16	Stop 16: Bapa Tere	S6 53.349 E108 25.688	2125	0,80	300	2 hr		
15	Stop 15: Batu Lingga	S6 53.391 E108 25.405	2200	0,60	75	1 hr		
14	Stop 14: Sangga Buana	S6 53.458 E108 25.258	2500	0,40	300	1 hr	Montane	
13	Stop 13: Sangga Buana II	S6 53.521 E108 25.093	2620	0,40	120	2 hr		Camping ground, near spring
12	Stop 12: Pangasinan	S6 53.586 E108 24.917	2800	0,40	180	2 hr	Sub Alpine	Camping ground
11	Stop 11: Pengasinan Peak	S6 53.677 E108 24.711	3078	0,50	278	2 hr	No vegetation (rocky zone)	Near crater

Table 9.6. Difficulty rating and its variable of ascending route through Linggajati Route, Cereme Volcano.

No	Stop Site	Route Slope	Route Surface Type	Volcanic Rock Unit	Route condition	Special Skill Needed	Slope Beside the Route	Difficulty Rating	Possible geological hazard
21	Stop 21: Cibunar	5°-10°	Soil	Undifferentiated volcanics and pyroclastic sediments of younger volcanic product (Qyu), Lava deposit of older volcanic product (Qvl)	Clear route, dominated by water erosion path, dense vegetation, roots and trunks both as obstacle and support. Disorientation is rare	Need grasp the root to ascend or to descend, might need ladder.	Gentle slope - steep slope	Easy	Possible soil slide. During rainy day, muddy soil might develop into mud, soil slides and small flash flood.
20	Stop 20: Kondang Amis	5°-15°							
19	Stop 19: Kuburan Kuda								
18	Stop 18: Pan-galap	10°-25°						Moderate	
17	Stop 17: Tanjakan Seruni	10°-30°		Undifferentiated volcanics and pyroclastic sediments (Qyu)				Strenuous	
16	Stop 16: Bapa Tere	15°-30°						Moderate	
15	Stop 15: Batu Lingga	10°-30°							
14	Stop 14: Sangga Buana							Moderate - Strenuous	
13	Stop 13: Sangga Buana II	15°-30°							
12	Stop 12: Pan-gasinan								
11	Stop 11: Pen-gasinan Peak	20°-30°	Compacted rock with less gravel and sand		Water-eroded path. Disorientation is rare		Steep slope	Strenuous	

Figure 9.8. (Left) Narrower track in water erosion path (arrow) between Stop 8 and Stop 9. (Right) Walet cave is composed of lava. Photos taken by Aridy Prasetya, 2012.

Figure 9.9. (Top) Walking in the crater rim (Stop 11) where the tree line (at the right) is in the crater rim. (Bottom) Soil slide (white arrow) in the route (black arrow) between Stop 18 and Stop 19. Photos were taken by Aridy Prasetya, 2012.

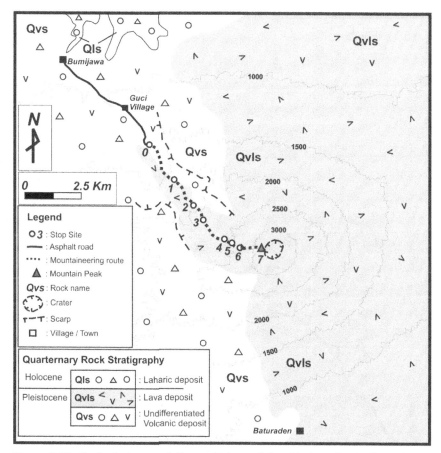

Figure 9.10. Geological map of Slamet Volcano (after Djuri et al., 1996). Rock unit description is given in Table 9.7. Numbers indicate stop site of ascending and descending routes. See Tables 9.8 and 9.9 for a more detailed description.

Table 9.7. Simplified volcanic rock unit of Slamet Volcano and its description (after Djuri et al., 1996).

Rock Unit	Description
Qls	Laharic deposit: Lahar, with boulders of andesitic-basaltic volcanics, 10-50 cm in diameters; produced by Old Slamet Volcanic. Its distribution occupied flat area.
Qvls	Lava: Andesitic lava, porous, mainly in eastern slope
Qvs	Undifferentiated Volcanic: Volcanic breccia, lava, and tuff; its distribution forming flat and hilly areas.

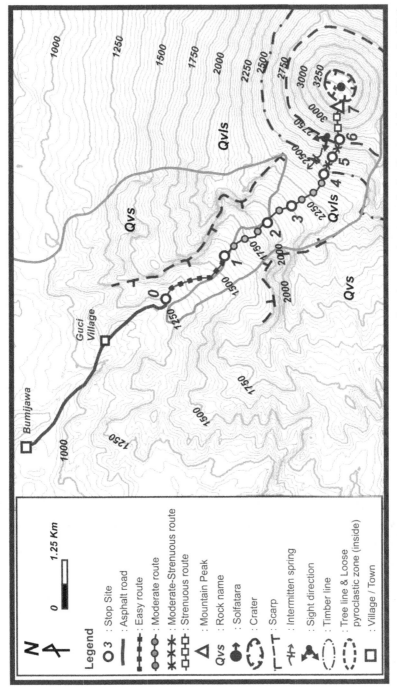

Figure 9.11. Mountaineering Route Map of Slamet Volcano. The map also shows volcanic rock distribution (after Djuri et al., 1996). Numbers indicate stop site. See Tables 9.8 and 9.9 for more detailed description.

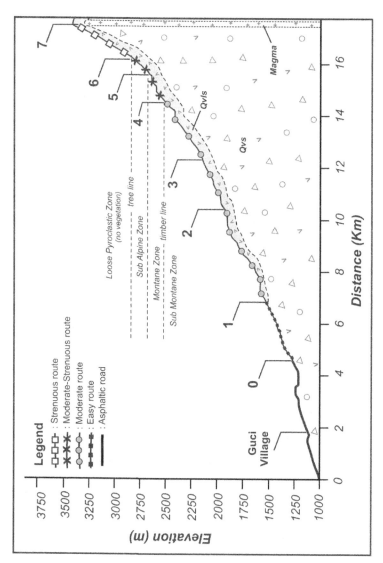

Figure 9.12. Geological section along the ascending route, Slamet Volcano. Geological subsurface is interpreted based on geological map of Slamet Volcano (after Djuri et al, 1996). Numbers indicate stop sites. See Tables 9.8 and 9.9 for detailed description.

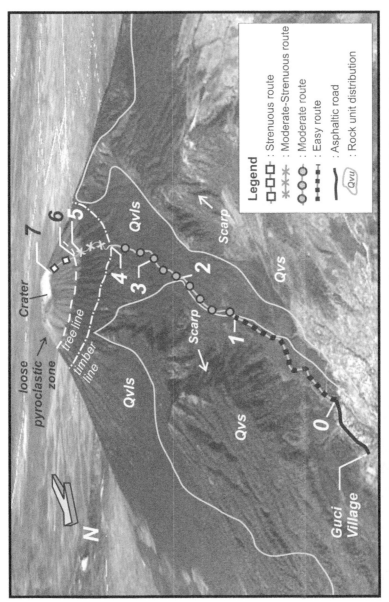

Figure 9.13. 3D topographic model of Slamet Volcano along ascending and descending routes. Rock distribution is based on the geological map of Slamet Volcano (after Djuri et al., 1996). Numbers indicate stop sites. See Tables 9.8 and 9.9 for detailed description. Image is taken from Google Earth.

Table 9.8. General information of ascending route through Guci Route, Slamet Volcano.

No	Stop Site	Coordinate	Elevation (m)	Distance (Km)	Elevation Gain (m)	Ascending Time Duration	Vegetation Zone	Remark
0	Pintu Rimba	S7 11.949 E109 10.008	1275	2,20	310	1 hr 30 mnt	Sub Montane	Registration site, the last village
1	Stop 1	S7 12.820 E109 10.627	1585	1,50	379	2 hr 30 mnt		Camping ground
2	Stop 2: Pondok Cemara	S7 13.424 E109 11.112	1964	0,80	176	1 hr 30 mnt		
3	Stop 3: Pondok Pasang	S7 13.765 E109 11.337	2140	1,40	451	2 hr 30 mnt		Camping ground. Near spring.
4	Stop 4: Pondok Kematus	S7 14.312 E109 11.982	2591	0,30	93	45 mnt	Montane	Shelter and Camping Ground
5	Stop 5: Edelweiss	S7 14.418 E109 12.086	2684	0,50	168	45 mnt	Sub Alpine	Camping ground
6	Stop 6: Pondok Cantigi	S7 14.451 E109 12.302	2852	1,00	576	3 hr	No vegetation (Loose pyroclastic zone)	Near crater
7	Peak	S7 14.512 E109 12.755	3428					

Table 9.9. Difficulty rating and its variables of ascending route through Guci Route, Slamet Volcano.

No	Stop Site	Route Slope	Route Surface Type	Volcanic Rock Unit	Route condition	Special Skill Needed	Slope Beside the Route	Difficulty Rating	Possible geological hazard
0	Pintu Rimba	0°-10°	The first 500 m is paved path, the rest is dirt path.	Undifferentiated volcanic deposit (Qvs)	Clear route. Track width generally 50 cm. Some route segments are water-eroded. Disorientation is rare.	No need special skill	Gentle slope	Easy	Almost no possible geological hazard
1	Stop 1	10°-20°	Soil						
2	Stop 2: Pondok Cemara			Lava deposit (Qvls)				Moderate	
3	Stop 3: Pondok Pasang	15°-20°							
4	Stop 4: Pondok Kematus								
5	Stop 5: Edelweiss							Moderate - strenuous	
6	Stop 6: Pondok Cantigi	20°-30°	Loose pyroclastic, dominated by peeble to cooble at the lower part, and sand dominated at the upper part		No clear route.	Might need to use hand for balance (scrambling)	Quite gentle - steep slope	Strenuous	
7	Peak								Probable slides of sand and stones. Strong sulphur smell observed. Poisonous gas present during higher volcanic activity

Figure 9.14. (Top) Tree line situated in the boundary of loose pyroclastic zone. The sight was clear to northwest area where the scarps seen from Stop 6. (Bottom) Finer-grained pyroclastic near Stop 7, close to the peak. Photos were taken by Febrio Baroes, 2012.

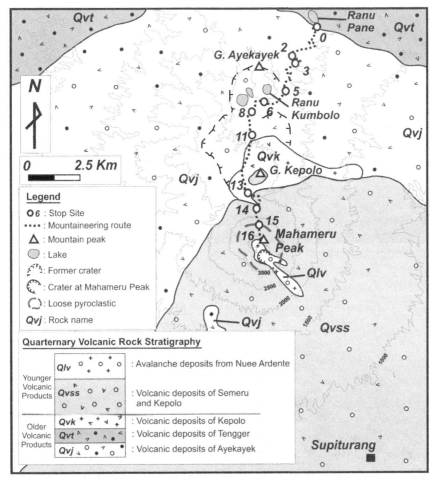

Figure 9.15. Geological map of Semeru Volcano and surrounding area (after Sujanto et al., 1992). Rock unit description is given in Table 9.10. Numbers indicate stop site. See Table 9.11 and 9.12 for detailed description. The letter "G" means "Mount."

Table 9.10. Simplified volcanic rock unit of Semeru Volcano and surrounding area and its description (after Sujanto et al, 1992).

Rock Unit	Description
Qlv	Avalanche deposit of Nuee Ardente of Semeru: Laharic deposit
Qvss	Lava of Kepolo-Semeru Parasite (augite hypersetene andesitic lava), Lava of Semeru Parasite (Pyroxene andesitic or olivine basaltic lavas) and Volcanic deposit of Semeru (Andesitic to basaltic lavas, volcano clastics and lahars)
Qvk	Volcanic deposit of Kepolo: Pyroxene olivine basaltic lava
Qvt	Volcanic deposit of Tengger: Pyroxene andesitic and olivine basaltic lava and pyroclastic falls
Qvj	Volcanic deposit of Ayekayek: Pyroxene olivine basaltic lava, tuff, sandy tuff, sand

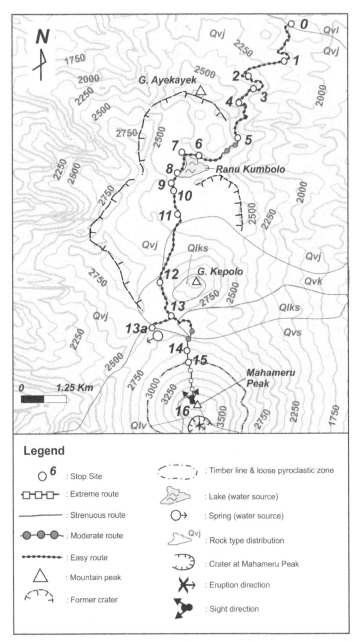

Figure 9.16. Mountaineering route map of Semeru Volcano on topographic map. The map also shows volcanic rock distribution (after Sujanto et al., 1992). Numbers indicate stop site. See Tables 9.11 and 9.12 for detailed description. The letter "G" means "Mount."

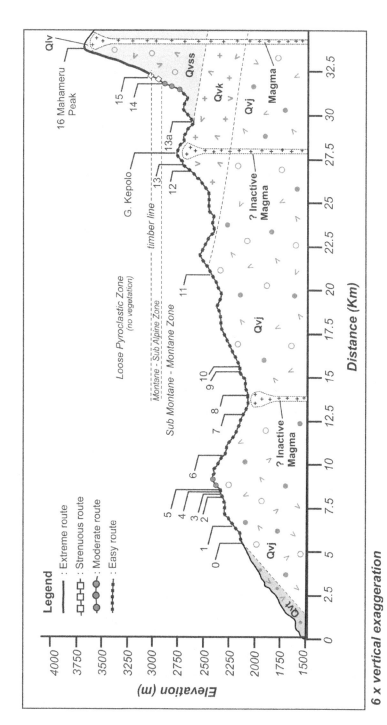

Figure 9.17. Geological section along the ascending route, Semeru Volcano. Geological subsurface is interpreted based on the geological map of Semeru Volcano and surrounding area (after Sujanto et al., 1992). Numbers indicate stop site. See Tables 9.11 and 9.12 for detailed description. The letter "G" means "Mount."

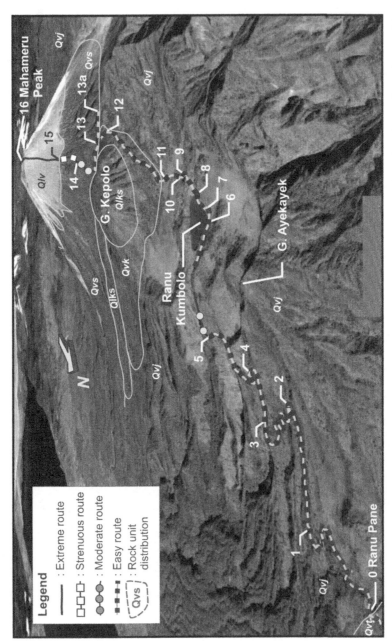

Figure 9.18. 3D topographic model of Semeru Volcano along ascending route. Rock distribution is based on the geological map of Semeru Volcano and surrounding area (after Sujanto et al., 1992). Numbers indicate stop sites. See Tables 9.11 and 9.12 for detailed description. The letter "G" means "Mount." Image is taken from Google Earth.

Table 9.11. General information of ascending route through Ranu Pane Route, Semeru Volcano.

No	Stop Site Name	Coordinate	Elevation (m)	Distance (Km)	Elevation Gain (m)	Ascending Time Duration	Vegetation Zone	Remark
0	Ranu Pane	S8 00.867 E112 56.733	2125					Registration site, the last village
1	Landengandowo	S8 01.418 E112 56.628	2194	3.5 (St. 0 to St. 2)	196	1 hr		Route name for long straight route
2	(no name)	S8 01.621 E112 56.091	2321					Shelter and camping ground
3	(no name)	S8 01.817 E112 56.167	2375	1.2 (St. 2 to St. 3)	54	30 mnt		Shelter
4	Waturejeng	S8 02.030 E112 55.955	2350	2.3 (St. 3 to St. 5)	81	1 hr		Blind turning point, near cliff
5	(no name)	S8 02.532 E112 55.937	2456					Camping ground, Shelter
6	(no name)	S8 02.793 E112 55.360	2443	1.6 (St. 5 to St. 6)	-13	1 hr		Shelter
7	Ranu Kumbolo	S8 02.784 E112 55.153	2389	1 (St. 6 to St. 8)	-43	30 mnt	Sub Montane - Montane	Camping ground, near lake (also as water source)
8	Pos Ranukumbolo	S8 03.054 E112 55.047	2400					Camping ground
9	Tanjakan Cinta Peak	S8 03.199 E112 54.949	2476	1.5 (St. 8 to St. 11)	100	1 hr		Highest point between route segments of Stop 8 to Stop 9 and Stop 9 to Stop10
10	Oro Oro Ombo	S8 03.291 E112 54.980	2442					Savanna
11	Cemoro Kandang	S8 03.653 E112 55.056	2500					Camping ground
12	Jambangan	S8 04.676 E112 54.781	2685	3.3 (St. 12 to St. 13)	200	2 hr, 30 mnt		Camping ground
13	Kalimati	S8 05.155 E112 54.931	2700					Camping ground
13a	Sumbermani	S8 05.330 E112 54.650	2604	1.5 (St. 13 to St. 14)	200	2 hr		Spring
14	Arcopodo	S8 05.648 E112 55.174	2900					Camping ground
15	Cemoro Tunggal	S8 05.920 E112 55.206	3000	0.7 (St. 14 to St. 15)	100	1 hr, 30 mnt	Montane - Sub Alpine	The last pine observed (already collapsed; timber line)
16	Mahameru Peak	S8 06.468 E112 55.325	3676	1 (St. 15 to St. 16)	676	3 hr, 30 mnt	No vegetation (loose pyroclastic zone)	Near Jonggring Saloko Crater

Table 9.12. Difficulty rating and its variables of ascending route through Ranu Pane Route, Semeru Volcano.

No	Stop Site Name	Route Slope	Route Surface Type	Volcanic Rock Unit	Route condition	Special Skill Needed	Slope Beside the Route	Difficulty Rating	Possible geological hazard
0	Ranu Pane	0°-10°	Soil	Volcanic deposit of Ayekayek (Qvj)	Clear route. Track width is up to 50 cm. Disorientation is rare.	No need for particular skill	Gentle slope	Easy	Almost no possible geological hazard
1	Landengandowo								
2	(no name)								
3	(no name)								
4	Waturejeng	0°-15°							
5	(no name)								
6	(no name)	10°-20°						Firstly Moderate, then Easy	
7	Ranu Kumbolo	0°-10°							
8	Pos Ranukumbolo				Clear route. Track width is up to 50 cm. Usually the route is also water erosion path. Disorientation is rare.				
9	Tanjakan Cinta Peak	0°-20°							
10	Oro Oro Ombo								
11	Cemoro Kandang			Volcanic deposit of Kepolo (Qvk), of Semeru (Qvs), and Lava of Kepolo - Semeru Parasite (Qlks)			A track in between has steep slope due to small stream. Trail surface is composed of loose sand to gravel	Easy	
12	Jambangan	0°-10°							
13	Kalimati								
13a	Sumbermani	5°-20°			Route is also water erosion path. Disorientation might occur when descending due to bifurcated footpath.		Gentle slope	Firstly Easy, then Moderate	Flash flood during rainy day, carrying sand and gravel load.
14	Arcopodo								
15	Cemoro Tunggal	10°-20°	Mixture of soil & loose stone, occasionally loose sand	Volcanic deposit of Semeru (Qvs)			Quite gentle slope	Strenuous	
16	Mahameru Peak	20°-30°	Loose pyroclastic (loose sand and stone)	Volcanic deposit of Semeru (Qvs) & Avalanche deposit from Nuée Ardente (Qlv)	No clear route. As a result there is no clear route, then it can be misdirected to the Blank 75 zone during descending.	Need hand for balance (scrambling). One step ascend, half steps descend.	Quite gentle - Steep slope	Extreme	Slides of sand and stones due to reach critical angle of repose. Usually poisonous gas at noon due to no wind.

Figure 9.19. (Top left) Steep slope in the loose pyroclastic zone between Stops 15 and Stop 16 (peak), which makes it hard to ascend. As shown in the picture, mountaineers used their hands or a walking stick for balance during ascent. (Top right) One of the authors (Aridy Prasetya) poses at the peak of the volcano, with a small ash plume as the background. (Bottom) Ranu Kumbolo (Kumbolo Lake) is one of the main attraction while the peak of Semeru volcano seen in the background. Photos were taken by Febrio Baroes, 2012.

Figure 9.20. 3D topographic model of 75 Blank Zone, Semeru Volcano, based on the description of Haryono (2012). The zone shows where most mountaineers get lost when descending from the peak due to disorientation. Numbers indicate stop sites. See Tables 9.11 and 9.12 for detailed description. Image is taken from Google Earth.

Highlights of the Geological-Related Attractions and Tourism Development of Rinjani - Lombok Geopark and Lombok Island

This chapter is written in collaboration with
Nicolaus Lumanauw and Heryadi Rachmat

Highlights

- This paper describes how the geology of Lombok Island is utilized for various tourist interests—such as geoscientific, scenic beauty, outdoor activity, and curative interests—which have consequences for various tourism markets.

- Lombok's geomorphology is characterized by four landscapes: volcanic, coastal, faulted hill, and karst landscapes.
  - Each landscape is able to fulfill unique tourist interests: some proven, many probable, and the remaining is possible.

- Tourism development is examined under three headings on those landscape and landform units that have a unique development strategy: exploration (of new destination), mitigation (of injury and fatality), and impact monitoring (of tourist activity).

- It is concluded that Lombok's proven destinations are poorly distributed.
  - Most other identified geological-related attractions have a probable or possible status.
  - A tourism development strategy offers more destination choices, better distributes tourist pressure within the environment, and increases the wealth of currently undeveloped community.

Content

10.1 BACKGROUND.. 397
10.2 PROBLEM STATEMENT 397
10.3 GEOLOGY OF THE LOMBOK ISLAND.. 398
10.4 METHODOLOGY.. 401
10.5 GEOLOGICAL-RELATED ATTRACTION CHARACTERS................................. 404
    10.5.1　Volcanic Landscape.. 404
        10.5.1.1　Rinjani Upper Cone (A1)... 404
        10.5.1.2　Rinjani Lower Cone (A2) 404
        10.5.1.3　Punikan Volcanic Cone (A3)... 405
        10.5.1.4　Pusuk-Nangi Volcanic Cone (A4)... 405
    10.5.2　Coastal Landscape... 405
        10.5.2.1　Pengulung – Kuta Rocky Coast (B1)...................................... 405
        10.5.2.2　Malimbu Rocky Coast (B2)... 406
        10.5.2.3　Rinjani Sandy Coast (B3) 406
    10.5.3　Faulted Hill Landscape 407
        10.5.3.1　Pengulung Undulated Area (C1)... 407
        10.5.3.2　Kuta Undulated Area (C2).. 407
    10.5.4　Karst Landscape.. 407
        10.5.4.1　Ekas Karst (D1) 407
        10.5.4.2　Pengulung Isolated Carbonate (D2) 408
10.6 TOURISM DEVELOPMENT HIGHLIGHT 408
    10.6.1　Development Highlight for Rinjani Upper Cone (A1) & Rinjani Lower
        Cone (A2) 409
    10.6.2　Development Highlight for Punikan Volcanic Cone (A3) & Pusuk-Nangi
        Volcanic Cone (A4) 410
    10.6.3　Development Highlight for Pengulung – Kuta Rocky Coast (B1) &
        Malimbu Rocky Coast (B2) 410
    10.6.4　Development Highlight for Rinjani Sandy Coast (B3)............................ 411
    10.6.5　Development Highlight for Pengulung Undulated Area (C1) & Kuta
        Undulated Area (C2).. 413
    10.6.6　Development Highlight for Ekas Carbonate (D1) & Pengulung Isolated
        Carbonate (D2) 413
10.7 CONCLUSION 414
FIGURES AND TABLES... 417

Abstract

Geological, biological, and cultural diversity of Lombok and Rinjani Volcano qualify them to become a member of the UNESCO Geopark network. This chapter describes how geological-related features are characterized to be utilized as various tourist interests, e.g., geoscientific, scenic beauty, outdoor activity, and curative attractions, which have consequence for various tourism markets. The approach is a desk study on a regional scale.

The results show that Lombok's geomorphology is characterized by four landscape types, consisting of eleven landform units, as follows: volcanic landscape with four landform units, coastal landscape with three units, faulted hill landscape with two units, and karst landscape with two units. In each landform unit, the tourist attractions and activities are rated as being proven, probable, or possible. In addition, tourism development is examined under three headings: exploration (of new destination), mitigation (of injury and fatality), and impact monitoring (of tourist activity).

It is concluded that Lombok's proven destinations are poorly distributed. Currently, tourist activities are mostly on the southern and the western coasts. Most other identified geological-related attractions have a probable or possible status. For instance, the volcanic black sediment of the northern coast has a potential for health tourism, while the faulted hill and karst landscapes in the southern part of the island have potential for outdoor tourism and recreation. The tourism development strategy in these areas offer more destination choices, better distributes tourist pressure within the environment, and increase the wealth of currently undeveloped community.

Keywords: attraction, activity, scenic beauty, outdoor activity

10.1. BACKGROUND

Lombok Island, an island to the east of Bali Island, is a well-known Indonesian tourist destination. The Lombok coast and Rinjani Volcano are tourism icons of the island. Since Mount Rinjani National Park won the World Legacy Award in 2004, an effort to make it be a member of the UNESCO Global Geopark Network began. In 2018, it has designated as one of the network, with 22 geological sites identified including 8 biological and 17 cultural sites. The geological sites identified are mainly to be developed for the geo(logical) tourism market segment within the Rinjani-Lombok Geopark area.

In reality, there are many tourist attractions related to geological features. Moreover, we should take into account the diversity of tourist interests. If we take a look the whole island, then to mention a few there are a karst area, volcano slope, faulted hill landscape, and volcanic black sand. Those geological-related attractions have a potential to fulfill various tourist interests and market types, ranging from sightseeing (recreation), outdoor activity (outdoor and sport tourisms), to health therapy (health or medical tourism).

In addition, recall Moreira and Melendez (2012, p. 205) study outcome of the other tourism types in 37 members of the Global Geopark Networks? The outcome suggested that Cultural Tourism is the most popular (94%), followed by Ecotourism (83%), Historical Tourism (81%), Rural Tourism (75%), Culinary Tourism (64%), and Adventure Tourism (61%). The others (25%) are religious tourism, beach tourism, fishing tourism, scientific tourism, cruise ship tourism, and thermal tourism.

10.2. PROBLEM STATEMENT

In this chapter, the problem that needs to be resolved is what is the character of Lombok in terms of its geological resources? And how can they be utilized for tourist activity? The main purpose is to demonstrate characterization of the Lombok geological features for tourist attractions and activities. The scope of this research is focused on the geological features that can support the non-living natural tourist attractions and activities or limit it.

This research uses a tourism geology perspective. This means the scope of geological-related attraction covers various tourist interests such as geoscientific or geologic history, scenic beauty, outdoor activity, and curative interests. Hence there are many tourist interests related to the geological features. This work is conducted based on desk study on a regional scale (scale 1:250,000) within the preliminary stage. The area of investigation is the Lombok Island, including Rinjani – Lombok Geopark and the smaller surrounding islands (Figs. 10.1 and 10.2).

10.3. GEOLOGY OF THE LOMBOK ISLAND

Based on the geological map of the Lombok Sheet, West Nusa Tenggara (Mangga et al., 1994; Fig 10.3), the rock unit was simplified into nine geological map units: one alluvium unit, one carbonate rock unit from the Late Miocene (Ekas Formation), one intrusive rock unit of the Middle Miocene, and the rest of the units related to volcanic rock of the Oligocene to Holocene age (Table 10.1).

Oligocene to Early Pleistocene rocks are mostly distributed in the southern part, where they are uplifted and exposed. Late Pleistocene to Holocene rocks are situated in the northern part, where the deposits of Rinjani, Pusuk, and Nangi volcanoes are distributed.

The large caldera in the northern part of the island is called Rinjani Caldera or Samalas Caldera. Today, the name of Rinjani refers to the highest peak of the caldera wall (3,726 m). The caldera was the result of a large explosion of the previous volcano, also called Older Rinjani or Samalas Volcano. The explosion timing of VEI 7 was in 1257, and it ranks among the greatest volcanic episodes of the Holocene (Lavigne et al., 2013, pp. 16745 - 16746).

The active volcanoes are inside the caldera, called Barujari and Rombongan volcanoes. They erupted at least 19 times between 1846 and 2016, with a Volcanic Explositivity Index (VEI) maximum of 3 (1994) and average of 2 (Venzke, 2013).

Hadisantono et al. (2008) constructed Volcanic Hazard Map of Rinjani Volcano (Fig. 10.4). It is a guidance map to identify the hazard degree of an area when an eruption occurred from the active volcano of Barujari. They divide the hazard area into three zones: Hazard Zone III, Zone II, and Zone I.

- The most inner part of hazard zone is called Hazard Zone III. It is characterized by an area that will be affected by lava flows, pyroclastic flows, toxic gas, and lahar. Within a 3-km radius from the eruption center, the area will also be affected by ballistic projectiles and ash falls.

- Hazard Zone II, the middle hazard area, is characterized as an area influenced by lava flows and base surge. In addition, within a 5 km radius from the eruption center, the area will be affected by ballistic projectiles and ash falls.

- The outer hazard area or Hazard Zone I is defined as an area that will be affected by lahars. Within a 8-km radius from the eruption center, it will be affected by ash falls. In addition, rivers might distribute laharic flow downstream.

A geological process that works today other than volcanic activity is earthquake. A set of earthquake data from the USGS catalog (2019) shows that most quakes occurred in 4.2 to 4.4 magnitudes for 51 times (Figs. 10.5 and 10.6), where 1979 was the oldest quake data recorded. A magnitude larger than 6 was a rare event, such as in the 2018 quake.

Suartika and Turjono (2009) produced Earthquake Hazard Prone Map of Lombok Island (Fig. 10.7). They divided the island into five hazard zones, as follows.

- Very high hazard zone: area potentially damaged by strong earthquakes with intensity scale of more than VIII MMI, potentially to have earthquake features such as ground fracturing, liquefaction, landslides on steep hills, and ground faulting.

- High hazard zone: area potentially affected by earthquakes with an intensity scale of VII MMI, potentially to have earthquake features.

- Moderate hazard zone: area potentially altered by earthquakes with an intensity scale of VI MMI, potentially to have earthquake features on a small scale.

- Low hazard zone: area potentially affected by earthquakes with intensity scale of V MMI.

- Very low hazard zone: area potentially influenced by earthquakes with an intensity scale of IV MMI.

- Generally, high to moderate hazard zones are dominant on Lombok Island.

A map of the ground motion vulnerability zone of the island was produced by the Volcanological Centre and Geological Hazard Mitigation (2009; Fig. 10.8). They divide the island into four zones, as follows.

- Very-low-degree zone: the area that almost never experienced ground motion.

- Low-degree zone: the area with rare ground motion if there is no disruption on the slope.

- Medium-degree zone: the area of ground motion occurring at the edge of a river valley, cliff, road cut, or when a slope is disturbed and might be triggered by heavy rain.

- High-degree zone: the area mostly ground motion active within a steep slope, that might be triggered by heavy rain.

Medium- to high-degree zones are situated in the southwestern part and the northern part of the island where it has higher elevation.

Geologically, Lombok Island is sandwiched by two main thrusts. The subduction zone is located to the south of the island, while Flores Back Arc Thrust is situated to the north of the island. The latter has the consequence of the existence of tsunami-prone areas on the northern coast, not only on the southern coast that faces the subduction zone. A tsunami-prone area map of Lombok Island was described by Distamben (2011, as quoted by Mueck, 2013; see Fig. 10.9).

10.4. METHODOLOGY

There were seven steps in this work as methodology, as follow (Fig. 10.10).

(a) Data Gathering. Today, it is easy to gather data and information regarding destinations through the internet, such as Google Maps and other internet sources. The sources are mostly tourist and local people reports on the destination (e.g., photos, blogs, and map coordinates). They recount proven activities on a particular site that has attraction. Twenty-two geological sites of Rinjani-Lombok Geopark are also used (Table 10.2).

(b) Mapping Attraction Zone. Satellite image (Fig. 10.2), geological map (Fig. 10.3), proven tourist activity types and their geographic situation are used to map the island into several geomorphological zones. It is conducted for the use of geological-related attraction characterization. The zone excludes urban areas, typically on the flat terrain, where many man-made structures are built. The map is called Landform Zone Map for Geological-Related Attractions (Fig. 10.11). The map is basically geomorphological map with modified zone for tourist attractions. It may contain known attraction spots. The outcome is four landscapes, which are further divided into eleven landform units, as follows.

  - Volcanic Landscape, composed of four landform units: Rinjani Upper Cone (A1), Rinjani Lower Cone (A2), Punikan Volcanic Cone (A3), and Pusuk-Nangi Volcanic Cone (A4).

- Coastal Landscape, consisting of three landform units: Pengulung-Kuta Rocky Coast (B1), Malimbu Rocky Coast (B2), and Rinjani Sandy Coast (B3).

- Faulted Hill Landscape, comprised of two landform units: Pengulung Undulated (C1) and Kuta Undulated (C2).

- Karst Landscape, composed of two landform units: Ekas Carbonate (D1) and Pengulung Isolated Carbonate (D2).

Rinjani Geopark Area covers the Volcanic Landscape (A1, A2, A3, A4), the Malimbu Rocky Coast Area (B2) and Rinjani Sandy Coast in the northwestern area; the northern and the northeastern area (B3) includes the smaller islands.

(c) Defining Attraction and Activity Types. The attraction type and activity are interpreted and plotted based on available data on each landform unit (Table 10.3). The attraction type is focused on geologic history, scenic beauty, and particular landform and curative attractions. The activity for each attraction is described as follows.

- Geologic history-related activity is learning geological information based on outcrop or other geological feature. It is related to the geotourism market.

- Sightseeing is activity on scenic beauty attraction for recreation.

- Therapy to improve health or cure disease based on geological features is the activity of curative attraction, which is related to the health tourism market.

- Physical outdoor activity is any physical activity conducted on particular landform that is strongly connected to outdoor and sports tourism markets.

(d) Defining Status of Attraction and Activity. The interpretation of attraction and activity are categorized into three status levels: proven, probable, and possible (Table 10.3). The statuses are regardless of whether or not the destination is developed. The three levels of status are described as follows.

- Proven: the attraction and activity have been confirmed to exist. It might be confirmed by tourist reports from various media types including social media and Google Maps, mentioned in a scientific report, or personal experience.

- Probable: the attraction and activity are probable because they have similar geological character compare to proven attractions. Moreover, the probable area is located near a proven area. However, there is no tourist report found, or there is a report but no geographical points reported.

- Possible: the attraction is identified from an analysis on data and/or information. There is no visitation recorded.

(e) Defining Impact. An impact is defined on each activity type when there is a physical contact on an attraction zone, such as soil erosion, soil compaction, and water quality. It provides awareness of environmental consequences for a monitoring program.

(f) Defining Natural Process as Hazard Potential. It is important to realize that some geological processes might lead to injury or fatality if there is tourist contact with the processes. Examples are earthquakes, landslides, volcanic eruptions, tsunamis, and rip currents. Hence, the Volcanic Hazard Map of Rinjani Volcano (Fig. 10.4), Earthquake Hazard Prone Map (Fig. 10.7), Ground Motion Vulnerability Zone Map (Fig. 10.8), and Tsunami Prone Map (Fig, 10.9) are overlaid with the Landform Zone Map (Fig. 10.11). Other dangerous natural processes such as rip current zones should be further explored. The outcome is mitigation issue for tourist activity on each landform unit.

(g) Tourism Development Highlight. Finally, a tourism development highlight as an example for each landform unit is constructed. It is composed of exploration, mitigation, and impact monitoring highlights. The highlight is constructed to be a scientific input within the decision-making process in tourism planning and development.

10.5. GEOLOGICAL-RELATED ATTRACTION CHARACTERISTICS

There are four landscapes with eleven landform units. Each landform unit is briefly discussed.

10.5.1. Volcanic Landscape

Four landform units in volcanic landscape are Rinjani Upper Cone (A1) and Rinjani Lower Cone (A2), where those two units are in the same volcano; and Punikan Volcanic Cone (A3) and Pusuk-Nangi Volcanic Cone (A4).

10.5.1.1. Rinjani Upper Cone (A1)

The most wanted destination is the Rinjani Peak and Segara Anakan Lake. This landform is situated in the middle of the northern part of the island, typically higher than 800 m elevation. Geomorphological character is volcano peak, caldera lake, parasitic cone, mountain slope, waterfall, cave, and hot spring, with a slope typically 10° to 20°. The slope in the crater wall might reach 40° to 70°. Rock type distributed is composed of lava, breccia, and tuff of undifferentiated volcanic rock unit (Holocene age).

Geological hazards in the upper cone are eruption, landslide, and earthquake. The upper cone where the Barujari volcano is situated is a particularly prone area to eruption. And so lava flow, ballistic projectiles, ash falls, wet ash falls, lahar, pyroclastic flows, and toxic gas will be distributed. Landslide hazard is dominated by a high to medium degree of ground motion vulnerability zones. The upper cone is also situated in very high, moderate, and low hazard zones.

10.5.1.2. Rinjani Lower Cone (A2)

The lower cone is within an elevation range of 400 to 800 m in the middle of the northern part of the island. In the eastern part, the elevation range is 1,200 to 1,400 m. Slope typically is 3° to 10°, with waterfall and valley. Rock type distributed is lava, breccia, and tuff of undifferentiated volcanic rock unit (Holocene age). Geological hazard in the lower cone is laharic flow area, moderate hazard zone of earthquake, and landslide hazard (medium to low degree of ground-motion vulnerability zones).

10.5.1.3. Punikan Volcanic Cone (A3)

This volcanic cone is situated on the northwestern part of the island. Geomorphological characteristics are mountain slope 10° to 45°, eruption crater, breccia and lava flow ridge, elevation range 100 to 1,490 m (the Punikan peak). Rock type distributed is mostly breccia and lava of Kalibabak Formation (Plio-Pleistocene age) and pumiceous tuff, laharic breccia, and lava of Lekopiko Formation (Pleistocene age). Landslide hazard degree is dominated by the high to medium degree of ground-motion vulnerability zones. This cone is also prone to earthquakes of high to moderate strength.

10.5.1.4. Pusuk-Nangi Volcanic Cone (A4)

On the northeastern part of the island is located this volcanic cone. Geomorphological character is mountain slope typically 8° to 45°, eruption crater, breccia and lava flow ridge, and hot spring, elevation range 1,200 to 2,330 m (the Nangi peak). Rock type distributed is lava, breccia, and tuff of undifferentiated volcanic rock unit (Holocene age). Landslide hazard degree in this cone is dominated by a high to medium degree of ground-motion vulnerability zones. The earthquake zone in this cone falls into very high and moderate hazard zones.

10.5.2. Coastal Landscape

There are three landform units in the coastal landscape: Pengulung-Kuta Rocky Coast (B1), Malimbu Rocky Coast (B2), and Rinjani Sandy Coast (B3).

10.5.2.1. Pengulung – Kuta Rocky Coast (B1)

This landform is one of the tourism icons of Lombok. This rocky coast is situated in the southern coast, to the south of Pengulung Undulated

Area (C1) and Kuta Undulated Area (C2). Coast character is curvature shoreline, gentle to steep slope of seabed to shore, pocket beach, sea erosional feature, headland, and sea cliff. Various sand types are reported, such as pink beach sand in the southeastern coast, white beach sand in the Gilis and southern coast, while a few beaches have sand-sized organism shells. Rock type distributed is breccia, lava, tuff of Pengulung Formation, and quartz sandstone and claystone of Kawangan Formation. Both formations are of Oligocene to Early Miocene age. There is calcarenite of Ekas Formation (late Miocene age) in the southeastern coast. This coast is also prone to tsunami hazard.

10.5.2.2. Malimbu Rocky Coast (B2)

This coast is situated on the western coast, to the west of Punikan Volcanic Cone (A3). This coast character is curvature shoreline, gentle to steep slope of seabed to shore, pocket beach, headland, sea cliff, and brown sand beaches. Rock type distributed is breccia and lava of Kalibabak Formation Plio-Pleistocene age. This coast is prone to tsunami hazard.

10.5.2.3. Rinjani Sandy Coast (B3)

This coast is located in the eastern to northern coast and also the coastal zone of the smaller islands (Gilis). The coast character is relatively straight shoreline, spit, volcanic black sand particularly in the northern coast, white beach sand in the Gilis, gentle to steep slope of seabed to shore. There is volcanic outcrop along the coast. This coast is prone to tsunami hazard.

It is interesting to examine Lugra and Arifin (2008) research outcome. They described the geology of the northern coast. In detail, they described the coast characteristics such as sand or gravelly sand sediment beach types, and described coastline change whether from accretion or abrasion (Fig. 10.12, p. 96).

10.5.3. Faulted Hill Landscape

There are two landform units of this landscape: Pengulung Undulated Area (C1) and Kuta Undulated Area (C2).

10.5.3.1. Pengulung Undulated Area (C1)

This area is located in the southwestern area of the island. The character is hilly area, slope typically 10° to 30°, with elevation range 5 to 400 m. Rock type distributed is breccia, lava, tuff of Pengulung Formation, and claystone of Kawangan Formation. Both formations are Oligocene to Early Miocene age. Domination of medium degree of ground-motion vulnerability zone is the landslide degree in this area. This area is also prone to earthquakes (high hazard zone).

10.5.3.2. Kuta Undulated Area (C2)

The southern part of the island is the location of this landform unit. The character is hilly area, slope typically up to 20°, and elevation range 5 m to less than 300 m. Mandalika exclusive economic zone is situated in this area. Rock type distributed is breccia, lava, tuff of Pengulung Formation, and quartz sandstone and claystone of Kawangan Formation. Both formations are from the Oligocene to Early Miocene age. Carbonate of Ekas Formation is located in some areas of this zone. This area has a medium degree of ground-motion vulnerability zone, while the earthquake-prone character in this area makes it a high hazard zone.

10.5.4. Karst Landscape

This landscape is divided into two units, Ekas Karst (D1) and Pengulung Isolated Carbonate (D2).

10.5.4.1. Ekas Karst (D1)

This karst is situated in the southwestern part of the island. It is characterized by conical hill, slope typically up to 15°, elevation range 5 m to less than 100 m, with cave features. Rock type distributed is calcarenite of Ekas Formation (Late Miocene age). This karst area is dominated by a very low degree of ground-motion vulnerability zone. Earthquake character in this area is moderate hazard zone.

10.5.4.2. Pengulung Isolated Carbonate (D2)

This unit is located in the southwestern area of the island. It is typically characterized by isolated carbonate hill area that is located in pengulung undulated area and kuta undulated area, slope that typically ranges from 10° to 30°, and an elevation range of 5 to 400 m. Rock type distributed is Carbonate of Ekas Formation. Domination of medium degree of ground-motion vulnerability zone is due to landslides in this isolated carbonate. Earthquake character in this area is moderate hazard zone. In addition, Fajri et al. (2014, p. 94) reported many cave collapses.

10.6. TOURISM DEVELOPMENT HIGHLIGHT

A development program highlight is arranged based on geological characteristics of landform, proven tourist (outdoor) activity, and considering various tourist interest that might be capable to be fulfilled by each landform unit. The attraction and activity status and proven outdoor activity as example are given in Table 10.3. The area that has similar characteristics as the proven character is categorized as probable. It is the reason why proven status always is coupled with probable.

In this work, the purpose of development program highlights, which are composed of exploration, mitigation, and impact-monitoring programs, is described, as follows.

- Exploration highlight is to explore new destination on probable and possible attraction and activity status.

- Mitigation highlight is to increase the safety level of an activity on proven, probable, and possible destinations related to geological hazard and other natural processes.

- Impact monitoring highlight is to minimize impact that is focused on proven attraction.

The highlight will be described as example. The Landform Zone Map (Fig. 10.11) can be used as guidance during ground check and development programs.

10.6.1. Development Highlight for Rinjani Upper Cone (A1) and Rinjani Lower Cone (A2)

Mountaineering to reach the peak is on tourists' to-do list. However, there should be other peaks, although lower than the Rinjani Peak. Hence, example exploration highlight on the upper cone is to establish other mountaineering routes to the other peaks, such as Tanaklayur Peak (2,664 m). It will have a different difficulty rating to reach the peak and different sight to the caldera. The other highlight is to explore aerosport take-off sites in the lower cone after reaching the peak (outdoor and sports tourism markets).

Particularly on the lower cone, there are many rivers for rafting and a mountain slope of 3° to 10° for mountain biking routes. Thus, exploration highlights on the lower cone are to explore other exploration rafting and mountain bike routes (outdoor and sport tourism markets). Waterfalls should expose the rocks that need to be interpreted for the geotourism market. If possible, a spring could be used for balneotherapy (health tourism market).

Mitigation highlight program is to establish early warning system for eruption in the upper cone, particularly for mountaineers. Mitigation highlight on the upper and lower cones is to establish early warning system for laharic flow and earthquake, and also identify landslide-prone slope in the high to medium degree of vulnerability zones. The 2018 earthquake that struck Lombok had a consequence of closing the mountaineering route. Moreover, the earthquakes of May 2019, with 5.4 and 5.1 magnitudes, caused landslide in Tiu Kelep waterfall (lower cone) where it had the consequence of three tourist fatalities.

The impact-monitoring highlight program is focused on soil erosion and soil compaction on proven routes and sites, which is mostly due to outdoor activities. Since this area is situated in a national park area, then the impacted routes and sites should be minimized.

10.6.2. Development Highlight for Punikan Volcanic Cone (A3) and Pusuk-Nangi Volcanic Cone (A4)

These two landform units have similar characteristics, so that what can be conducted in one cone most likely can be done in the other cone. Wrapping up the proven attractions and activities on those two, then the exploration program for those cones is to explore other hiking and mountain bike routes and aerosport takeoff sites (outdoor and sports tourism markets), other scenic view sites (recreation), and a spring for balneotherapy (health tourism market).

The mitigation highlight program is to establish early warning system for earthquake and identified landslide-prone slope in the high to medium degree of vulnerability zones.

Impact monitoring highlight program is focused on soil erosion and soil compaction on proven routes and sites, which is mostly due to outdoor activities. Those two volcanic cones are situated in Rinjani Lombok Geopark Area. Hence, the impacted routes and sites should be greatly minimized.

10.6.3. Development Highlight for Pengulung – Kuta Rocky Coast (B1) and Malimbu Rocky Coast (B2)

It is hard to find what needs to be further explored on these rocky coasts. The coasts are well known as a main destination. Beach character has high cliff exposed at an excellent outcrop, such as submarine volcano outcrop of the Tanjung Aan (Rachmat, 2013, p. 27).

Some exploration highlight is to explore other outcrops (geotourism market) and cliff-jumping sites (outdoor and sport tourism markets).

Bile sayak beach is well known for sand therapy (psammotherapy). Other beaches should be explored to increase the attraction related to health tourism market.

Mitigation highlight program is to identify safe waters for swimming (sun and beach tourism market). Based on local newspaper reports, there were a few proven fatalities where beachgoers were caught by rip current in Are Guling, Mawun, and Torok nearshore in the southern nearshore. Proven fatalities were also reported in Setangi, Klui, Kerandangan, and Gili Trawangan of the western nearshore of Malimbu Rocky Coast. Since the coast is prone to tsunami hazard, establishing a tsunami early warning system and the evacuation route to a higher area are needed. Impact-monitoring highlight needs to be aimed on water and sand quality on the proven beaches.

10.6.4. Development Highlight for Rinjani Sandy Coast (B3)

Within this sandy coast, particularly the northern part, there are no tourist spots recorded. Nevertheless, this study shows many potential attraction.

Geologically, the volcanic sediment is the main character on the coast, whether finer or coarser grain size. It should be packaged to have an attraction. Curative attraction is one of them, for the health tourism market. Thus, exploration highlights are to explore sand-based therapy (psammotherapy), mud-based therapy (pelotherapy), and stone therapy on the northern coast. Those therapies are based on volcanic mud or sand coupled with pebble-sized gravel. It might be integrated with a geothermal spot.

Many health center models can be used. Ibusuki beach in Japan used geothermal energy to heat the body through beach sand. If no geothermal energy is found, then artificial heating systems can be constructed to heat the sand, mimicking a natural geothermal system. Other health therapy centers use volcanic sand or pebbles as the therapy ingredient: for instance, volcanic sand as the main massage ingredient, or pebbles for hot stone therapy.

Lugra and Arifin (2008) suggest that the northern beach areas meet requirement for tourist destinations, most likely for sightseeing. Those beaches are Karang Bedil – Kolotumbu, the east of Kolotumbu to Sesait, Salangan village - Ambar - Ambar - Sukadana, Tanjung Batu, Sungian to Labuhan Pandan, and the eastern beach of Gili Sulat and Gili Lawang (Fig. 10.12, p. 102). Moreover, they recommend the best areas for snorkeling and diving were in Tanjung Awar-awar, Tanjung Menangis, and Tanjung Batu (p. 102).

Lavigne et al. (2013, p. 16743) concluded the area of pumice-rich pyroclastic density current deposit that formed as a result of Samalas eruption spread to the northern, southeastern, and southwestern coasts of Lombok Island. Those deposits contain charcoal that record when the eruption occurred. The charcoal is an important scientific prove. Thus, highlight is to explore outcrops that contain charcoal (geotourism market). Pillow lava boulders in seabed surrounding the Gili Trawangan, Gili Meno, and Gili Air were also interesting geological sites (Astjario and Astawa, 2005, p. 33).

Riyanto et al. (2018) observed land suitability on several beaches and nearshore zones in the eastern sandy coast for swimming and sightseeing. Their outcome suggests that swimming activity was best at the area surrounding Lampu, Labuan Haji, Gili Bidara, and Gili Kondo beaches.

Mitigation highlight is to establish a tsunami warning system and tsunami evacuation structure, particularly on the Gilis' coast. Identifying safe waters for swimming (for the sun and beach tourism market) is another mitigation program. Local newspapers reported that there were proven fatalities in Ketapang and Padak nearshore in the eastern nearshore where beachgoers were caught by rip current. An impact-monitoring highlight program is focused on water and sand quality on the proven beaches.

10.6.5. Development Highlight for Pengulung Undulated Area (C1) and Kuta Undulated Area (C2)

There are many proven outdoor activities in Kuta Undulated Area. Unfortunately, no Google Maps data are available for the Pengulung Undulated Area for where it has steeper slopes and higher elevation range. Absolutely, it has a challenging terrain. Probably, it could be an interesting event if the area was utilized as motocross off-road route competition like Hare Scramble Racing in United States. Aerosport takeoff sites in the area might also be interesting to be explored, where tourists would get a different sight from the sky.

In those two areas, there should be many outcrops that need to be interpreted for the geotourism market. Exploring scenic view sites from hilltop (recreation) and a spring for balneotherapy (health tourism market) are needed to increase the attraction.

Highlights of mitigation are to establish an earthquake early-warning system, particularly in Kuta Undulated Area; and also identify landslide-prone slopes in the medium degree of vulnerability zones, particularly during heavy rain. Impact monitoring highlight programs are focused on soil erosion and soil compaction.

10.6.6. Development Highlight for Ekas Carbonate (D1) and Pengulung Isolated Carbonate (D2)

Carbonate is a rock type that is highly soluble by meteoric water. The outcome is dissolution features, such as caves. However, only two caves are available in Google Maps data, Bangkang Cave (D2) and Raksasa Cave (D1). Fortunately, Fajri et al. (2014, p. 94) reported other caves in D1—Gale-Gale, Buwun Kenculit, and Surga Caves—although no coordinates or positions were given. It is probable there are other caves.

Thus, highlight example on exploration program is to explore other caves and other karst features (cave tourism, speleotherapy for health tourism). Particularly in Ekas Carbonate, an aerosport takeoff site (outdoor and sports tourisms) is interesting to be explored where the hill faces the ocean. Many calcarenite outcrops should be exposed, which need to be interpreted for the geotourism market. Mitigation highlight is to identify areas prone to cave collapse. Cave monitoring is a program for impact monitoring.

10.7. CONCLUSION

This research uses a perspective where there are various tourist interests related to geological features. This work is at the level of a preliminary stage to understand characteristics of geological-related attractions and tourism development highlights. Characterizing the Lombok geology by using this perspective was conducted by desk study on a regional scale. The outcome suggests eleven landform units of four landscapes. They are volcanic, coastal, faulted hill, and karst landscapes. Furthermore, for each landform unit, the status of proven, probable, and possible of attractions and tourist activities are defined.

The attractions of Scenic Beauty and Particular Landform are the best-known attractions by tourists (proven and probable statuses). On the other hand, curative attractions are the least-known attractions (possible status).

In addition, a set of program highlights on each landform unit is arranged. It is related to exploration of new destinations in probable and possible attractions, mitigation to increase safety level of tourist activities, and impact monitoring to minimize environmental consequences, particularly on proven attractions.

Well-known destinations in Lombok are poorly distributed. Tourist activities are concentrated in Pengulung-Kuta and Malimbu Rocky Coasts, and the Rinjani Sandy Coast, particularly in the Gilis. Development highlights for those areas are expected to be able to offer destination choices, distribute tourist pressure to the environment, increase satisfaction, and increase undeveloped community wealth.

Reference Cited

Astjario, P. & Astawa, I.N., (2005) Proses Terbentuknya Pulau-Pulau Wisata, Gili Trawangan, Meno dan Air, Akibat Aktifitas Gunungapi Bawah Laut di Pamenang, Kabupaten Lombok Barat, Jurnal Geologi Kelautan, Vol. 3, No.1, Pusat Penelitian dan Pengembangan Geologi Kelautan, Bandung. p.33. pp.28-34 pp.

Badan Nasional Penanggulangan Bencana. (2016) Rencana Kontinjensi Menghadapi Ancaman Bencana Erupsi Gunungapi Rinjani/Barujari Provinsi Nusa Tenggara Barat Tahun 2016, Workshop, Hotel Golden Palace, Mataram, 30 Maret – 2 April 2016, p.64-66, 70 pp.

Fajri, S.R., Idrus, A.A. & Hadiprayitno, G. (2014) Kelimpahan Spesies Kelelawar Ordo Chiroptera di Gua Wilayah Selatan Pulau Lombok NTB, Jurnal Biologi Tropis, Vol. 14, No.2, Juli 2014, p.94, pp.93-99.

Global Volcanism Program (2013) [Semeru (264030)]. In: Volcanoes of the World, v. 4.7.6. Venzke, E (ed.). Smithsonian Institution. Downloaded 30 Mar 2019.

Hadisantono, R.D., Heriwaseso, Pujowarsito, Riyadi, & Dahlan, A., (2008) Volcanic Hazard Map of Rinjani Volcano, West Nusa Tenggara Province, Scale 1:100,000, Pusat Vulkanologi dan Mitigasi Bencana Geologi, Bandung.

Lavigne, F., Degeai, J-P., Komorowski, J-C., Guillet, S., Robert, V., Lahitte, P., Oppenheimer, C., Stoffel, M., Vidal, C.M., Surono., Pratomo, I., Wassmer, P., Hajdas, I., Hadmoko, D.S., & de Belizal, E., (2013) Source of the Great A.D. 1257 mystery eruption unveiled, Samalas Volcano, Rinjani Volcanic Complex, Indonesia, Proceeding of the National Academy of Sciences of the United States of America, Vol. 110, No. 42, p.16743, 16745, 16746, pp.16742-16747.

Lugra, I.W. & Arifin, L. (2008) Potensi Objek Wisata Pantai Dan Bahari Di Perairan Utara Lombok Ditinjau Dari Aspek Geologi Kelautan, Jurnal Geologi Kelautan, Vol. 6, No. 2, Pusat Penelitian dan Pengembangan Geologi Kelautan, Bandung. p.96,102. pp.93-103.

Mangga, S. A., Atmawinata, S., Hermanto, B., Setyogroho, B. & Amin, T.C. (1994) Geological Map of the Lombok Sheet, West Nusatenggara, Scale 1:250,000. Geological Research and Development Centre, Bandung, Indonesia.

Moreira, J.C. & Melendez, G. (2012) It's Not Only Geotourism! Types of Tourism in Geoparks, An Analysis Based in 37 Geoparks. p.205, 206, pp.205- 206, In: Sa, A.A., Rocha, D., Paz, A. & Correia, V. (eds) Proceedings of the 11th European Geoparks Conference, 19 – 21 September 2012, Arouca Geopark Portugal, 319 pp.

Mueck, M. (2013) Tsunami Hazard Maps for Lombok, Technical Documentation, May 2013, Joint Publication by GIZ IS and DLR in the frame of the PROTECTS project.

Pusat Vulkanologi dan Mitigasi Bencana Geologi, (2009) Peta Zona Kerentanan Gerakan Tanah Provinsi Nusa Tenggara Barat, Pusat Vulkanologi dan Mitigasi Bencana Geologi, Bandung.

Rachmat, H., (2013) West Nusa Tenggara Geotourism, Geological Museum, Ministry of Energy and Mineral Resources, First Edition, August 2013.p.27, 118 pp.

Riyanto, I.A., Khoiriyah, U., Damayanti, M., Siregar, E. M., Marfai, M.A., Cahyadi, A., (2018) Kesesuaian Lahan Pantai Untuk Wisata dan Berenang di Kabupaten Lombok Timur, Seminar Nasional IV Pengelolaan Pesisir dan Daerah Aliran Sungai, Yogyakarta, 24 Oktober 2018

Suartika, K.P. & Turjono, G., (2009) Earthquake Hazard Prone Map of Lombok Island West Nusa Tenggara, Scale 1:250,000. Pusat Vulkanologi dan Mitigasi Bencana Geologi, Bandung.

USGS (2019) Earthquake Catalog, Lombok Island, Indonesia, earthquake.usgs. gov/earthquakes or go to tinyurl.com/ujn3bf9. Accessed March 2019.

Figures and Tables

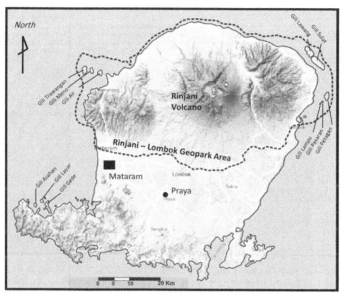

Figure 10.1. Geographical map of Lombok Island. Rinjani-Lombok Geopark Area is situated in the northern part of the island.

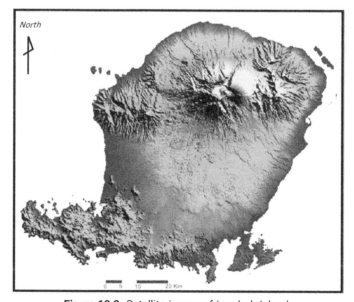

Figure 10.2. Satellite image of Lombok Island.

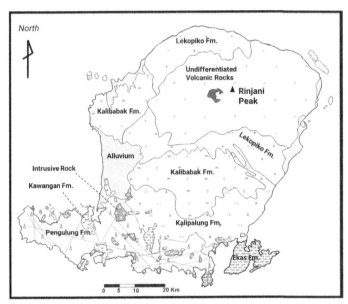

Figure 10.3. Geological map of Lombok Island (simplified from Mangga et al., 1994). In total it is composed of nine rock units (see Table 10.1 for rock unit stratigraphy).

Table 10.1. General stratigraphic column of Lombok Island.

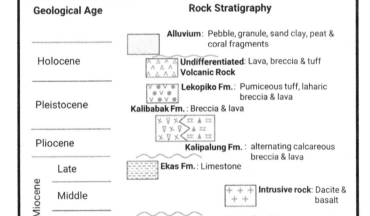

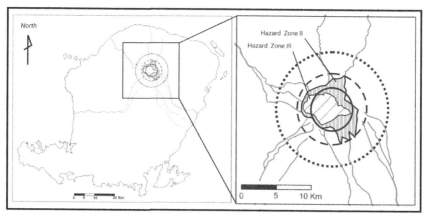

Figure 10.4. Volcanic hazard map of Rinjani Volcano (right), and where the volcano is situated in the northern part of the island (left). The inner circle (radius 3 km) is hazard zone III, the medium circle (radius 5 km) is hazard zone II, and the outer circle (radius 8 km) is hazard zone I. White area with diagonal lines in the center volcano is also hazard zone III, while the gray area with white vertical lines is hazard zone II. Rivers might distribute laharic flow. Map is simplified from Hadisantono et al., 2008.

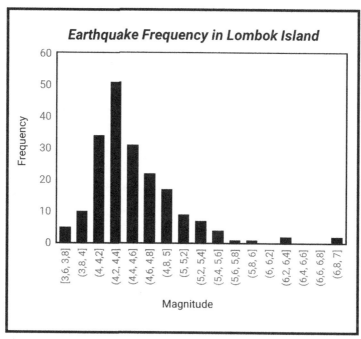

Figure 10.5. Earthquake frequency in Lombok Island from 1979 to 2019. USGS Catalog, 2019.

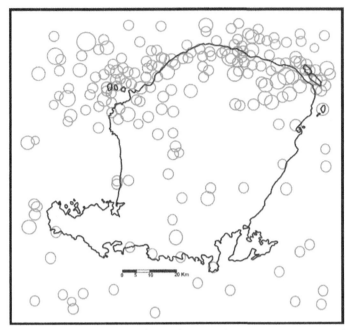

Figure 10.6. Earthquake epicenters (circles) on Lombok Island and surrounds during 1979 to 2019. USGS Catalog, 2019.

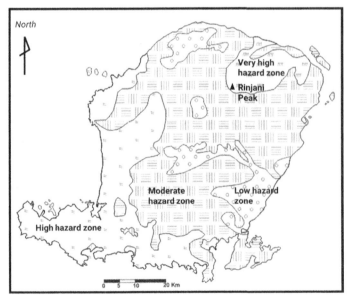

Figure 10.7. Earthquake hazard prone map of Lombok Island, which shows most of the island is in the moderate hazard zone. Simplified from Suartika and Turjono, 2009.

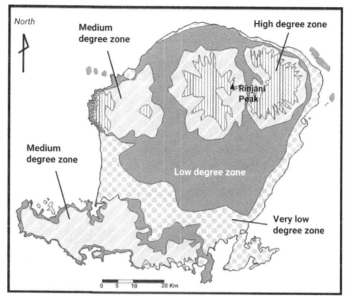

Figure 10.8. Ground motion vulnerability zone map of Lombok Island. Simplified from Vulcanological Centre and Geological Hazard Mitigation, 2009.

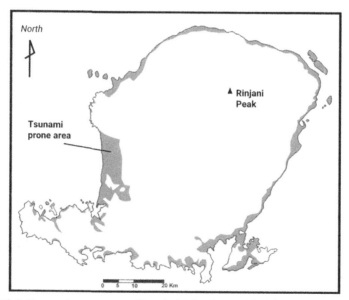

Figure 10.9. Tsunami prone map of Lombok Island. Simplified from Distamben, 2011, as quoted by Mueck, 2013.

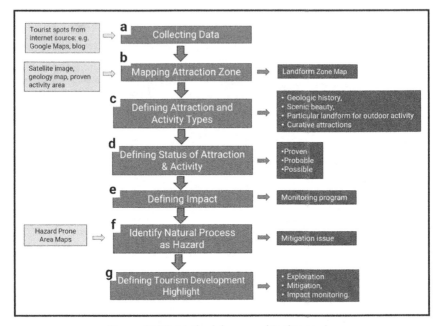

Figure 10.10. Methodology used in this study.

Table 10.2. The 22 geological sites of the Rinjani-Lombok Geopark. Personal communication with Heryadi Rahmat, 2019. These locations are shown in Figure 10.11.

No	Geological Site	Description
1	Samalas Caldera	Caldera from the eruption of Samalas Mountain in 1257 can be viewed from Pelawangan Senaru viewpoint (1a), Pelawangan Sembalun (1b), Pelawangan Aik Berik/ Batubelah (1c) and Pelawangan Timbanuh/Cemara Rompes (1d)
2	Barujari Volcano	Volcanic activity in the caldera after the eruption in 1257. In the area there are cone of Barujari Mt. (2a), Middle and Side Crater of Barujari (2b, 2c), Cone of Rombongan Mt. (2d) with lava spread from year 1944, 1966, 1994 and 2004-2009.
3	Rinjani Volcano	The peak of second highest volcanoe in Indonesia is at 3716 meter above mean sea level, consisted of Rinjani Volcano's Cone (3a) and Rinjani Crater / Segara Muncar (3b) which is separated from the Samalas Caldera.
4	Segara Anak Lake	Highest caldera lake in Indonesia at 2009 m above mean sea level

No	Geological Site	Description
5	Aik Kalaq	Hot spring and waterfall near Segara Anak lake.
6	Susu Cave	A Cave in the lava stream with hot springs
7	Payung Cave	Cave with bicarbonate springs
8	Charcoal of Samalas Eruption	Upraised wood from Samalas eruption in 1257 is located at Punikan (8a), Batukliang (8b), Pantai Luk (8c)
9	Sembalun Valley	Old volcanic caldera aged around 0.45 million years with geothermal potential. In this complex there are Sembalun Valley (9a), Gawir Sesar Pusuk (9b), Caldera Wall of Sembalun (9c), Lava Flow Structure (9d), Lentih Lava (9e) and Aik Kalaq Sembalun Hotsprings (9f)
10	Sebau Hot Springs	Chloride hotsprings in Sembalun geothermal system
11	Volcanic Beach	Beaches that indicate geological process in Lombok Island are Batubolong Beach (11a) Malimbu Beach (11b), and Kerandangan Beach (11c)
12	Gili	Small islands serving as marine tourism area are Gili Meno (12a) and Gili Trawangan (12b)
13	Waterfalls in Gangga	Tiu Pupus (13a) and Kerta Gangga (13b)
14	Waterfalls in Kayangan	Tiu Teja waterfall (14a), Sekeper (14b) and Tiu Bombong (14c)
15	Waterfalls in Bayan	Sendang Gi le waterfall (15a), Tiu Kelep (15b) and Batara Lejang (15c)
16	Waterfall in Kerandangan and Senggigi	Semporonan Waterfall–Senggigi (16a), Gua Walet Waterfall (16b) and Putri Kembar Waterfall (16c) in Kerandangan Nature Park.
17	Waterfall in Ai Berik	Benang Stokel Waterfall (17a), Benang Kelambu (17b), Pengkelep Udang (17c), Sesere (17d) and Kliwun (17e)
18	Joben Waterfall	Joben Waterfall in Otak Kokok Gading
19	Jeruk Manis Waterfall	Waterfall inside Kembang Kuning Resort, Mount Rinjani National Park
20	Semporonan Waterfall-Timbanuh	A 30-meter high waterfall before Rinjani trekking route from Timbanuh
21	Narmada Spring	Spring Complex inside the garden of King's Palace
22	Lemor Spring	Spring in Lombok Lemor Botanical Garden

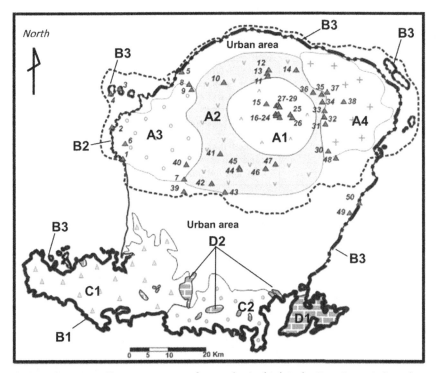

Figure 10.11. Landform zone map for geological-related attractions. It has four landscape and eleven landform units. Rinjani-Lombok Geopark Area (dashed line as boundary) is within Volcanic Landscapes (A1, A2, A3, A4), Malimbu Rocky coast (B2) and northern part of the Rinjani Sandy Coast (B3). Triangles are the 22 geological sites of the Geopark (Table 10.2).

Table 10.3. Status of attraction and activity on each Landform Unit.

Land-scape Type	Landform Unit Code	Landform Unit Name	Attraction & Tourist Activity Status			
			Geologic History	Scenic Beauty	Particular Landform	Curative
Volcanic Landscape	A1	Rinjani Upper Cone	proven	proven	proven-probable	proven-probable
	A2	Rinjani Lower Cone	proven	proven	proven-probable	possible
	A3	Punikan Volcanic Cone	proven	proven-probable	proven-probable	possible
	A4	Pusuk-Nangi Volcanic Cone	proven	proven-probable	proven-probable	proven-probable
Coastal Landscape	B1	Pengulung-Kuta Rocky Coast	proven	proven	proven-probable	proven
	B2	Malimbu Rocky Coast	proven	proven	proven-probable	possible
	B3	Rinjani Sandy Coast	proven	proven-probable	proven-probable	possible
Faulted Hill Landscape	C1	Pengulung Undulated	possible	proven-probable	proven-probable	possible
	C2	Kuta Undulated	possible	proven-probable	proven-probable	possible
Karst Landscape	D1	Ekas Carbonate	possible	proven-probable	possible	possible
	D2	Pengulung Isolated Carbonate	possible	possible	proven-probable	possible

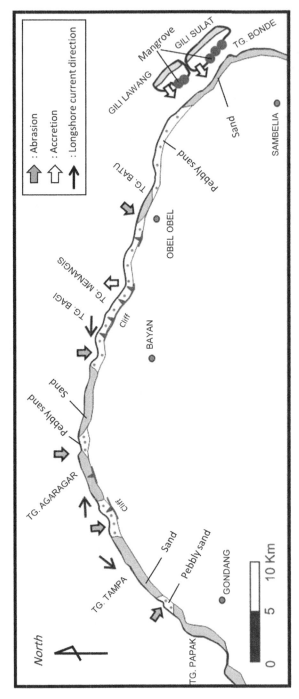

Figure 10.12. Northern coast characteristics of Lombok Island. TG stands for tanjung, or cape. Simplified from Lugra and Arifin, 2008.

Glossary

Abandoned well: In the oil and gas industry it means a well that is not used because it ceased to produce hydrocarbon or because it was fail to find hydrocarbon (dry hole) during exploration.

Aeolian: relating to action the wind.

Anastomosed river: a river which has distributary channels that separates from the main river and flow parallel then rejoin to the main river.

Andesite: A very finely crystalline extrusive rock of volcanic origin composed largely of plagioclase feldspar (oligoclase or andesine) with smaller amounts of dark colored mineral (hornblende, biotite or pyroxene). The extrusive equivalent of diorite.

Andesitic: Pertaining to andesite.

Angle of repose: The maximum slope, measured in degrees from the horizontal, at which loose solid material will remain in place without sliding.

Anticlinal valley: a valley which structurally formed by anticline structure.

Anticline: A fold in which layered strata is in fold form.

Anticlinorium: A series of anticlines and synclines.

Arc volcano: a volcano chain that formed above a subducting plate.

Asthenosphere: the upper part of the earth's mantle but below the lithosphere.

Back Arc Spreading: a geological basin that forms among the mainland and an island arc.

Barchan dunes: a crescent shape dune where the wind blows predominantly from one direction.

Basalt: An aphanitic crystalline rock of volcanic origin composed largely of plagioclase feldspar and dark minerals, such as pyroxene and olivine.

Basaltic: Pertaining to, made of or resembling basalt; as, basaltic lava. See also: basalt.

Bathymetry: The measurement of the depths of oceans, seas or other large bodies of water.

Beach: A loose sediment accumulation in surface and positioned from lowest tide to highest tide (Van Zuidam, 1985); distribution of sand or pebbles along a shore; the area adjacent to the seashore.

Berm: A horizontal portion of a beach or backshore formed by deposit of material as a result of wave action. Also known as backshore terrace; coastal berm.

Boulder: A stone, usually spherical form, has minimum diameter 256 mm.

Braided river: a river consists of a number of small channels separated by bar.

Breaker: A wave breaking on a shore.

Breccia: A rock made up of very angular coarse fragments; may be sedimentary or may be formed by grinding or crushing along faults.

Butte: small, isolated and flat-topped hill.

Caldera: A large collapse depression at a volcano summit that is typically circular to slightly elongate in shape, with dimensions many times greater than any included vent. It ranges from a few miles to 60 kilometers in diameter. It may resemble a volcanic crater in form, but differs in that it is a collapse rather than a constructional feature.

Chronic polyarthritis: Any of several diseases of the joints, such as osteoarthritis or rheumatoid arthritis, characterized by pain, swelling and often stiffness and usually involving inflammation.

Cinder cone: a cone built by pyroclastic material surround the volcanic vent.

Clay plug: Fine grained size sediment deposited in a cut off river meander with a great deal of organic mud.

Coast: the land near the sea.

Coastal: denoting to coast.

Collovium: A general term applied to any loose, heterogeneous and incoherent mass of soil material or rock fragments deposited chiefly by mass-wasting, usually at the base of a steep slope or cliff; e.g. talus, cliff debris and avalanche material.

Colluvial: Pertaining to colluvium.

Columnar joint: Parallel, prismatic columns that are formed as a result of contraction during cooling in basaltic flow and other extrusive and intrusive rocks.

Continental Crust: the earth's crust that forms the continent, mainly composed of granitic rocks.

Convergent margin: the plate boundary where the oceanic plate is consumed or moved beneath the continental plate.

Crater: A large, bowl-shaped topographic depression with steep sides.

Delta Front: A zone in a delta between the Delta Plain and the Pro Delta where the main processes are terrestrial and marine processes. It consists of a continuous sheet of sand and occurring at the effective depth of wave erosion.

Delta Plain: A zone in a delta between the Fluvial and the Delta Front, where the main processes similar to fluvial environment but the salinity is brackish.

Delta: An alluvial deposit, triangular in shape and exhibits a positive feature compare to the adjacent shoreline, where sediments from a river enters the standing body of water, e.g. sea or lake.

Desert: an area typify by evaporation exceeds precipitation.

Distributary channel: An irregular branch flowing out from a main stream and not returning to it, as in a delta. Distributary channels are situated in the Delta Plain zone.

Dolina: A hollow in a karstic region, usually funnel-shaped.

Dolostone: a sedimentary rock comprises predominantly of dolomite minerals.

Dolostone: rock type comprised of dolomite.

Dry hole: a well that produce no oil or gas.

Early Miocene: A geologic epoch of the Tertiary period, extending from 16-23 Ma.

Earthquake focus or **earthquake hypocenter**: the point, usually on subsurface, where the rocks begin to break.

Echo-sounder: A sounding instrument that measures water depth by measurement of the time that it takes a sonic or supersonic sound signal to travel to and return from the sea floor, river bed or lake floor.

Endogenic process: the energy originated deep from earth, e.g. tectonic forces, volcano eruption.

Engineering Geology: Geology as applied to engineering practice, esp. mining and civil engineering.

Estuary: the mouth of the river onto the sea or lake.

Exogenic process: the energy originated solar radiation, e.g. weathering, erosion, wind, wave.

Fault scarp: A steep cliff formed by movement along one side of a fault.

Fault: A fracture in rock along which the adjacent rock surfaces are differentially displaced.

Fault-block mountain: a mountain range produced by faulting.

Fault-related fold: A fold which during its formed related to fault.

Fluvial meandering: a river with sinuous form.

Fluvial: Pertaining to or produced by the action of a stream or river.

Fold and thrust belt mountain: a mountain range produced by thrusting and folding.

Fold: A bend in a layer of rock.

Foreshore: The zone that lies between the ordinary high- and low-watermarks and is daily traversed by the rise and fall of the tide. Also known as beach face.

Formation: Any assemblage of rocks which have some common character and are mapable as a rock unit.

Fumarole: A hole, usually found in volcanic areas, from which vapors or gases escape.

Gemstone: A mineral or petrified organic matter suitable for use as jewelry.

Geoconservation or **Geological Conservation**: An action taken with the intent of conserving and enhancing geological and geomorphological features, processes, sites and specimens (Burek and Prosser, 2008, in Burek and Prosser (eds), 2008).

Geodiversity: the diversity of the earth material, process and forms.

Geologic Map: A representation of the geologic surface or subsurface features by means of signs and symbols and with an indicated means of orientation; includes nature and distribution of rock units and the occurrence of structural features, mineral deposits and fossil localities.

Geological Heritage (or **Geoheritage**): all of geological feature which is inherited from the earth processes.

Geomorphologic Map: A representation of the geomorphologic process and its features by means of sign and symbol.

Geomorphology: The study of the origin of secondary topographic features which are carved by erosion in the primary elements and built up of the erosion debris.

Geopark: A geographical area where geological heritage sites are part of a holistic concept of protection, education and sustainable development (UNESCO, 2014).

Geophagy: the practice of eating earthy substances, particularly clay mineral.

Geyser: a small opening on surface that periodically spouts water into the air.

Glacial: denoting to, resulting from or relating to the presence of ice, particularly in the form of glaciers.

Glacier: a slowly moving mass or river of ice formed by the accumulation and compaction of snow on mountains or near the poles.

Graben valley: a valley which structurally formed by graben structure.

Granite: igneous rock characterized by light-colored, coarse-grained, mostly consist of quartz, feldspar and mica.

Gravitational sedimentation: a sedimentation process which gravity force is the main process. It is instantaneous process instead of continuous process.

Gravity flow: a flow due to gravity force, esp. flow in a steep slope.

Gullies: a feature of rain erosion.

Gynecological disorders: disorders that affect to the female reproductive system.

Head of Passes: a point between the Fluvial and the Delta Plain where the fluvial might branch into several Distributary Channels.

Headland rip: a rip current that occur around the headland.

High Density Chained Ball: a chain of concrete balls designed to stop Sidoarjo mud flow center.

Holocene: An epoch of the Quaternary Period from the end of the Pleistocene, around 10,000 years ago, to the present. Also known as Post-glacial; Recent.

Homocline ridge: a ridge in which structurally the bedding of the rock layer has uniform dip direction.

Hornblende: A general name given to the monoclinic calcium amphiboles mineral that form an extensive solid-solution series between the various metals in the generalized formula $(Ca,Na)_2(Mg,Fe,Al)_5(Al,Si)_8O_{22}(OH,F)_2$.

Hot spring: A thermal spring whose temperature is above that of the human body.

Hotspot: volcanic regions thought to be fed by underlying mantle that is anomalously hot compared with the surrounding mantle. Their position on the Earth's surface is independent of tectonic plate boundaries (Wikipedia).

Impact crater: a crater formed by meteorite impact.

Inselberg: Isolated and steep sided large hill of big rocky outcrops stands above adjacent nearly flat plains

Interfingering: The disappearance of sedimentary bodies in laterally adjacent masses owing to splitting into many thin units, each of which reaches an independent pinch-out termination; the intergradation of markedly different rocks through a vertical succession of thin interlocking or overlapping wedge-shaped layers.

Intertidal zone: area between mean high-water level and mean low-water level in coastal region.

Intraplate Volcano: a volcano which occurs in the middle of the tectonic plate where it is strongly related to hotspot volcanism.

Intrusive: igneous rock that is emplaced within pre-existing rocks.

Karst: An area of limestone terrane characterized by rocky ground, caves, sinkhole, ravines and underground streams.

Karstification: The process by which karst is formed; The processes of solution and infiltration by water whereby the surface features and subterranean drainage network of a karstland are developed to form a karst topography.

Lahar: A mudflow or landslide of pyroclastic material occurring on the flank of a volcano.

Landform: All the physical, recognizable, naturally formed features of land, having a characteristic shape; includes major forms such as a plain, mountain or plateau and minor forms such as a hill, valley or alluvial fan.

Landscape: The distinct association of landforms that can be seen in a single view.

Landslide: The perceptible downward sliding or falling of a relatively dry mass of earth, rock or combination of the two under the influence of gravity.

Lapilli: Pyroclasts that range from 0.04 to 2.6 inches (1 to 64 millimeters) in diameter of grain sized.

Late Miocene: A geologic epoch of the Tertiary period, extending from 5.3 - 11.6 Ma.

Lateral accretion: The digging away of material at the outer bank of a meandering stream and the simultaneous building up to the water level by deposition of material brought there by pushing and rolling along the stream bottom.

Lava: the molten rock issues from a volcano or volcanic vent.

Limestone: A sedimentary rock composed dominantly (more than 95%) of calcium carbonate, principally in the form of calcite; examples include chalk and travertine.

Limestone: rock mainly comprised of calcium carbonate.

Lithosphere: the outer part of the earth which comprised of the crust and upper mantle.

Lithostratigraphy: A branch of stratigraphy concerned with the description and interpretation of sedimentary successions in terms of their lithic character.

Locked fault zone: a fault zone that was not moving (stuck), while the other zone was moving. It is due to frictional resistance on the fault is greater than the shear stress across the fault. Such faults may be released when frictional resistance is overcome.

Long shore current: A current, caused by wave action, that sets parallel to the shore; usually in the near shore region within the breaker zone.

Longshore current: current moving along the shore or parallel the shore.

Magma: The molten rock material from which igneous rocks are formed.

Mass wasting: a natural process which involved solid material (e.g. rock, soild, sand) move downslope.

Medical Geology: The study of human health related to geology. Examples would include the correlation of disease or vitality with residences over specific types of bedrock or health problems associated with exposure to specific mineral materials.

Mesa: small, isolated and flat-topped hill, but larger than butte.

Mid Oceanic Ridge: an underwater mountain system formed by plate tectonics that moved away from each other. It also forms volcano chain.

Middle Miocene: A geologic epoch of the Tertiary period, extending from 11.6 - 16 Ma.

Mineral: A naturally occurring, solid, inorganic element or compound having a uniform composition and a regularly repeating internal structure. Minerals typically have a characteristic hardness and color or range of colors, by which they can be recognized. Rocks are made up of minerals.

Mineralogy: the science or study of minerals.

Mogote: a steep-sided hill resemble tower and might reach more than 100 m high.

Mohs Scale: The scale of mineral hardness. The order of the mineral hardness is Talc (scale 1, the softest), Gypsum (2), Calcite (3), Fluorite (4), Apatite (5) orthoclase (6), Quartz (7), Topaz (8), Corundum (9) and Diamond (10 as the hardest). For instance, Quartz able to scratch Orthoclase, but unable to scratch Topaz.

Montane zone: Vegetation zone situated in the middle altitude of a mountain, below the sub alpine zone. The vegetation is usually characterized by rare the high and big trees, smaller leaves, shorter height (up to 20 m height), shorter trunk branch compared to vegetation in the sub montane zone and less vegetation density.

Moraine: a mixture of rock mass and sediment carried and deposited by a glacier.

Mouth Bar: A bar composed of sand deposit formed where moving water enters a body of still water, due to decreased velocity.

Mud volcano: A conical accumulation of variable admixtures of sand and other finer grain size sediment. Might include rock fragments, resulting from eruption of wet mud and impelled upward by fluid or gas pressure. It is not necessarily related to volcano.

Musculoskeletal disorder: disorders or injury that affect the musculoskeletal system (all the bones, muscles and tendon of the body) or human body's movement.

Nearshore: region of the sea that close to the shore.

Normal fault: A fault, usually of 45^0 to 90^0, in which the hanging wall appears to have shifted downward in relation to the footwall.

Nuée ardente: hot gas and ash cloud that moving fast produced during volcano eruption.

Oceanic Crust: the earth's crust that underlies the ocean basins, composed of basaltic rock and overlain by sedimentary rock.

Oceanography: The scientific study of oceans, the life that inhabits them and their physical characteristics, including the depth and extent of ocean waters, their movement and chemical makeup and the topography and composition of the ocean floors

Offshore: A marine zone extending from water depth of 20 m to 200 m.

Oil / gas / hydrocarbon seepages: An area, generally small where oil/gas percolates slowly to the land surface.

Olivine: A mineral composed of $(Mg,Fe_2)SiO_4$ of a neosilicate group of olive-green magnesium-iron silicate minerals crystallizing in the orthorhombic system and having a vitreous luster.

Osteoarthritis: degeneration of joint cartilage and the underlying bone.

Outcrop: Exposed stratum or body of a rock at the surface of the earth.

Periglacial: an environment where the action of freezing and thawing are dominant surface process.

Petrified forest or Petrified wood: fossilized vegetation which the outer structure still exhibit wooden texture.

Petroleum Engineering: The technology of exploiting petroleum fluids from subsurface reservoirs. Petroleum engineering is concerned with the design and implementation of methods to recover commercial amounts of oil and gas.

Petroleum Geology: The branch of economic geology dealing with the origin, occurrence, movement, accumulation and exploration of hydrocarbon fuels.

Petroliferous gas: Containing petroleum (gas).

Petrology: The scientific study of the origin, composition and structure of rocks.

Placer deposit: mineral accumulation by gravity separation from a particular rock in upstream. The accumulation might be alluvium in river bank or beach sediment.

Plateau valley: a valley between plateau mountain.

Plateau: a large flat area, relatively situated in high ground, much larger than mesa.

Pleistocene: The older of the two epochs of the Quaternary Period, spanning about 1.8 million to 10,000 years ago. It represents the interval of geological time (and rocks accumulated during that time) extending from the end of the Pliocene Epoch (and the end of Tertiary Period) to the start of the Holocene Epoch. It is commonly characterized as an epoch when the earth entered its most recent phase of widespread glaciation. Also known as Ice Age.

Pliocene: The youngest of the five geological epochs of the Tertiary Period. The Pliocene represents the interval of geological time (and rocks deposited during that time) extending from the end of the Miocene Epoch to the beginning of the Pleistocene Epoch of the Quaternary Period. Modern time scales assign the duration of 5.0 million to 1.8 million years ago to the Pliocene.

Pocket Beach: Beach bounded by hard rock formed the headland where the wave eroded those rocks.

Psoriasis: a skin disease marked by red, itchy, scaly patches.

Pyroclastic: Fragmented volcanic products ejected from volcanoes in explosive events.

Pyroxene: A family of diverse and important rock-forming minerals having infinite (Si_2O_6) single inosilicate chains as their principal motif; colors range from white through yellow and green to brown and greenish black.

Quaternary: The second period of the Cenozoic geologic era, following the Tertiary and including the last 2–3 million years.

Quicksand: soft bed of unconsolidated sediment, usually comprised of sand, saturated with water and easily to be pressed so that objects on its surface tend to sink and engulfed.

Relief well: a well that drilled to intersect another oil / gas well that experienced blow out.

Reservoir: a rock strata or rock body where fluid accumulated, it might be water or hydrocarbon, e.g. oil reservoir, gas reservoir.

Rheumatic illnesses: conditions of pain affecting the joints and/or connective tissue.

Rheumatoid arthritis: a chronic disease causing inflammation in the joints, particularly in the ankles, feet, wrists and fingers.

Ring of Fire: zone in the Pacific Ocean margin that marked by active volcanoes and frequent earthquake.

Rip channel: A channel which is formed by rip current.

Rip current: A current that flow perpendicular to the beach which usually dragged swimmer into the open ocean.

Rock mechanics: science of the mechanical behavior of the rock and rock masses when it is put for buildings, tunnels, roads, dams, bridges and other use of civil engineering

Sand dunes: a dune of sand formed by the wind action.

Sand sea: a broad and flat area of desert covered by sand with little or no vegetative cover.

Sandstone bed: a rock layer mainly composed of sand grain sized, usually dominated by quartz, feldspar and lithic component.

Scarp: A cliff or steep slope of some extent, generally separating two level or gently sloping areas and produced by erosion or by faulting.

Sciatica: pain affecting the back, hip and outer side of the leg.

Scleroderma: a chronic hardening and contraction of the skin and connective tissue, either locally or throughout the body.

Sea stack: Rock column formed by wave erosion.

Sediment suspension: Mixture of fine particle / sediment sized, composed of organic and / or inorganic, in a fluid supported by buoyancy.

Sedimentary rock: A rock formed by consolidated sediment deposited in layers.

Serpentinite: a metamorphic rock type that mostly composed of serpentine group minerals.

Shallow marine: A marine area within water depth column from highest tide to 200 meter depth.

Shear Zone: A zone where there are rock fractures, where it might be filled by minerals

Sheeting joint: A fracture or joint formed by pressure-release jointing or exfoliation.

Shore: the land along the edge of a sea, lake.

Shoreface: A marine area within water depth column from highest tide to 20 meter depth.

Side tracking: a secondary hole beside the original wellbore, which parallel to the original wellbore.

Snow avalanche: A rapid flow of snow down a hill or mountainside.

Snubbing unit: a heavy well intervention type which performed in oil and gas wells to control the borehole environment.

Soil mechanics: science concerned with the properties and behavior of soil.

Soil movement: The movement down slope of soil mass under influence of gravity.

Solfatara: A fumarole from which sulfurous gases are emitted.

Speleothem: a structure formed in a cave by deposition of minerals from water dissolution.

Speleothem: a structure formed in a cave wall, ceiling or roof by the water dissolution and later on deposition of minerals, e.g. stalactite, stalagmite.

Stalactite: A conical or roughly cylindrical speleothem formed by dripping water and hanging from the roof of a cave; usually composed of calcium carbonate.

Stalagmite: A conical speleothem formed upward from the floor of a cave by the action of dripping water; usually composed of calcium carbonate.

Stratigraphic / Stratigraphy: A branch of geology concerned with the form, arrangement, geographic distribution, chronologic succession, classification, correlation and mutual relationships of rock strata, especially sedimentary.

Stratovolcano: A volcano built up of alternating layers of lava and pyroclastic.

Sub Alpine zone: Vegetation zone situated on the higher slope of mountain, below the tree line. The vegetation is usually characterized by stunted trees (usually up to 2 meter height), smaller trunk diameter and smaller leaves.

Sub Montane zone: Vegetation zone situated in the foothills of lower slope of a mountain, below the montane zone. The vegetation is characterized by wooden tree.

Subducting Plate: a plate that moves under another plate due to gravity into the mantle.

Submarinescape: the scape entirely situated below sea and formed by erosion, sedimentation, mineralization and/or tectonic.

Suiseki: a stone which has naturally formed aesthetic appearance e.g. in shape, colour or texture.

Swash zone: a zone where the water rushing to the coast from wave breaks in coastal region.

Syncinal valley: a valley which structurally formed by syncline structure.

Tephra: pyyroclastic material ejected by volcano eruption.

Terrestrial: The earth's land area, including its human-made and natural surface and subsurface features and its interfaces and interactions with the atmosphere and the oceans.

Thrust fault: a gentle fracture that crossing rock strata where the older rocks are pushed to be positioned relative on top of the younger rocks.

Tidal channel: a narrow inlet caused by flow of ocean tides.

Timber line: The upper altitude limit where no wooden vegetation grows. The timber line is situated below the tree line.

Tombolo: a sand deposit connecting an island to the mainland or to another island.

Topography: The three-dimensional arrangement of physical attributes (such as shape, height and depth) of a land surface in a place or region, include mountains, valleys, plains and bodies of water.

Tor: An exposed bedrock, isolated blocky hills about the same size as a house, standing abruptly above its surroundings and typically but not exclusively developed on granitic rocks.

Transtensional lake: a lake formed by extensional structures, e.g. normal fault and wrench structures, e.g. strike-slip faults.

Tree line: The upper altitude limit where no tress grows.

Triple junction: a place on earth where three tectonic plates meet.

Tsunami: An ocean wave or series of waves generated by any large, abrupt disturbance of the sea-surface by an earthquake in marine and coastal regions, as well as by a sub-oceanic landslide, volcanic eruption or asteroid impact.

Tuff: Consolidated volcanic ash, composed largely of fragments (less than 4 millimeters) produced directly by volcanic eruption; much of the fragmented material represents finely comminuted crystals and rocks.

Undifferentiated volcanic rock: a mixed rock that might be composed of lava, lahar, breccia, tuffaceous sand and lapilli.

Veins: mineral deposits formed in a preexisting rock fracture.

Ventifact: a stone shaped by the erosive action of windblown sand.

Volcanic breccia: A pyroclastic rock that is composed of angular volcanic fragments having a diameter larger than 2 millimeters and that may or may not have a matrix.

Volcanic gas: Volatile matter composed principally of about 90% water vapor and carbon dioxide, sulfur dioxide, hydrogen, carbon monoxide and nitrogen, released during an eruption of a volcano.

Volcanic rock: Finely crystalline or glassy igneous rock resulting from volcanic activity at or near the surface of the earth. Also known as extrusive rock.

Volcanic: denoting to volcano.

Volcano: A mountain or hill, generally with steep sides, formed by the accumulation of magma erupted through openings or volcanic vents.

Wentworth Scale: The scale for grain size of sedimentary particle in diameter. The order of the grain size from the finest to the coarsest is clay (finer than $1/_{256}$ mm of grain size diameter), silt ($1/_{256}$ mm to $1/_{16}$ mm), sand ($1/_{16}$ mm to 2 mm), granule (2 mm to 4 mm), pebble (4 mm to 64 mm), cobble (64 mm to 256 mm), boulder (coarser than 256 mm). It is used in sedimentary rock and sediment.

Index

A

adventure interest 116
adventure tourism 8, 18, 86, 110, 250, 251
aero sport 69, 340
aesthetic 9, 19, 65, 66, 105, 134, 220, 226, 278, 280, 281, 289, 435
anticline 45, 243, 427
applied geology viii, 16, 18, 21, 22, 23, 27, 28, 40, 53, 54, 56, 59, 60, 61, 62, 63, 64, 76, 88, 89, 90, 217, 220, 236, 238, 239, 248, 250, 251, 252, 253, 449
applied science 216, 217, 233
attraction vii, 3, 5, 7, 9, 10, 16, 18, 29, 30, 32, 33, 34, 39, 40, 61, 62, 63, 64, 68, 71, 72, 73, 74, 75, 76, 81, 89, 96, 98, 99, 101, 102, 103, 104, 105, 106, 107, 108, 109, 114, 117, 119, 120, 122, 128, 131, 132, 134, 135, 138, 141, 145, 152, 161, 162, 163, 164, 169, 170, 171, 173, 177, 178, 182, 193, 194, 195, 196, 197, 198, 199, 201, 202, 203, 204, 214, 216, 217, 218, 219, 221, 223, 224, 225, 226, 230, 231, 232, 233, 244, 249, 250, 251, 252, 253, 258, 260, 261, 264, 271, 280, 281, 316, 318, 319, 320, 324, 326, 328, 330, 339, 340, 351, 396, 398, 401, 402, 403, 408, 409, 411, 413, 425

B

balneotherapy 123, 409, 410, 413
beach 8, 18, 37, 66, 86, 106, 127, 134, 135, 180, 201, 241, 243, 246, 250, 278, 280, 281, 282, 285, 287, 288, 289, 291, 292, 293, 297, 306, 310, 397, 406, 411, 412, 428, 429, 433, 434

beach sediment 289, 433

Bentonite 123

breaker 281, 282, 284, 285, 286, 287, 292, 293, 294, 432

C

caldera 157, 184, 323, 398, 399, 404, 409, 422, 423

carbonated 122, 124

cave 7, 106, 112, 114, 115, 121, 122, 131, 132, 145, 146, 147, 148, 149, 150, 151, 154, 155, 159, 194, 195, 197, 202, 203, 245, 246, 249, 258, 266, 329, 354, 371, 375, 404, 407, 408, 414, 435

cave mine 7, 106, 145, 149, 150, 151

cavescape 114

Cereme 10, 70, 71, 75, 341, 342, 343, 344, 345, 351, 352, 362, 366, 367, 368, 369, 370, 371, 372, 373, 374

Ciantir 65, 66, 278, 279, 280, 287, 288, 290, 291, 292, 293, 294, 302, 304, 307, 308, 309, 313

Ciantir Bay 279, 280, 288, 291, 292, 293, 294, 304, 307, 308, 309, 313

civil engineer 5, 41, 42, 44, 47, 55, 57, 60, 61, 243, 250

civil engineering 27, 40, 41, 43, 44, 53, 54, 58, 250, 429, 434

conservation 4, 8, 19, 40, 43, 78, 79, 80, 81, 83, 85, 203, 204, 236, 238, 252

crater 7, 101, 106, 140, 143, 144, 152, 153, 155, 156, 157, 158, 159, 177, 199, 227, 228, 264, 344, 346, 347, 354, 355, 356, 357, 358, 361, 371, 373, 376, 381, 404, 405, 428, 431

curative 7, 11, 71, 96, 98, 123, 131, 132, 221, 230, 245, 249, 394, 396, 398, 402, 414

curative interest 249

D

Danakil Depression 215, 226, 228, 229, 231, 233

deep ocean floor tourism 8

delta 7, 159, 160, 261, 262, 263, 265, 266, 276, 289, 429

difficulty rating 10, 11, 22, 70, 75, 96, 98, 99, 103, 117, 119, 120, 200, 204, 220, 221, 246, 249, 292, 325, 342, 344, 345, 350, 351, 353, 356, 358, 359, 360, 361, 365, 409

drilling 5, 7, 45, 46, 50, 55, 58, 59, 96, 98, 105, 106, 138, 139, 140, 141, 142, 195, 197, 219, 247, 250, 265

drilling accident 105, 138, 197

drilling engineer 5, 55, 58, 59, 105, 250

E

Earthing 97, 133, 195, 207

earthquake 7, 12, 27, 49, 67, 69, 106, 109, 141, 161, 162, 165, 166, 167, 169, 170, 171,

173, 174, 177, 195, 196, 199, 211, 221, 231, 233, 318, 320, 323, 324, 325, 326, 346, 399, 400, 404, 405, 407, 409, 410, 413, 416, 429, 434, 436

economic geology 28, 433

ecotourism 18, 20, 29, 77, 78, 86, 87, 106, 111, 253

end-user 44, 51, 53, 54, 61, 63, 76, 83, 85, 86, 87

engineering geologist 41, 42, 43, 44, 58, 63, 64, 86, 236, 238, 239, 242, 248

engineering geology 16, 18, 21, 23, 28, 40, 41, 43, 44, 47, 53, 54, 55, 58, 60, 61, 86, 90, 250

environmental geology 252, 253

environmental impact 78, 84, 96, 98, 103, 104, 203, 204, 252

exploration viii, 5, 11, 28, 45, 46, 47, 48, 49, 51, 52, 53, 58, 59, 64, 72, 90, 138, 141, 149, 159, 179, 197, 243, 244, 248, 250, 265, 273, 323, 394, 396, 403, 408, 409, 410, 411, 414, 427, 433

exploration geologist 48

F

Fault 112, 120, 121, 171, 221, 264, 322, 323, 324, 325, 331, 337, 340, 429
    fault-related fold 264
    fault scarp 323, 337

flammable gas 263, 264, 265, 274

fluvial 156, 261, 262, 265, 270, 429, 430

Fluvial and Tide-dominated Delta 262
    fluvial-deltaic 261, 262

focus of interest 8, 18, 25, 26, 33, 38, 39, 41, 43, 44, 50, 51, 52, 53, 54, 56, 57, 58, 59, 60, 61, 62, 76, 81, 86, 87, 89, 220, 238, 242, 245, 247, 248

fossil 7, 24, 106, 109, 159, 160, 197, 320, 329, 430

G

Gemstone 97, 128, 136, 430

geoconservation 3, 4, 18, 19, 40, 77, 78, 79, 80, 82, 84, 203, 226, 230, 231, 244, 245, 248, 249, 250, 252, 320, 328, 329
    geodiversity 40, 68, 80, 251

geodiversity value 68

geoheritage 3, 4, 79, 80, 109

Geological attraction 320, 324

Geological Conservation 207, 430

Geological Heritage 430

geological knowledge viii, 3, 5, 10, 13, 18, 20, 40, 46, 49, 50, 56, 57, 58, 59, 62, 63, 68, 74, 76, 83, 84, 85, 86, 87, 88, 89, 90, 96, 98, 99, 101, 104, 204, 214, 216, 222, 223, 224, 225, 251, 253, 281, 318, 326, 449

geological process 68, 144, 162, 320, 399, 423

geological variable 22, 56, 62, 70, 74, 85, 103, 104, 119, 218, 220, 222, 249, 342, 344, 345, 351, 352, 359

geology vii, viii, ix, xi, 2, 3, 4, 5, 6, 8, 10, 11, 16, 18, 19, 20, 21, 22, 23, 24, 25, 26, 27, 28, 38, 39, 40, 41, 43, 44, 47, 49, 50, 51, 52, 53, 54, 55, 56, 58, 59, 60, 61, 62, 63, 64, 65, 71, 74, 76, 77, 78, 80, 81, 82, 83, 84, 85, 86, 87, 88, 89, 90, 96, 98, 99, 100, 101, 102, 103, 104, 105, 108, 109, 110, 135, 140, 199, 203, 204, 205, 214, 216, 217, 218, 219, 220, 224, 226, 230, 231, 232, 233, 236, 238, 239, 243, 245, 247, 248, 249, 250, 251, 252, 253, 255, 319, 320, 321, 324, 394, 398, 406, 414, 432, 433, 435, 449

geomorphology 19, 71, 78, 197, 321, 394, 396

Geopark xiii, 11, 19, 36, 71, 72, 75, 78, 92, 109, 110, 209, 210, 251, 254, 393, 396, 397, 398, 401, 402, 410, 416, 417, 422, 424, 430

Geophagy 129, 430

geophysicist 47, 48, 50, 51

Geophysics 48, 49, 51, 210, 212

Geoscience 20, 52, 83, 91

geoscientific 11, 16, 18, 39, 40, 54, 60, 74, 76, 78, 83, 86, 87, 89, 98, 102, 105, 108, 230, 248, 249, 258, 260, 261, 262, 263, 264, 265, 266, 267, 272, 394, 396, 398

geoscientific interest 40, 74, 83, 86, 102, 105, 260, 263, 265, 266

geoscientist 51, 82

geothermal 27, 122, 123, 124, 125, 126, 127, 134, 138, 139, 195, 199, 202, 229, 411, 412, 423

geotourism vii, 2, 3, 4, 5, 6, 8, 11, 16, 18, 19, 20, 23, 65, 71, 77, 78, 79, 80, 81, 82, 83, 84, 85, 86, 87, 88, 89, 110, 216, 226, 227, 230, 232, 236, 238, 239, 244, 245, 248, 249, 250, 251, 402, 409, 411, 412, 413, 414, 449

Geotourism aims 18

Geotourism Background 17, 78

Geotourism concept 87, 110

Geotourism definition 19, 80, 81, 89

Geotourism practitioner 11, 81, 236, 238, 239, 244, 248

Geotourism products 85, 244

Geotourism Purpose 17, 79

Geotourism Research 17, 82, 215, 230

Geotourism scope 80

Geotourism study 78, 82

giant crystal cave 146, 197, 203

Grand Canyon National Park 34, 36, 91, 92

Gunung Batu 10, 68, 69, 75, 93, 315, 316, 317, 318, 319, 321, 322, 323, 324, 325, 326, 330, 331, 332, 333, 335, 336, 337, 338, 339, 340

H

Hawaii 17, 67, 75, 171, 175, 186

hazard 69, 70, 162, 164, 166, 169, 172, 173, 196, 198, 199, 200, 201, 264, 265, 266, 318,

320, 325, 326, 328, 330, 344, 351, 358, 361, 365, 372, 374, 382, 390, 399, 400,
    404, 405, 406, 407, 408, 411, 419, 420
health tourism 8, 18, 86, 245, 250, 396, 402, 409, 410, 411, 413, 414
hot spring 124, 179, 404, 405
HSSE xii, xiii, 200
Hydrothermal Vent 12, 97, 106, 179, 180, 206, 207, 209, 219

I

impact 3, 6, 11, 31, 67, 72, 78, 83, 84, 96, 98, 99, 102, 103, 104, 133, 152, 153, 154, 155,
    156, 157, 159, 171, 182, 194, 199, 202, 203, 204, 214, 216, 217, 219, 221, 224,
    225, 230, 232, 238, 242, 245, 247, 250, 252, 253, 258, 260, 263, 264, 265, 266,
    267, 328, 394, 396, 403, 408, 409, 410, 413, 414, 431, 436

J

John Day Fossil Beds National Monument 34, 91

K

kaolin 129, 130
karst 72, 102, 106, 109, 112, 113, 131, 132, 195, 241, 243, 244, 247, 394, 396, 397, 407,
    408, 414, 431
Krakatau 178

L

landform 71, 72, 73, 96, 98, 105, 107, 111, 112, 115, 117, 119, 120, 195, 197, 219, 233,
    241, 245, 320, 324, 337, 361, 394, 396, 401, 402, 403, 404, 405, 407, 408, 410,
    414, 424
landscape 8, 26, 71, 72, 77, 80, 81, 107, 109, 111, 112, 113, 114, 115, 123, 137, 152,
    163, 194, 226, 236, 238, 239, 240, 241, 242, 243, 244, 245, 246, 247, 248, 287,
    319, 320, 324, 394, 396, 397, 404, 405, 407, 424
landslide 7, 25, 161, 163, 164, 167, 195, 199, 334, 346, 350, 353, 404, 405, 407, 409,
    410, 413, 431, 436
lava tube 114, 154, 155
Lebak 9, 65, 66, 75, 92, 93, 278, 280, 281, 287, 288, 289, 304
Legon Pari Bay 279, 288, 293, 302, 304, 310, 311, 314
Lembang Fault 322, 323, 324, 331, 337, 340
loess deposit 226
Lumpur Sidoarjo xiii, 141

M

Mahakam Delta 113, 258, 259, 260, 261, 262, 265, 266, 269, 271, 272, 273
Mahakam River 261, 262, 267

Manuk Island 65, 66, 67, 278, 279, 280, 287, 288, 290, 293, 294, 302, 304, 305, 306, 312
Mars 2, 3, 4, 7, 8, 96, 97, 98, 105, 106, 138, 151, 152, 155, 156, 157, 158, 159, 196, 198, 207, 209, 210, 219, 221
medical geology 21, 28
mitigation 11, 28, 41, 43, 44, 57, 58, 72, 90, 201, 394, 396, 403, 408, 410, 413, 414
Moon 2, 3, 4, 7, 96, 97, 98, 105, 106, 138, 151, 152, 153, 154, 157, 159, 196, 198, 219
Mountaineering 17, 70, 341, 342, 343, 344, 345, 349, 350, 351, 352, 355, 363, 368, 378, 386, 409
  mountaineering difficulty rating 10, 75, 342, 344, 345, 350, 351, 360, 361, 365
mud volcano 7, 122, 125, 126, 141, 144, 203, 212, 260, 264, 274

N

Naica cave 7, 149, 150
NASA xiii, 151, 154, 155, 156, 158, 160, 196, 206, 210
National Park 34, 36, 37, 91, 92, 112, 113, 114, 139, 202, 207, 210, 252, 397, 423
natural peloid 126, 134
Nature Based Tourism 78
next-user 44, 51, 54, 56, 57, 58, 59, 60, 61, 63, 68, 74, 83, 85, 98, 104, 204, 216, 220, 222, 223, 224, 225, 232, 247, 326

O

ocean floor 2, 3, 4, 7, 8, 106, 115, 116, 138, 179, 194, 214, 222
oceanography 65
Ore 97, 132
ore mine tunnel 132
outdoor activity 7, 11, 71, 105, 116, 117, 119, 120, 195, 199, 200, 231, 232, 320, 325, 330, 340, 394, 396, 397, 398, 402, 408
outdoor enthusiast viii, 105

P

park manager viii, 202, 204, 223
park managers 5, 68, 85, 353
peloid 125, 126, 134
pelotherapy 125, 145, 411
petroleum 5, 16, 18, 21, 23, 28, 40, 44, 45, 46, 47, 48, 49, 50, 51, 52, 53, 54, 55, 58, 59, 60, 61, 63, 64, 86, 90, 138, 140, 141, 197, 236, 238, 239, 243, 244, 247, 248, 250, 262, 273, 433
  petroleum engineer 47, 50, 53, 60, 61, 86, 250
  petroleum engineering 46, 50, 51, 52, 53, 54, 250
  petroleum exploration 45, 46, 47, 52, 273
  petroleum geologist 47, 48, 59, 63, 64, 197, 236, 238, 239, 243, 248

Petroleum geology 47, 49

Petroleum System 52, 92

physical outdoor activity 105, 116, 117, 199, 231, 330

possible viii, 7, 8, 11, 63, 72, 73, 152, 161, 164, 172, 193, 203, 204, 217, 219, 221, 223, 230, 232, 236, 251, 266, 294, 312, 314, 325, 340, 348, 356, 358, 382, 390, 394, 396, 402, 408, 409, 414, 425

powerful 7, 96, 98, 105, 138, 162, 163, 173, 175, 196, 198

probable 10, 72, 73, 193, 394, 396, 402, 403, 408, 414, 425

Proven 193, 403, 411

psammotherapy 101, 411

Q

Quarternary 352, 355, 357

R

radioactive 124, 125, 127

radon gas 132, 195

recreation 5, 85, 106, 116, 117, 396, 397, 402, 410, 413

recreationist 99

Rinjani 11, 71, 72, 73, 75, 112, 176, 346, 393, 395, 396, 397, 398, 399, 401, 402, 403, 404, 405, 406, 409, 410, 411, 415, 417, 419, 422, 423, 424, 425

Rip channel 434

rip current 66, 117, 201, 249, 278, 280, 282, 284, 285, 286, 294, 298, 403, 411, 413, 430, 434

risk 5, 43, 57, 58, 69, 116, 150, 178, 198, 199, 201, 204, 232, 292, 316, 318, 320, 325, 326, 350, 351, 365

S

safety 3, 5, 6, 9, 65, 66, 75, 84, 96, 98, 99, 102, 103, 117, 119, 120, 121, 164, 194, 198, 199, 200, 201, 204, 218, 221, 230, 232, 278, 280, 281, 289, 319, 350, 359, 408, 414

salt 45, 102, 106, 122, 124, 131, 132, 195, 221, 229

salt mine tunnel 106, 131, 132

Samalas 398, 412, 415, 422, 423

Samarinda 9, 64, 75, 92, 257, 258, 259, 260, 261, 262, 263, 264, 265, 266, 267, 268, 269, 270, 271, 272

scenic 7, 10, 11, 25, 34, 36, 64, 65, 71, 86, 96, 98, 103, 108, 110, 111, 112, 115, 152, 194, 196, 197, 220, 221, 230, 260, 262, 263, 266, 267, 319, 321, 394, 396, 398, 402, 410, 413

scenic beauty 7, 10, 11, 25, 64, 71, 86, 96, 98, 103, 108, 111, 112, 152, 194, 196, 220, 221, 230, 260, 262, 266, 267, 319, 394, 396, 398, 402

scenic beauty interest 111, 112, 220, 260, 262, 266

Semeru Volcano 343, 357, 384, 385, 386, 387, 388, 389, 390, 391, 392

Sibayak Volcano 215, 226, 227, 230, 233

Slamet Volcano 343, 355, 360, 377, 378, 379, 380, 381, 382

smectite 129, 144

sport tourism 106, 409, 411

subterranean 2, 4, 112, 114, 131, 431

suiseki 102, 135, 197, 221, 245

sun and beach tourism 8, 18, 86, 246, 250, 411, 412

swimming 9, 65, 66, 67, 75, 101, 121, 197, 202, 220, 243, 245, 249, 278, 280, 281, 284, 285, 286, 287, 288, 289, 291, 292, 293, 294, 411, 412

T

Tangkuban Parahu 327

tectonic 26, 167, 171, 181, 228, 229, 242, 281, 323, 324, 429, 431, 435, 436

therapy 105, 122, 123, 125, 126, 127, 128, 131, 132, 195, 397, 411, 412

tidal channel 266, 276, 284

tourism framework 33

tourism geology vii, xi, 2, 3, 4, 5, 6, 8, 10, 11, 16, 18, 20, 21, 22, 23, 38, 39, 40, 53, 61, 62, 63, 74, 76, 77, 81, 83, 84, 85, 86, 87, 88, 89, 90, 96, 98, 99, 101, 102, 103, 104, 105, 108, 135, 199, 203, 204, 205, 214, 216, 217, 218, 219, 220, 224, 226, 230, 232, 233, 236, 238, 239, 245, 247, 248, 249, 250, 251, 252, 253, 255, 398, 449
  tourism geology definition 87

tourism market 8, 83, 86, 98, 104, 106, 247, 250, 397, 402, 409, 410, 411, 412, 413

tourism planning 33, 84, 227, 231, 403

tourism problem 18, 74, 83, 252

tourism-related professional 2, 3, 5, 6, 18, 33, 61, 62, 63, 74, 76, 83, 84, 85, 88, 89, 96, 98, 99, 204, 236, 238, 250

tourist vii, 2, 3, 4, 5, 6, 7, 9, 10, 11, 16, 18, 24, 29, 30, 32, 33, 34, 39, 40, 61, 62, 63, 64, 65, 66, 68, 69, 71, 72, 73, 75, 76, 78, 79, 81, 83, 84, 85, 86, 87, 89, 96, 98, 99, 100, 101, 102, 103, 104, 106, 107, 108, 124, 138, 139, 145, 146, 148, 151, 161, 162, 164, 169, 176, 182, 183, 184, 192, 193, 196, 197, 198, 200, 201, 203, 204, 214, 216, 217, 219, 223, 225, 229, 230, 231, 233, 244, 245, 246, 248, 249, 250, 251, 252, 258, 260, 261, 263, 267, 271, 272, 280, 281, 289, 316, 318, 319, 320, 326, 394, 396, 397, 398, 401, 403, 408, 410, 411, 412, 414, 415, 449

tourist attraction vii, 3, 5, 7, 16, 18, 33, 39, 40, 61, 62, 63, 68, 72, 75, 76, 89, 96, 98, 99, 101, 102, 106, 145, 161, 162, 164, 169, 197, 233, 250, 251, 252, 258, 260, 261, 271, 281

tourist destination 10, 34, 39, 61, 64, 65, 66, 68, 69, 75, 99, 100, 229, 251, 252, 316, 318, 319, 320, 326, 397, 449

tourist interest 11, 39, 40, 65, 78, 83, 86, 87, 98, 102, 104, 108, 193, 196, 219, 230, 245, 248, 249, 260, 267, 408

tsunami 7, 8, 31, 106, 109, 161, 162, 167, 170, 171, 172, 173, 174, 177, 195, 196, 199, 201, 221, 401, 406, 411, 412

U

UNESCO xiv, 19, 71, 78, 93, 109, 110, 211, 229, 396, 397, 430

V

Vent 12, 97, 106, 179, 180, 183, 185, 191, 192, 206, 207, 209, 219
volcanic 24, 25, 28, 66, 67, 68, 71, 72, 106, 109, 113, 114, 119, 120, 124, 125, 126, 127, 130, 134, 153, 154, 160, 161, 163, 165, 170, 175, 177, 178, 180, 185, 195, 199, 200, 201, 220, 221, 227, 228, 231, 264, 288, 291, 292, 293, 319, 346, 350, 352, 353, 355, 357, 358, 360, 367, 368, 372, 374, 377, 378, 382, 385, 386, 394, 396, 397, 398, 399, 403, 404, 405, 406, 410, 411, 412, 414, 423, 427, 428, 430, 431, 432, 434, 436, 437
volcanic eruption 28, 67, 109, 161, 163, 177, 195, 199, 200, 350, 357, 436
volcano 7, 8, 67, 69, 70, 101, 106, 119, 122, 125, 126, 141, 144, 157, 161, 175, 176, 177, 178, 184, 185, 186, 195, 196, 199, 203, 212, 221, 227, 228, 260, 264, 265, 271, 274, 318, 319, 320, 321, 323, 326, 330, 345, 351, 352, 355, 357, 358, 366, 385, 391, 397, 398, 399, 404, 410, 419, 427, 428, 429, 431, 432, 433, 435, 436, 437
volcano eruption 7, 8, 106, 161, 175, 177, 178, 429, 433, 436
Volcanology 327, 362

Y

Yellowstone National Park 34, 36, 37, 91, 92, 112, 114, 139

Visit **www.yudispurnama.com**
for my progress of Tourism Geology

➡️ *There are more that geologists can do to support tourism-related professional's job*

➡️ *The spirit of Tourism Geology is to explore the usage of geological knowledge for tourism*

➡️ *Tourism geology offers new opportunities:*
- ❑ *New tourist attraction*
- ❑ *New tourist activity*
- ❑ *New profession*
- ❑ *New business opportunity*

➡️ *Tourism Geology:*
- *Context: Tourist Attraction*
- *Content: Delivering proper geological knowledge for Tourism-related Professional*

Follow me ......

✉️  yudigea93@gmail.com
yudi@yudispurnama.com

📷 @yudi_s_purnama   💼  @yudi_s_purnama

Author Bio

Yudi Satria Purnama is a geologist, live in Jakarta, Indonesia. His first interest in tourism characterized by his first book of *Panduan Wisata Geologi Bandung Utara* (Geological tour guide to the Northern Bandung Area), published in 2001. He also designed the interpretative geological panels in Tangkubanparahu Volcano (a tourist destination) in 2005, the first in the country.

In 2009, he received the IAGI (Indonesian Geologists Association) Award for his contribution in geotourism development.

However, since 2001, he has different mindset that is to establish applied geology for tourism. He calls it: tourism geology, which present in this book.

Tourism geology is the beginning of his interest to develop any applied geology for society interests. He believe geological knowledge is able to be applied to many society needs, more than we already know.

Contact him through his email: yudigea93@gmail.com; yudi@yudispurnama.com and also through his website: www.yudispurnama.com

The world is changed by those who dare to act differently

Made in the USA
Las Vegas, NV
29 December 2023

83698090R00277